DESTINY

HOW TO READ YOUR OWN HAND

A PALMISTRY HANDBOOK

BY
SALLY FRY
AND
ROSALIND CRAIG

Virgin

First published in Great Britain in 1986 by
Virgin Books,
328 Kensal Road, London W10 5XJ

ISBN 0 86369 133 1

Printed and bound in Great Britain by
Richard Clay Ltd
(The Chaucer Press), Suffolk

Typeset by Keyline Graphics, London NW6
and Transcript, London WC1

Cover and design by Sue Walliker
and Ursula Shaw

Distributed by Arrow Books

CONTENTS

SALLY FRY is an international Palm Reader to the famous and infamous, royalty and the public at large. She has tried to adapt the ancient art of Chiromancy (study of the lines of the hand) to modern-day living, helping people with their problems and assessing their potential. She is an honest woman and believes that life is for living. Thus, with her expertise in this field, she hopes to help and guide people to understand themselves a little better, so that they in turn can make the most of what life has to offer.

ROSALIND CRAIG is the mother of three teenage children, a Marriage Guidance Counsellor and a Magistrate in that order! She has been involved in the practice of Palmistry for a number of years and her knowledge of the subject has been invaluable in all aspects of her work.

To Sam

'HE SEALS UP THE HAND OF EVERY MAN
THAT ALL MEN MAY KNOW HIS WORK'

Job 37.7

INTRODUCTION

This book is written for all people as an easy approach to understanding the secrets of the palm and fingers. It is to intrigue, amuse and share with your friends and to give an insight into your negative, as well as positive, qualities; and to a certain extent to help direct you to your own Destiny.

There is no better way to learn the true nature of individuals than by studying palmistry. Discover who are the Leaders in Life, who are the Faithful, the Good or Bad Lovers, the Introvert or the Extrovert simply by scrutinizing their palm.

The science of palmistry is said to date back almost to the creation of time and the human body has always been looked upon as a means of foreseeing omens and portents.

Palmistry can be divided into two main areas: CHIROGNOMY, which deals with the basic character and potential reflected by the size, shape and outward appearance of the hand; and CHIROMANCY, the ability to predict past, present and future from the lines and signs on the palm itself.

DERMATOGLYPHICS is the name given to the study of the skin ridges and patterns covering the palm and fingers. This system is used throughout the world by the police to identify fingerprint patterns.

When analysing or reading a palm it is essential to remember that the subject is very vulnerable. Great care must be taken to use the information in a positive and constructive way.

As you use this book, your skill will improve. You should always limit your readings to what you have learnt. Don't attempt to make guesses. Reading palms is much more a question of a skill to acquire than an intuitive ability.

Used carefully and intelligently, palmistry is a fine way to judge character, health and potential.

PALMISTRY – AN ANCIENT SCIENCE

The use of hand prints can be traced back to early Stone Age cave drawings. As far back as 563 BC it was noted that Buddha had certain markings on his feet which were proof of his greatness, and it is believed that palmistry was first recognised in Europe around the time of Alexander the Great. Fingerprints were often used instead of signatures and in China the Emperor's thumb print was used on State documents. In 1595 a book was published by Joannes Rothmann entitled *Chiromantiea Theorica Practica* and in 1661 a collection of writings on Chirology appeared which incorporated over 70 books on the subject.

One of the best-known palmists was Count Louis Hamon, who was better known by the name of 'Cheiro', meaning hand. He was the author of several books on the subject which mainly followed the theories of two well-established authorities, D'Arpentigny and Desbarrolles. D'Arpentigny was born in March 1798 and his first book, *La Chirognomia*, published in 1839, caused a new wave of interest in the form of the hand. Desbarrolles was born in August 1801 in Paris and it was his study of the Kaballa (the mystical Hebrew theosophy which flourished between the twelfth and sixteenth centuries) that led him to record his chirological findings in a highly detailed system of classification with fine illustrations of the palm.

Another important contributor to the scientific study of the hand was Dr Carl Gustav Carus, personal physician to the King of Saxony, who during the mid nineteenth century published several books on the subject. His theory was that the human hand was a cross between a fin and a wing, and that the palm was the elementary part of the hand from which the fingers grew. He saw the palm as the key to the subconscious and the fingers, developing parallel with the thought processes and the key to the conscious mind. Hands were classified into two types: the first was the prehensive – those best adapted to the sense of touch – which was subdivided into two further types, the elementary and motoric. The second was the sensitive and psychic. Carus used these classifications to identify the various levels of intellect.

Today, hand analysis has a role to play in medical and psychological diagnosis, a vocational function and the ability to provide a personal analysis. All these possibilities are a direct result of the findings of many years of intensive study by people all over the world.

HOW TO TAKE HAND AND FINGER PRINTS

If you want to undertake a thorough study of your hands, you should take prints. If you are only doing it for fun, a magnifying glass can be used, although this will not give such accurate results as a print.

To take prints you will need: a roller (as used in lino work), fingerprint ink (water-based), a pane of glass or the inside of a biscuit-tin lid – something with a completely smooth surface – a small rubber pad large enough to fit under the narrow part of the palm, tissues, magnifying glass, ruler and paper.

Method: place a sheet of paper with the rubber pad beneath it on a flat table. Squeeze a small amount of ink onto the glass (or other smooth surface) and roll the roller backwards and forwards in the ink until the roller is evenly covered. You are now ready to take the print. The help of another person would be an advantage at this stage. They should take the roller and roll it evenly over the whole of your palm and fingers. Relax your hand and place it down on the paper in the most comfortable position. The other person should then press down on the back of the whole hand. Take your hand off carefully so as not to smudge the ink, and you should have a clear print.

Once a print has been taken, it should be dated immediately and, if it is not your own hand, it should be identified either by a name or by a code number, if the owner objects to their name being used. It can be quite an interesting exercise to take further prints in future years and to ascertain the changes that have taken place.

•CHIROGNOMY•

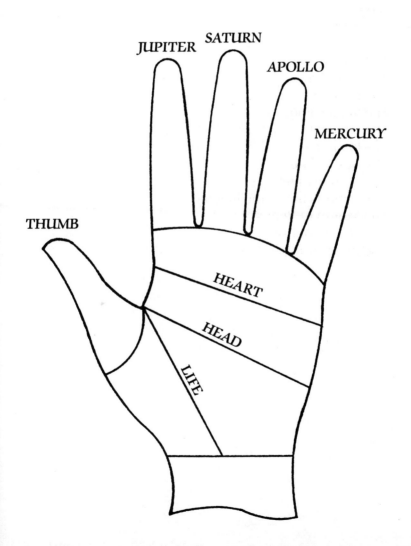

HOW TO ANALYSE THE HAND

The hand and its various aspects are dealt with in the following order:

The shape of the hand
The fingers
The heart line
The head line
The Simian line
The fate line
The life line
The Apollo line
The Mercury line
The Mounts under the fingers
The Mount of Venus
The Moon Mount
The fingerprint patterns

MASCULINE AND FEMININE HANDS

It is possible to assess the proportion of male and female within a human being from their hand. When you are considering the whole hand, the fact that the hand looks delicate does not necessarily mean that the person is particularly feminine. The same with the male – a strong, sturdy hand does not necessarily indicate a masculine personality.

Generally speaking, the round shaping on the hands and fingers suggests female attributes, whereas square shapings on the hands and fingers suggests masculine attributes.

As for the lines on the palm, the straighter the horizontal lines are the more female the personality, and the more curves the more masculine.

A line dropping from the end of the heart line to the head line suggests homosexual tendencies.

THE SHAPE OF THE HAND

There are several basic types of hand shapes: the square, the conical, the knotty, the pointed and the spatulate. There are additional shapes, namely the elementary and the mixed hand, but we will be confining our study to these five. The square hand enjoys order and regularity, whilst the conical or artistic hand has a strong tendency towards sensuality and aesthetics. The knotty or philosophical hand belongs to the analyst and meditator whereas the pointed hand is the least practical, revealing a tendency towards the abstract and, generally, indicating that such people should not be in a position of authority. Finally, the spatulate hand's main characteristics are action, movement and energy.

The left hand is used to determine events and character traits and is called the Hand of Destiny. It is the hand of hereditary factors. The other hand shows how your life develops, and what you make of your potential.

For the purpose of this book, the diagrams have been prepared for the left hand in each case to make it easier to locate and identify lines and markings.

On each diagram, the shaded area indicates the part of the hand which is being dealt with.

The Square or Useful hand	
The Conical or Artistic hand	
The Knotty or Philosophical hand	
The Pointed or Psychic hand	
The Spatulate or Active hand	

Doctors, mathematicians, scientists and computer programmers	Square hand	
Artists, actors, singers and orators	Conical hand	
Philosophers, analysts and pure scientists	Knotty hand	
Members of religious orders, clairvoyants and social workers	Pointed hand	
Engineers and mechanics, members of the Armed Forces		

Stubborn and reactionary, with little vision. Family-oriented, tends to take jobs which serve others. Dislikes change.

Loves life and people. Good-humoured and charming but also rather shallow and selfish. Publicity-seeking.

Abhors the grossness of life, believes that the next life will be better than this. Remote and ascetic, idealistic and critical.

Quiet nature, loving beauty and living on an exalted emotional level. Easily hurt, good intuition and often academically bright.

Restless and indecisive, this practical and inventive person dreams obsessively of the future and constantly thinks up new ideas and concepts.

COLOUR OF THE PALM

Very pale skin on palm	Selfish and could suffer from bad circulation
Yellow skin on palm	Morbid and could suffer from bilious attacks
Pink and mottled skin on palm	Cheerful disposition, well-balanced
Red skin on palm	Quick-tempered
Very red skin on palm	Violent disposition, should watch blood pressure
Silky skin on palm	Tendency to rheumatism and gout
Dry skin on palm	Runs temperatures easily, prone to fevers
Damp skin on palm	Ill-balanced moral nature, prone to liver and kidney disorders

HAIR ON THE HAND

Hairy hands on a woman – mannish and cruel

Hairy hands on a man – energetic and sexy

Very hairy hands on a man – violent nature

No hair on a man's hands – effeminate and passive

Light-coloured hair on hands – passionless

Dark hair on hands – passionate disposition

Reddish-coloured hair on hands – excitable nature

Air sign	Aquarius Gemini Libra	Round hands with Conic type fingers
Fire sign	Aries Leo Sagittarius	Long hands with short thick fingers
Water sign	Pisces Cancer Scorpio	Long hands with long thin fingers
Earth sign	Taurus Virgo Capricorn	Square hands with short square fingers

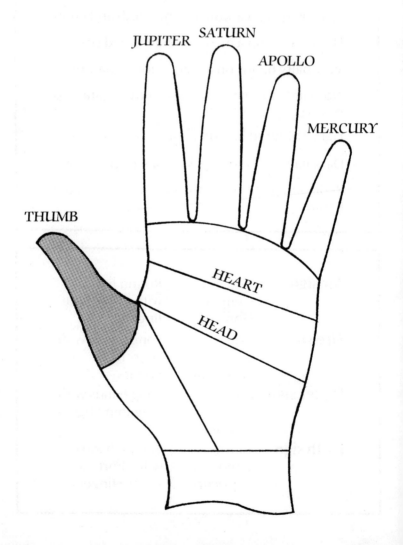

THE THUMB

The Thumb or 'Thenar Eminence' is the most important digit on the hand; without it one would find it difficult to cope with everyday living. It also has the most significant meaning in reading hands. The main thing to remember is that the thumb represents one's self-control and to some extent the control of others. The thumb must be adequately proportioned in relation to the hand or there will be insufficient firmness of purpose.

The thumb has three phalanges and not two as is commonly supposed. The upper nail phalange determines the will, the middle phalange logic and reason, and the lower phalange, which is the Mount of Venus, love, energy and sympathy.

A longer thumb in comparison with the other fingers suggests a person who is out to impress, and who is, at the same time, impressionable. People in high places, such as Prime Ministers, tend to have noticeably large thumbs.

A short stunted thumb betrays a lack of will, swinging moods and an outlook which is not based on logic. A short thick thumb implies primitive taste, and a person who is uncouth, albeit blunt and honest. If, however, the thumb is proportionately long, then thickness shows health and vitality. Thin thumbs indicate a nervous disposition.

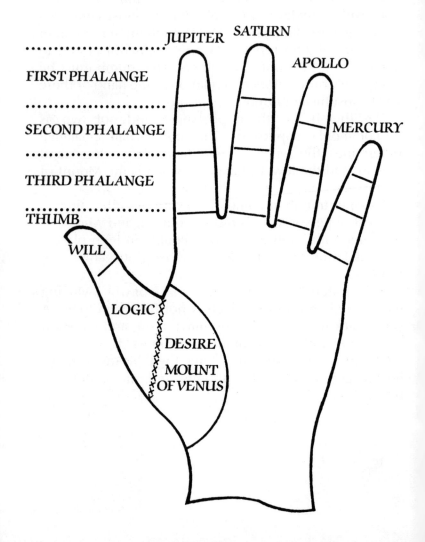

Fun-loving	45° to Jupiter	
Wants to impress people	90° to Jupiter, and large	
Sycophantic	Close to hand	
Overbearing	Thick	
Rather cold and distant	Medium	

Generous and tends towards extremes	90° to Jupiter	
Snake in the grass	Long and close to hand	
Pervertedly cruel	Short, thick and chubby	
Bad-tempered	Short	
Refined	Thin	

Impulsive	Conic	
Violent tendencies: *the Murderer's Thumb*	Short, chubbed	
Practical	Square top	
Weak-willed	Short	

Very determined	Long, strong and broad	
Strong will-power	Long	
Craves excitement; an extrovert	Angled over	
Obstinate	Narrowing	
Under stress	Horizontal bars	

Logical	Second phalange equal to first	
Diplomatic and unbearably charming	Second phalange longer than first and thin	
Reasonable and never brutish	Much longer than first phalange	
Loves family life; egocentric	Family Ring	
Excellent timing and patience; good musician, orator or sportsman	Angle of Time	

Very sensitive and easily upset; afraid of marriage	Line running across	
Boasts openly and crudely about love-life; could have an incestuous relationship	Crosses on Venus	
Easily upset and totally unpredictable; has select but strong friendships	Jointy or knotty	
Acts on instinct and intuition, won't listen to logical arguments	Short	
Argumentative and violent; avoid conflicts with such a person	Very short	

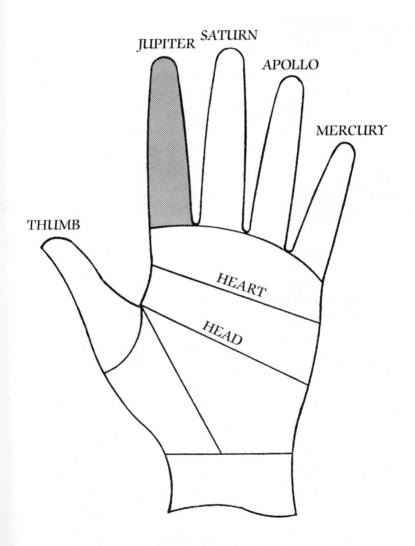

THE JUPITER OR INDEX FINGER

The Jupiter or index finger represents pride, self-esteem and the capacity to dominate. Its length should be equal to that of Apollo and both the Jupiter and Apollo fingers should at least reach the base of the top phalange of Saturn.

A poor Jupiter finger, shorter in length than Apollo, denotes an inferiority complex – short Jupiter finger people do not like responsibility.

When the Jupiter finger is large, long and heavy in comparison to the other fingers, the person has power to lead others and to assume responsibility. These people like to feel important and are therefore susceptible to flattery.

The Jupiter finger must always be judged along with the thumb because together they show the conscious attitude of the person to the world.

If the thumb is held close to the hand and the Jupiter finger stands out, while the rest of the fingers turn into the palm, you have a person who is socially awkward and unadaptable but with great pretension and power to realise their potential.

When the Jupiter finger leans away from the Saturn finger and outwards from the hand, one can deduce a very strong independence of thought.

When the Jupiter finger stands straight then the person stands on their own feet; if it leans towards the Saturn finger (second finger), there is a strong involvement with the home and a love of domesticity.

Ambitious and not afraid to take responsibility	Large and heavy	
Very studious	Straight, long and knotty	
Bossy and domineering	Pointed	
Good company; unconventional	Isolated	
Happy as a bachelor; wise	Solomon's Ring	

Hates responsibility	Shorter than Apollo	
Lack of self-esteem	Bent, withered	
Wilful	Inclined to Saturn	
Has difficulty relating to others	Gap between Jupiter and Saturn	
Withdrawn	Short	

Spiritual	Fleshy	
Likely to be involved in politics; very religious	Long	
Great orator or politician	Very big	
May not have many genuine friends	Dry and thin	
Bossy	Pointed	

Love of self	Plump and short	
Charitable and caring but weak-willed	Short	
Rheumatic, prone to gout	Top phalange inclines to Saturn	

Desire for recognition	Long	
Very subjective	Jointy or knotty	
Excellent cook	Plump	
Glutton	Fat	
Martyr-like withdrawal	Thin	

Dominant and materialistic	Long	
Desire for glory, domination	Thin	
Material ambition	Plump	
Order in personal things	Jointy	
Realistic	Long and thin	

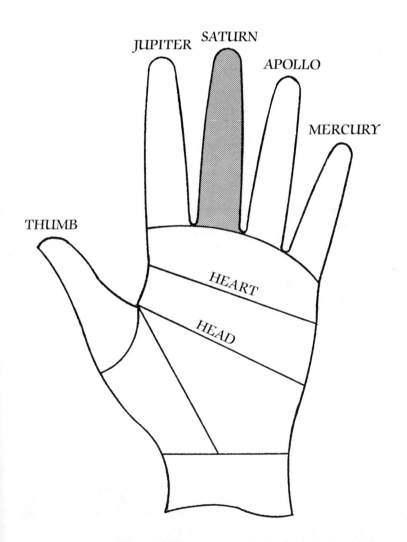

THE SATURN OR MIDDLE FINGER

The Saturn or middle finger should ideally be the longest on the hand, half a phalange longer than Apollo. If longer than this, it denotes an over-serious disposition. A short Saturn finger indicates a flippant attitude to life.

The Saturn finger is the balancing finger of the hand, mediating between the conscious and unconscious side of our nature. If it is too long on the hand it shows a morbid preoccupation with one's situation in life, and also a tendency towards depression. Intellectually, such a person will often be out on a limb.

A short Saturn finger denotes an impulsive person with Bohemian traits – artists, writers and so on.

A bent or curved Saturn finger suggests the person is sensitive and prone to bilious upsets. A bent top phalange turning to Apollo suggests neck or back problems.

Prone to depression	Heavy and broad	
Loyal, serious	Longest on hand	
Perceptive	Bends back	
Unable to face up to life	Bends in	
Harbours a guilty secret	Saturn and Apollo wilt towards each other	

An intellectual who may be less than sparkling socially	Leans to Apollo	
Flippant	Thin	
Morbid outlook on life	Heavy	
Prone to spine trouble	Crooked	
Non-achiever	Short	

Natural gift for clairvoyance	Long and fleshy	
Loves magic, mystery and freemasonry	Long	
Psychic	Pointed	
An accurate judge of others; good at figure work and music	Square top	
Can be too serious about the occult – a fanatic!	Thin	

Mystical	Conical top	
Bad at figure work	Short, pointed	
Influenced by superficial considerations	Short	
Interested in the occult	Large and heavy	

Very good director of scientific projects	Jointy or knotty	
Very scientific	Long	
Will see a project to its end	Thin	
Can't see beyond theory	Plump	
Finds it difficult to complete tasks	Short	

Greenfingers	Long	
Cut off from reality	Ringed	
Lazy and rather parasitic	Fleshy	
Spendthrift	Thin	
Poor money sense	Short	

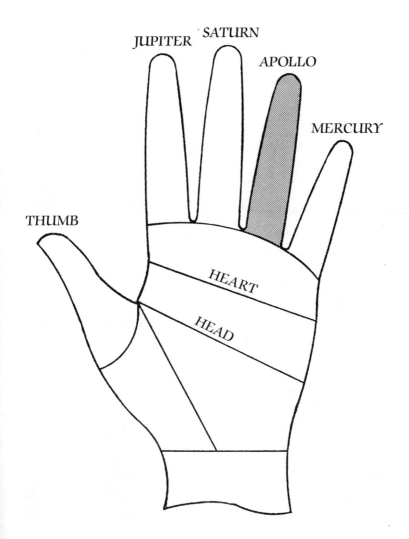

THE APOLLO OR SUN FINGER

The Apollo or Sun finger is traditionally supposed to indicate the artistic and creative ability of the individual and to relate to their potential, their ambitions and their future wealth.

It is this finger which represents our sense of belonging. That the wedding ring is worn on this finger is significant since it is a symbol of attachment and mutual belonging. Its length should ideally be equal to that of Jupiter, indicating a balanced personality.

If the Apollo finger is longer than Jupiter it makes a person a 'gambler of life'. A short Apollo finger indicates that the person will be active in achieving their goals. In other words, the Jupitarian emotions will predominate and the person will be determined to ensure their own good fortune. People with a short Apollo finger tend to be very individualistic and do not conform to stereotypes. They can often be affected and make a great show of their emotions.

An inwards bend of the top phalange towards Saturn is also indicative of emotional difficulties. A bend of the whole finger towards Saturn indicates feelings of guilt and an unrealistic approach to love.

The Apollo should be straight, giving outlets to artistic and other types of expression. Bends indicate all sorts of physical problems.

An island under the Apollo finger often denotes eye trouble. Over-long Apollo fingers – as long as Saturn – suggest intellectual bores but also born dreamers, with a vision of beauty too idealistic to be realised.

Balanced personality	Equal to Jupiter	
Sunny disposition	Straight	
Will take risks	Longer than Jupiter	
Needs to marry an older person	Wilts to Saturn	
Great artistic potential	Long with spatulate tip	

Hidden sorrow	Bent over	
Cautious, never gambles with life	Shorter than Jupiter	
Could be spiritual leader	Clings to Mercury	
Should take more exercise	Crooked	
Riddled with guilt	Clings to Saturn	

An intellectual person with an interest in art	Long	
Sensitivity of thought in artistic matters; refined	Thin	
Love of beauty in all forms	Plump	
Good taste	Conic	
Enigmatic	Pointed	

Destroys and never rebuilds	Jointy or knotty	
Lacks breeding	Square	
Lacks finesse	Short	

Skilled at translating ideas into concrete form	Plump	
By dint of hard work this person will usually succeed	Long	
Idealistic, artistic and precise	Thin	
This person has a need for beauty and order in their life	Jointy or knotty	

Yearns for riches and likes to be surrounded by art	Long	
A perfectionist	Jointy or knotty	
Little respect for fame and money	Thin	
Remarkably bad taste and ostentatious too!	Plump	
One of the less refined types; likely to fail, especially if the task requires artistic talent	Short	

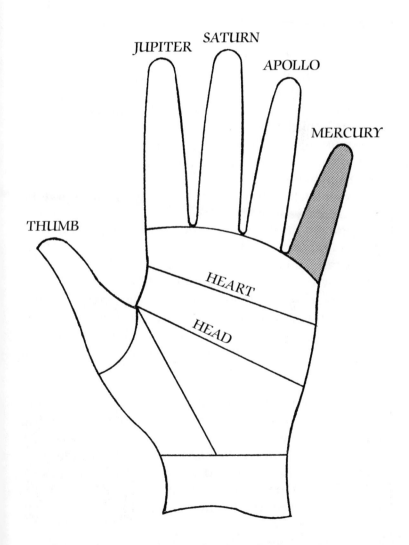

THE MERCURY OR LITTLE FINGER

The Mercury finger in conjunction with the Mount of Venus shows the sexual potential of the individual.

This finger should be the shortest finger on the hand. A longer finger indicates masculinity, gifts for speech, musical ability in general and a sense of form. A long thin Mercury denotes a cunning and creative person.

A thick third phalange and a firm, well-padded Mount of Venus are sure signs that this is the sexy lover; with an added curved heart line, the passionate soul we all long to be – or to be with.

Sexual relationships permeate our whole lives and the correct analysis of the place of sex in the life of an individual is an important step in the evaluation of their psychological disposition.

Sex can either be an integrated part of the individual's life or it can cause disharmony. It can either be an immense force for creation or an equally strong force for destruction. Disharmony in sex accounts for the majority of problems and it is almost certain that sex, or, more exactly, repressed sexual energy, is the basis for most crimes and mental illness.

A low-set Mercury finger, set deep into the palm so that the finger looks well-rooted in the palm, indicates parent fixation which results in sexual inhibitions, fear and uncertainty.

A finger inclining to the palm conveys prudishness but can also indicate tact and secretiveness. An outward bend, away from the palm, shows a person who is extremely sensitive to noises, and to unexpected reactions to the environment.

A broad, physical finger shows a broad mind. A plump Mercury is for a person who understands business and knows how to make money.

The Mercury finger is the only finger without a nail moon. If there is one it will disappear early in life.

A Mercury finger which arcs towards Apollo shows self-sacrifice and a person well-suited to the caring professions.

Thrives on knowledge; excellent hearing	Long with long first phalange	
Very sexy, and fulfilled in all aspects of life	Thick base and knotty joints	
A cunning mind; clever and successful negotiator	Long	
Self-sacrificing nature makes them ideal as nurses or doctors	Curved towards Apollo	
Sublimates their sexual urge into a money-making drive	Ring	

Avoids commitment to relationships, prefers to keep a distance	Wide apart from Apollo	
Tactful and secretive	Clings to Apollo	
Longs for affection	Clings to hand	
May be rather immature or even retarded	Shorter than second phalange of Apollo	
Intellectual	Halfway up first Apollo phalange	

Gift for languages	Jointy or knotty	
Flair for business	Thin	
Ability for science	Long	
Will make a good and lasting marriage	One line	
More than one love	More than one line	

Great at listening and giving advice	Several lines: 'Samaritan lines'	
Teeth need attention	Straight lines under Mercury	
Excellent hearing	Pointed	
Little finesse	Plump	
Intellectual bore	Short	

Natural gift for business or law	Jointy or knotty	
Gift for making money	Thick	
Practical and materialistic	Long	
Unrealistic	Thin	
Always tired	Lines going down	

Good sex life	Plump	
Cunning and hypocritical; likely to be a charlatan	Long	
Has problems achieving orgasm	Ringed	
May find it difficult to relate to parents, one of whom may come from another country	Low set	
Poor sex life	Flat	

Frustrated	Thin	
Stupid	Short	

THE NAILS

The nails are most informative. For instance, we all know that people who bite their nails show a nervous disposition. Flecks on the nails donate a tired, run-down condition. Short nails which are broader than they are long show a stubborn nature. Broad, long nails indicate clear judgement. Long, almond-shaped nails suggest a less energetic person, whilst white nails show a cold nature. Long, ridged nails, bluish in colour, betray problems. Brittle nails with the first phalange of the index finger (the 'Jupiter' finger) inclining reveal gout.

●CHIROMANCY●

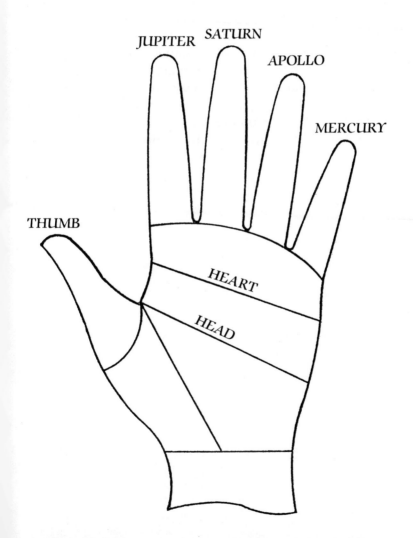

LINES ON THE HAND

Chiromancy or the study of lines on the palm reveals not only our habits but also past, present and future events. Lines should be clear in relation to the overall colour of the skin of the palm – continental hands have pinker palms, black hands have pink palms with brown lines, and oriental hands have their own shade of mushroom.

A hand showing numerous breaks in the lines indicates a lack of continuity; islands show a divided mind; little cuts across the lines indicate inner tensions and little dots on the lines have a similar meaning.

THE MAIN LINES ON THE HAND

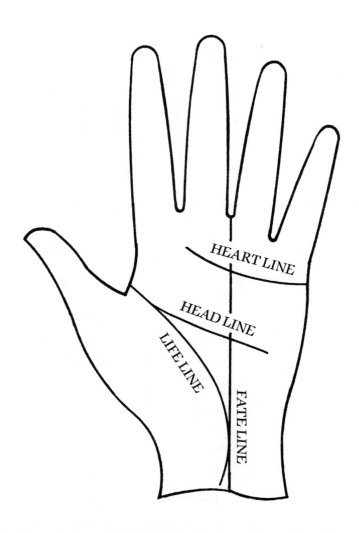

TIME ON THE HAND

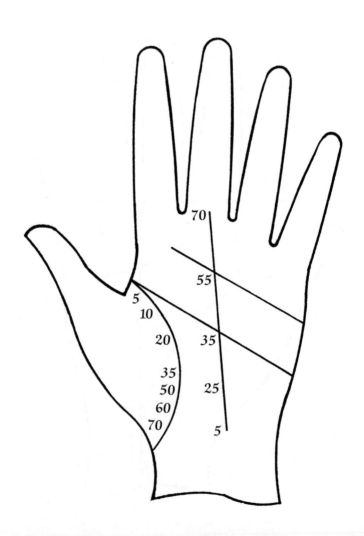

THE HEART LINE

Read from below the Mount of Mercury across the hand, this represents the unconscious expression of emotions, the circulation, and the affections.

It also suggests the sexual motivation of the person; the straighter the line, the more 'feminine' and the more calculating. The deeper the curve, the more 'masculine' and the more forceful the feelings.

If the line is made up of uneven chains, the person has a normal sexual appetite. If it runs straight across the hand this is an indication of jealousy due to excesses of affection. Breaks in the heart line show great inconstancy in relationships and, on man's hand, often indicate a woman-hater.

White marks on the line show love affairs; red spots on or gaps in the line represent physical or emotional wounds.

This fair-weather friend is fickle, inconstant and vain; don't take your problems to them	Broken line	
Jealous, possessive and selfish in love; quick to anger, slow to forgive; will never see your point of view	Long, straight heart line	
Prone to illness and allergy, always under emotional strain; complains a lot	Even-chained heart line	
Impatient in life and love; emotionally over the top	Deep, long heart line	
Miserly and rather selfish	Short and faint	

A great lover and a flirt, boundless charm	Branches on heart line	
Always more than just a friend; hot-blooded and passionate but easily upset	Ideal heart line	
Sincere and warm, will make close friendships and will always be very understanding	Set low beneath fingers	
Too charming to be true; a smooth, impenetrable exterior hides shallow emotions	Tram lines	
A closed, defensive character who is difficult to get to know; the island hints at a guilty secret	Island on line	

THE HEAD LINE

The head line represents the conscious and unconscious thought processes.

The straighter and shorter the line, the less likely the person is to be an initiator.

Straight with a sudden drop shows extremes of moods, sudden and unexpected, which can make a person seem thoughtless and cruel.

The line should suit the type of hand – a damaged line can suggest a tendency to alcoholism; too fine a line, an explosive situation; too broad, no energy to back up ideas; low on the hand and curved, passionate thoughts. The deeper the line towards the Moon Mount, the more imagination and fantasy.

Modest and likeable; a good all-rounder with a steady success rate	Ideal head line, lightly attached to life line	
Imaginative and creative with a particular skill for one art; may have suicidal tendencies	Deeper dip to Moon Mount	
Very down to earth; will always attempt to be objective	Follows own course	
Friends are merely contacts in this type's ceaseless search for money	Sharp upturn towards Mercury	
Combines imagination and practicality; very good listener	'Writer's fork' on head line	

Hurtful, poor self-control, rather dull	Gap at beginning of life line from head line	
The islands indicate times of great strain which this type will avoid if at all possible	Islands on head line	
Lacks self-confidence, very critical of own failings	Turning down	
Finds it difficult to take criticism and is generally of a nervous disposition	Barbed	
Lacking in confidence, unaware of own potential, too quick to agree with others	Tied to life line with short Jupiter finger	

THE LIFE LINE

Usually this line is long, completely encircling the Mount of Venus. It is used to determine time in a person's life and is divided up into periods of five and ten years.

Like all the major lines on the hand, it will differ from person to person. A short life line *does not* necessarily mean a short life, but does usually mean that the person has wasted their life and has not followed their true destiny.

Reckless and hysterical	Wide gap between beginning of life line and head line	
More evenly balanced and easier approach to life	Head line joining life line at beginning	
Cautious, lacks self-confidence	Head line tied to life line into palm	
Change	Break in life line	
Planned change	Overlapping break in life line	

Tries too hard	Life line etched deeply into palm	
Good health, success and financial benefits	Small branches running upwards on each side of life line	
Warning of financial losses; poor health	Small branches running down: 'dropping lines'	
Very good health, plenty of energy	Double life line	
Heavily influenced by the family	Life line connected to the fate line	

Tapeworm present at time indicated (see Time Chart p.72)	Blue spot on life line	
Great healing power	Square on life line	
Wasted, not necessarily a short, life	Short life line	
Bilious constitution	Island on life line	

THE FATE LINE

The fate line normally ends at the top of the hand below the fingers. A woman's hand without a fate line means she has an unstressful life and can afford to be very feminine, in the traditional sense of not having a career, because she has responsibility taken away from her by a man.

This isn't often the case today as women have to work, so the fate line is generally deep and strong – showing women are heavily involved in life and work.

Men should show a fate line as it indicates direction in life. The point where it starts indicates the beginning of a career and the point where it ends shows the final destination of their life.

Unlucky in love; may take early retirement	Fate line ending at heart line	
Lives a life of great variety with much travel; wealth is dependent on someone of the opposite sex	Fate line starting from Moon Mount to Saturn finger	
Ambitious, will achieve power and authority over others	Fate line which runs towards Jupiter	
A sign of good luck, popularity and success; fame and fortune are in the pipeline	Fate line which runs to Apollo	
Science is the key to success for this type; they will be a business tycoon or a well-known scientist	Fate line to Mercury	

Missed chances to develop natural gifts in early years of life	Fate line from life line to Saturn	
Positive approach to life	Strong fate line	
Uncertain approach to life	Faint fate line	
Forced to assume position of responsibility at an early age	Fate line starting from wrist to Saturn	
Family is a helpful influence; an excellent start to life	Fate line from Mount of Venus to Saturn	
As a result of their own efforts, will become successful from the age of 35 onwards	Fate line from head line to Saturn	

Success and prosperity will be gradually achieved	Fate line with rising lines	
Warning of loss of money and possessions	Fate line with lines dropping	
Bad start or bad end to life; hardship	Fate line crossed or chained at start or end	
Change at time indicated (see Time Chart p.72)	Cross alongside fate line	
Unlucky omen; warns against financial loss	Cross on fate line	

An influence coming into life such as a close relationship	Influence line coming up to fate line	
A source of protection	Square on fate line	
Planned change	Overlapping line on fate line	
Unforeseen change in life	Broken fate line	

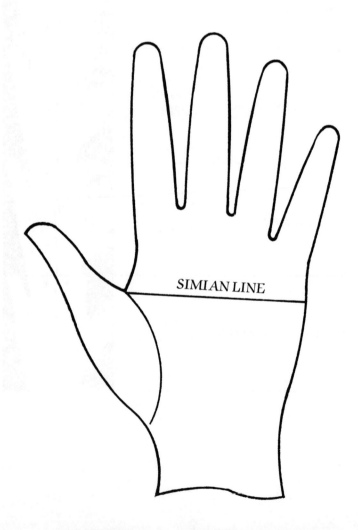

SIMIAN LINE

THE SIMIAN LINE

The Simian line runs horizontally across the palm and is the head and heart line combined.

It is rarely found on both the left *and* right hand. When found on both hands it denotes a person high in a religious order and a potential genius.

When the Simian line appears on the left hand only it usually implies a high intellect, a difficult disposition and is often associated with great disappointments in life.

When the Simian line appears on the right hand only it shows great intensity of being, a selfish and treacherous nature – someone who could be a hypocrite and who achieves their successes at the cost of others.

MOUNTS ON THE HAND

The Mounts are the highest fleshy parts in the hand. These Mounts are named after the seven principal planets and each Mount has certain characteristics. They are as follows:

The Mount of Venus:	Sensuality, passion, love
The Mount of Jupiter:	Domination, power, ambition
The Mount of Saturn:	Melancholy, seriousness, withdrawal
The Mount of Apollo:	Brilliance, success
The Mount of Mercury:	Commerce, science, mortality
The Mount of Mars:	Courage and vitality
The Moon Mount:	Changeability, romance, imagination

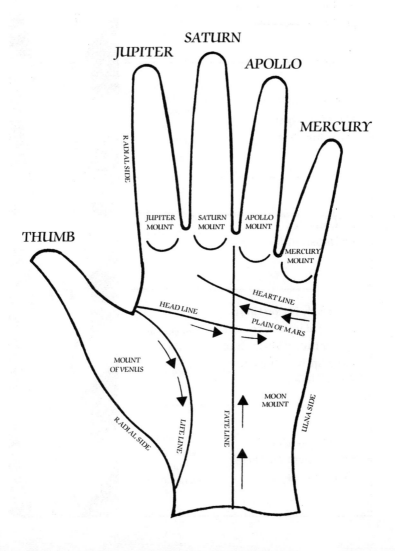

Love affair which must be kept secret because one partner is married	Line running from Venus through life, head and heart lines	
Person who keeps two affairs going at the same time	Two lines running from Venus to star on fate line	
Full-blooded and passionate	Many crosses on Mount of Venus	
Somebody is exerting a powerful influence – the nearer the influence line is the life line, the stronger the influence	Influence line running close to life line	
A good omen; great achievement will bring rich rewards	Line from Venus ending with a star under Jupiter	

Represents our capacity for love and friendship; appreciation of beauty	Fleshy ball at base of thumb	
Warm, uncritical, and sexy; attracted to opposite sex; adores children	Broad, firm and rounded	
Cold and suspicious with a pessimistic outlook; not very attractive sexually, poor health in general	Narrow and flat	
On right hand, people one likes; on left hand, people who like you	Influence lines running parallel to life line	
Symbol of great charm, luck in love and sex appeal	Star in middle of Mount of Venus	

LINES ON THE HAND FROM THE MOUNT OF VENUS

Wealth will come as a result of family help	Line from Venus to Saturn	
A very lucky line denoting wealth, fame and influential associates	Line from Venus to Apollo	
Any chance of success is undermined	Line cuts through into Apollo finger	
Achievement in business of scientific pursuits	Line from Venus to Mercury	
Denotes greed and a love of luxury	Soft, fleshy Mount of Venus	

A marriage or relationship will dominate an entire lifetime	Star just under base of thumb	
Difficulties in path to true love	Star at base of Venus	
Denotes a calculating attitude and a marriage made for money and status	Triangle on Mount of Venus	
One love only in life	One large cross	
Denotes the influence of loved ones	Lines running across Venus	

Sensual indulgence or unnatural vice will be uncovered	Star low down on Mount of Venus	
Two simultaneous love affairs – one will end in disaster	Two lines from Mount of Venus to Mercury	
Perfect health and a long life	Double life line	
Excess of tenderness	Branches at beginning and end of heart line	
Hysterical emotions and unusually intense attachments	Two lines beginning from centre of Venus and joining on palm	

LINES ON THE HAND TO AND FROM THE MOUNT OF APOLLO

Will achieve recognition for success helped by devotion of family	Line from life line to Apollo	
Success and honour by own merit in whatever occupation is taken up	Line from fate line to Apollo	
Success and fame in any occupation	'Sun line' – line from wrist to Apollo	
This line indicates success in life and especially in love	Line from Moon Mount to Apollo	
May mean suffering in old age but also indicates a marriage or close relationship late in life	Apollo line to heart line	

Success in later life, but accompanied by bitterness	Large star under Apollo	
Realisation of ambitions	'Tree of Success' – tree under Apollo	
Sense of humour	Loop under Apollo	
Recognition in middle age due to own efforts	Apollo line to head line	
Shock Hardship Scandal Protection	Small star on Apollo line Bars across Island Square	

Success line	Line to heart line under Apollo	
Success in two different careers or activities	Two lines from Apollo to heart line	
Achievement of aims	'Tree of success' from beneath Apollo to heart line	

THE HEALTH OR LIVER LINE

The health or liver line originates on the Moon Mount towards Mercury. When it is well-traced it denotes a good stomach.

When it is not traced on the hand it suggests great agility. It also indicates a tight-closed skin which does not sweat; it makes the person more prone to headaches and migraines.

A liver line which is discoloured, brown or yellow, suggests a liverish person who is bad-tempered and irritable.

The healthiest hands have no health line; the deeper the line is etched, the more serious the condition	Deep line	
Bilious attacks; if the line cuts through head line stress is present	Wavy or brownish health line	
Infertility or complications in childbirth	Star	
Lung trouble	Many islands on health line	
Sign of healing and protection in health	Square on health line	

THE THREE BRACELETS OR RASCETTES

These should be three clearly traced lines at the base of the palm which denote health, wealth and good luck respectively. They are sometimes known as the 'bracelets of life' and they are said to be the indication of 25-30 years of life, respectively.

Health	First bracelet	
Wealth	Second bracelet	
Happiness	Third bracelet	
Happiness in old age	More than three bracelets	
Possibility of miscarriage	Light, short, acute line from top bracelet	
Abortion	Short, dark, acute line from top bracelet	
Empty life	No bracelets	

Struggles, hard work and worries but success will come eventually	First bracelet chained or islanded	
In a woman's hand, high uterus and difficulty in becoming pregnant	First bracelet arching into palm	
Mother had difficulty in having you (left hand); difficulty in having own baby (right hand)	First bracelet deep in colour	
A legacy can be expected	Star in middle of top bracelet	

Again, this can indicate an inheritance	Angle in top bracelet	
Will have some difficulties in life; situation will improve in middle years	Cross in top bracelet	
Sudden wealth	Line from bracelet to Mercury	
Money problems throughout life	Second bracelet chained	

THE GIRDLE OF VENUS

In actual fact, a hand has a better reading without the Girdle of Venus. It always denotes a craving for excitement, a hysterical, nervous nature, and a tendency towards acute depression.

A normal Girdle of Venus starts between the first and second fingers and ends between the third and fourth fingers.

A very deep, red line suggests the person will have vicious tendencies and their career will suffer because of this. On no account should they consider a career in medicine.

A very thin line suggests the person will be talented in literature, have a strong will-power and a generally pleasant disposition.

A double or triple Girdle of Venus indicates bad features in the character, increasing in proportion to the number of lines. The Girdle of Venus is associated with vices and bad habits.

The ancients considered the Girdle of Venus to be an undesirable sign on the hand, unless there were several of them, or it showed significant markings (see diagrams). Today it is simply thought of as a sign of craving for excitement. If it is joined all the way along with no breaks, then the longing for excitement will never be satisfied.

Person has straightforward human passions	Normal Girdle of Venus	
A tendency to be hysterical	Double Girdle of Venus	
Venereal disease	Triple, shredded Girdle around Saturn	
An erotic nature	Girdle of Venus cut through by small lines	

UNUSUAL MARKINGS

Eye problems	Circle on life line	
Outstanding success in career	Circle on Mount of Apollo	
Protection from accidents	Square on Venus	
Could serve term of imprisonment	Large square on Venus	
Unhappiness caused by love	Star on Mount of Venus	

Military honour	Star on Plain of Mars	
Kleptomaniac	Star on Mount of Mercury	
Ill-fated wealth, fortune which brings unhappiness	Star on Mount of Apollo	
Death by the scaffold*	Star on Mount of Saturn	
One capable of murder	Symbol on Mount of Venus with short, thick tip to thumb	

(*old reading)

An amorous but inconstant disposition	Many lines encircling base of thumb	
One good marriage		
Honour and distinction, unexpected glory	Star on Mount of Jupiter	
One good marriage	One cross on Mount of Jupiter	
Two good marriages	Two crosses on Mount of Jupiter	
Riches achieved by own endeavours	Grille on second phalange of Jupiter	
Capable of adultery	Grille on third phalange of Jupiter	

Highly successful in marriage; great insight into others' minds	Cross under Jupiter	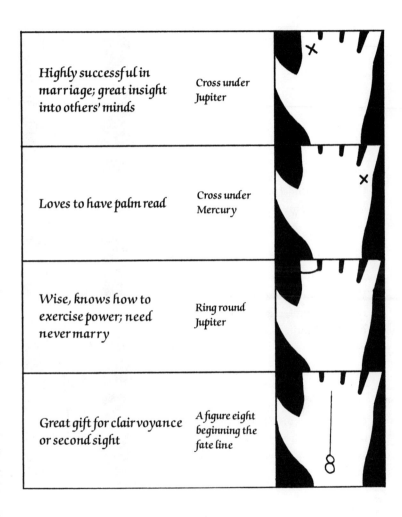
Loves to have palm read	Cross under Mercury	
Wise, knows how to exercise power; need never marry	Ring round Jupiter	
Great gift for clairvoyance or second sight	A figure eight beginning the fate line	

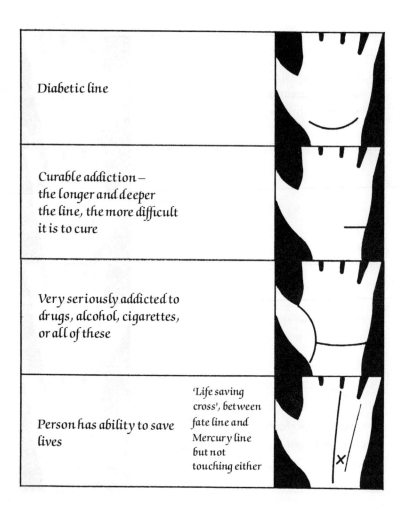

Diabetic line	
Curable addiction – the longer and deeper the line, the more difficult it is to cure	
Very seriously addicted to drugs, alcohol, cigarettes, or all of these	
Person has ability to save lives	'Life saving cross', between fate line and Mercury line but not touching either

A cowardly and mean disposition	Small triangle	
Can bear physical pain	Narrow triangle with hard, rough skin	
Business will be a failure	Narrow triangle and poor head line	
Spendthrift	Bulging on Plain of Mars	

Loop of Vanity	
Loop of Courage	
Loop of Humour	
Loop of Noble Birth – 'Rajah Loop'	
Loop of Serious Intent	

Love of Music	Loops at base of Venus	
Loop of Good Memory		
Loop of Humanism		

●DERMATOGLYPHICS●

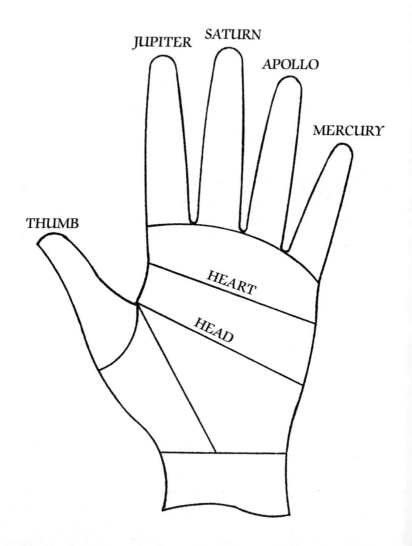

SKIN PATTERNS OR DERMATOGLYPHICS

Dermatoglyphics is the name given to the study of ridge and furrow patterns on the palms and on the soles of the feet. (Derma is the Greek word for skin.)

Each person's skin pattern is totally unique, a fact which is upheld by the important use the police make of fingerprint patterns in identifying criminals. Dermatoglyphics is also used extensively in the fields of genetics and medicine. More specifically, a great variety of problems relating to chromosome abnormalities can be detected in this way. One such example is Down's Syndrome (mongolism) where the palm and sole ridge patterns are very definitely different from those of a normal person. Similarly, distinctive peculiarities occur in the dermatoglyphs of people with sex chromosome abnormalities. Today, research workers can recognise with certainty the prints of ninety-five per cent of all Down's Syndrome babies.

Medical research has found that certain diseases frequently manifest themselves on the palm as follows:

Heart disease – Heart line thin and dotted

Gonorrhoea – Broken down skin pattern and islanded head line

Colitis – Split fate line and islanded life line

Cystitis – Islanded lines and malformed patterns

Low blood pressure – Very flexible hands

Work on the study of the skin began in the seventeenth century and in 1684 an English doctor, Nehemiah Grew, published a paper for the Royal Society of Medicine on his findings regarding ridges and patterns on the palm and fingers. Various other theories followed – in 1892 Sir Francis Galton published a book *Fingerprints* which laid the foundations for what we know as Dermatoglyphics.

On both the hands and the feet ridges run in different directions and cover different areas. There are three types of pattern found on the fingertips – the arch, the loop and the whorl. There are differences between the sexes and races; women, for instance, seem to have narrower ridges than men.

After severe burning which necessitates skin grafts, the patterns have been known to reappear in their original form after healing.

Physiologically speaking, the linear formations found on the epidermis of the hand serve a three-fold purpose. They act as secretion channels for the sweat, they form a rough surface to aid gripping, and they form a corrugated texture which heightens the stimulation of the nerve endings beneath the epidermis and facilitates tactile sensitivity. Epidermal ridges are developed in the foetus by the eighteenth week of pregnancy and the individual pattern formation remains without natural change until death.

The reading will vary according to where the peacock's eye is positioned. When it is high towards the tip of the finger, the subject will have high ideals, abstract thoughts and theories. When it is low down towards the base of the finger, a physical and practical approach will be found. When it is in the centre, the effect will be that of a well-balanced individual who is able to give their thoughts free expression.

Determined but not stubborn	Tented arch		
Very persistent will-power	Whorl		
Secretive nature	Whorl (on all digits)		
Knows own mind	Loop		
Hesitant	Composite		

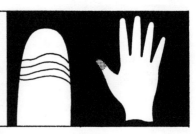

| Tendency to categorise people | Arch | |

RINGS ON THE HAND

Rings worn on the thumb denote an ego-centric personality.

Rings worn on the Jupiter finger indicate a person wishing to dominate.

Rings worn on the Saturn finger suggest a serious-minded person.

Rings worn on the Apollo finger disclose a person influenced by the superficial aspects of life who has no time for deeper feelings.

Rings worn on the left-hand Mercury finger show the possessor has a sexual obsession or complex. The heavier and flashier the ring, the coarser the complex.

Rings worn on the right-hand Mercury finger show a sublimated sexual urge, diverted into making money, and are therefore often found on business men.

Good legal mind, can see both sides of an argument	Composite	
Practical person, good manager	Radial loop	
Skilled in business but not destined for the top	Loops	
Should work in communication	Whorl	
Devoted to causes, could be a nurse	Tent	

Self-determined	Whorl		
Open-minded in metaphysical matters	Loops		
Combines the spiritual and the material, practical yet dreamy	Composite		
Desires pomp and circumstance	Arch		
Follower of 'isms'	Tented arch		

Gift for music	Tented arch	
Charming with close friends, but otherwise tough and earthy	Composite	
Individualistic, artistic	Whorl	
Appreciative of new ideas in fashion	Loops	
Conforms to standards	Arch	

PATTERNS ON THE MERCURY FINGER

Ninety per cent of Mercury fingerprint patterns are loops. It is the ideal pattern for this finger. It denotes humour and freedom in all forms of expression, as well as aiding harmony in working with other people. Loops always turn towards the Ulna side of the hand.

Whorls on Mercury show sincerity in everything that is undertaken. When the subject feels strongly about a topic they will defend their viewpoint passionately.

Arches on the Mercury finger tend to restrict artistic expression.

BIBLIOGRAPHY

Having read this book and, we hope, become more interested in the whole subject of palmistry, you might like to consider reading further publications on this topic. Here is a suggested reading list which will provide some starting-points.

Henry Frith, *Palmistry, Secrets Revealed*
(Ward Lock 1952)

Louise Owen (editor of revised edition),
Cheiro – You and Your Hand (Jarrolds – 1969)

Jo Sheridan, *What Your Hands Reveal* (Arco 1963)

Walter Sorell, *The Story of the Human Hand*
(Weidenfeld and Nicolson 1968)

J.Spier, *The Hands of Children*
(Routledge and Kegan Paul 1955)

Dr Charlotte Wolff, *Studies in Hand Reading*
(Methuen 1951)

East of England Ambulance Service

Clinical
Manual

2013

CLASS
PROFESSIONAL
PUBLISHING

East of England Ambulance Service

Clinical
Manual

CLASS
PROFESSIONAL
PUBLISHING

Printing history
First published 2013
10 9 8 7 6 5 4 3 2 1

The authors and publishers welcome feedback from the users of this book.
Please contact the publishers.

Class Professional Publishing, The Exchange, Express Park, Bristol Road,
Bridgwater, Somerset TA6 4RR, UK
Telephone: +44 (0)1278 427843
Fax: +44 (0)1278 421077
www.classprofessional.co.uk

The information presented in this book is accurate and current to the best of
the authors' knowledge. The authors and publisher, however, make no
guarantee as to, and assume no responsibility for, the correctness,
sufficiency or correctness of such information or recommendation. Any
product mentioned in the book should be used in accordance with the
manufacturer's prescribing information and ultimate responsibility rests with
the prescribing doctor.

A CIP catalogue record for this book is available from the British Library.
ISBN: 978 185959 380 6 (printed book)
ISBN: 978 185959 381 3 (ebook)

Project managed by Cambridge Publishing Management Ltd
www.cambridgepm.co.uk.
Designed and typeset by Typematter, Basingstoke.
Printed and bound in Italy by L.E.G.O.

Contents

Foreword

It is often said that 'knowledge is power', and safe clinical practice is definitely based upon the ability to put theory into practice. It is with this in mind that we welcome you to the first edition of the *East of England Clinical Manual*. We have constructed this manual to provide you with an easy reference guide of knowledge to help you practice clinically.

The manual serves as a truly Trust-wide document. Wherever you are working in the region, you should find the information you need to navigate the right care for your patient.

It is designed to complement other clinical guidance endorsed by the Trust such as *JRCALC* and *UK Resuscitation Council Guidelines*. The manual should be used alongside these to achieve the best possible care for patients.

Within healthcare we are constantly pushing the boundaries through research to develop the evidence base for improved care. The Trust has a clinical development process to pick up these changes and to adjust treatments and pathways accordingly. We aim now to publish a new edition of this manual annually to coincide with the professional update programme, and this will become the foundation for disseminating those changes in practice.

We have published the same manual for all members of the Trust so that, as members of the care delivery team, we all know the different parts we have to play. We hope this manual will act as a key resource in delivering excellent patient care.

John Martin

Consultant Paramedic

Abbreviations

4Hs	hypoxia, hypovolaemia, hypothermia, hypo/hyperkalaemia
4Ts	tension pneumothorax, tamponade, toxins, thromboembolism
A&E	accident and Emergency
AAA	abdominal aortic aneurysm
ABC	airways, breathing, circulation
ABCD²	age, blood pressure, clinical features, duration and diabetes
ACE	Anglian Community Enterprise
ACS	adult care services
ADRT	advanced decision to refuse treatment
AED	automated external defibrillator
AF	atrial fibrillation
AGM	Area General Manager
ALS	advanced life support
AMPDS	Advanced Medical Priority Dispatch System
APGAR	appearance, pulse, grimace, activity, respiratory effort
AVPU	alert, responsive to verbal, painful stimuli or unresponsive
BASICS	British Association for Immediate Care
BM	Boehringer Mannheim (blood glucose monitoring)
BP	blood pressure
BLS	basic life support
BURP	backwards, upwards, rightwards pressure
BVM	bag valve mask
cABCDE	C-spine, airway, breathing, circulation, disability, environment
CABG	coronary artery bypass graft
CAD	computer-assisted dispatch
CAT	Combat Application Tourniquet™

cath lab	catheterisation laboratory
CBRN	chemical, biological, radiological and nuclear
CCD	clinical coordination desk
CCL	Cardiac Catheter Laboratory
CCP	Critical Care Paramedic
CCU	Critical Care Unit
CECS	Central Essex Community Services
CEN	European Committee for Standardization
CFR	community first responders
CGM	Clinical General Manager
COM	Clinical Operations Manager
COPD	chronic obstructive pulmonary disease
CPAP	continuous positive airway pressure
CPD	continuous professional development
CPR	cardiopulmonary resuscitation
CQI	Clinical Quality Instructions
CRT	capillary refill time
CSD	Clinical Support Desk
CSFPPP	compliant, social history, family history, patient medical history, present history, physical
CSOP	Clinical Standard Operating Procedure
CT	computed tomography
CVS	cardiovascular system
D&V	diarrhoea and vomiting
DGH	District General Hospital
DH	drug history
DNA CPR	do not attempt cardiopulmonary resuscitation
DNAR	do not attempt resuscitation
DOB	date of birth
DoH	Department of Health
DOM	Duty Operations Manager
DRA	dynamic risk assessment

DSA	double-staffed ambulance
DVT	deep vein thrombosis
E&V	eye opening, verbal response
EAU	emergency assessment unit
ECA	emergency care assistant
ECG	electrocardiogram
ECTC	Essex Cardiothoracic Centre
ED	Emergency Department
EDT	emergency duty team
EEAST	East of England Ambulance Services Trust
EJV	external jugular vein
EOE	East of England
EOLC	end-of-life care
ePCR	electronic Patient Care Record
ET	endotracheal tube
ETA	estimated time of arrival
ETCO$_2$	end-tidal carbon dioxide concentration in the expired air
FAST	Face Arms Speech Test
FB	foreign bodies
FH	family history
FPV	falls partnership vehicle
GCS	Glasgow coma scale
GIS	gastrointestinal system
GM	General Manager
GMC	General Medical Council
GSF	Gold Standards Framework
GTN	glyceryl trinitrate
GUS	genito-urinary system
HART	Hazardous Area Response Team
HCP	healthcare professional
HDU	High Dependancy Unit

HEOC	Health and Emergency Operation Centre
HR	heart rate
Hx	history
ICCS	Integrated Communications Control System
ICP	intracranial pressure
ICT	Intermediate Care Team
IHT	inter-hospital transfers
IM	intramuscular
INR	international normalised ratio
IO	intraosseous
IPPA	inspect, palpate, percuss, auscultate
ISS	Injury Severity Score
ISSI	Inter-RF Subsystem Interface
IT	information technology
ITU	Intensive Care Unit
IV	intravenous
JAM THREADS	jaundice, anaemia, myocardial infarction, tubercule/thyroid, hypertension, rheumatic fever, epilepsy, asthma, diabetes, stroke
JRCALC	Joint Royal Colleges Ambulance Liaison Committee
JVP	jugular venous pressure
KED	Kendrick Extrication Device
KTD	Kendrick Traction Device
LCP	Liverpool Care Pathway
LHS	left-hand side
LMA	laryngeal mask airway
LMP	last menstrual period
LOC	loss of concentration
LPA	Lasting Power of Attorney
LSU	Laerdal suction unit
LVF	left ventricular failure
MCA	Mental Capacity Act

MDT	multidisciplinary team
MH	mental health
MI	myocardial infarction
MIU	Minor Injury Unit
MMP	Medicine Management Policy
MOI	mechanism of injury
MSC	motor, sensory and circulation
MTC	Major Trauma Centre
NCS	Network Co-ordination Service
NES	Non-emergency Service
NIAP	National Infarct Angioplasty Project
NIBP	non-invasive blood pressure
NIV	non-invasive ventilation
NNUH	Norfolk and Norwich University Hospital
NOF	neck of femur
NPA	nasopharyngeal airway
NS	neurological system
NSRH	Neurovascular/Stroke Rehabilitation Hospitals
OD	overdose
OOH	out-of-hours
OP	oropharyngeal
OPOA	Ordinary Power of Attorney
OT	occupational therapist
OTC	over-the-counter
PAS/VAS	Private Ambulance Service/Voluntary Ambulance Service
PAU	Paediatric Assessment Unit
PCC	Primary Care Centres
PCR	Patient Care Record
PCT	Primary Care Trust
PE	pulmonary embolism
PEA	pulseless electrical activity

SOB OE/AR	Short of breath – on exertion/at rest
SpO$_2$	oxygen saturation measured by pulsometer or CO oximeter
SPOC	single point of contact
SpR	Specialist Registrar
SIRO	Senior Information Risk Officer (SIRO)
STEMI	ST elevation myocardial infarction
SWAH	safe working at height
TBC	to be confirmed
T2T	tablet to tablet
TB	tuberculosis
TIA	transient ischaemic attack
TTA	to take away
USAR	urban search and rescue
UTI	urinary tract infection
VDI	vehicle daily inspection
WGC	Welwyn Garden City

Introduction

The Clinical Manual is the first trust publication of its kind to cover all the different grades of staff.

In order for staff to understand what sections apply to them and to prevent them working, outside their scope of practice, each section of the manual is colour-coded.

Each staff group has been assigned the following colours shown on the right.

The colour-coded markers will always be located at the edge of each entry of the clinical manual.

The colour marker shows the skills that are expected of a specific staff group. Before undertaking any procedure you should be confident that it is within your scope of practice, that you have had appropriate training, and that you have been deemed competent in its use. If there is any doubt then guidance should be sought from a manager.

Staff Group

Community First Responders (CFR)

CFR

Ambulance Care Assistants (ACA)

ACA

Emergency Care Assistants (ECA)

ECA

Qualified/Student Ambulance Paramedic (QSAP)

Q/SAP

Technicians (TECH)

TECH

Paramedics (PARA)

PARA

Specialist Paramedics (Critical Care)

SP CC

Specialist Paramedics (Primary Care)

SP PC

Acknowledgements

Thanks to:
Resuscitation Council UK,
National Institute for Health and Clinical Excellence,
South East Coast Ambulance Service,
World Health Organisation,
East of England Trauma Network,
Joint Royal College Ambulance Liaison Committee
(JRCALC)
and all staff within EEAST who have contributed
to this significant project.

Editor
Alice Berrill

Contributors
Eloise Murphy
Lisa Liszewski

1

Aide-memoire

Abbey Pain Score

What is it for?
It is used in the measurement of pain in people with dementia, or any other severe cognitive impairment, who cannot verbalise.

How do I use it?
Each question is scored from 0 to 3; the total score is calculated by the sum of each question to produce a score between 0 and 18. This is then assessed against the score criteria, which will give a pain level.

Please remember to record this value on your electronic Care Record (ePCR).

What does it look like?
See facing page.

ECA

Q/SAP

TECH

PARA

SP CC

SP PC

The Abbey Pain Scale

For measurement of pain in people with dementia who cannot verbalise.

How to use scale: While observing the resident, score questions 1 to 6.

Name of resident:..

Name and designation of person completing the scale:...

Date: .... Time: ....

Latest pain relief given was.. at ....hrs.

Q1. **Vocalisation**
e.g. whimpering, groaning, crying
Absent 0   Mild 1   Moderate 2   Severe 3

Q1 ☐

Q2. **Facial expression**
e.g. looking tense, frowning, grimacing, looking frightened
Absent 0   Mild 1   Moderate 2   Severe 3

Q2 ☐

Q3. **Change in body language**
e.g. fidgeting, rocking, guarding part of body,withdrawn
Absent 0   Mild 1   Moderate 2   Severe 3

Q3 ☐

Q4. **Behavioural change**
e.g. increased confusion, refusing to eat, alteration in usual
patterns
Absent 0   Mild 1   Moderate 2   Severe 3

Q4 ☐

Q5. **Physiological change**
e.g. temperature, pulse or blood pressure outside normal
limits, perspiring, flushing of pallor
Absent 0   Mild 1   Moderate 2   Severe 3

Q5 ☐

Q6. **Physical changes**
e.g. skin tears, pressure areas, arthritis, contractures,
previous injuries
Absent 0   Mild 1   Moderate 2   Severe 3

Q6 ☐

Add scores for Q1 to Q6 and record here ➡ Total pain score ☐

Now tick the box that
matches the Total Pain Score ➡

0–2	3–7	8–13	14+
No pain	Mild	Moderate	Severe

Finally, tick the box which
matches the type of pain ➡

Chronic	Acute	Acute on chronic

Abbey J, De Bellis A, Piller N, Esterman A, Gilles L, Parker D, Lowcay B. The Abbey Pain Scale.
Funded by the JH & JD Gunn Medical Research Foundation 1998–2002.
(This document may be reproduced with this reference retained.)

ECA

Q/SAP

TECH

PARA

SP CC

SP PC

ATMISTER Pre-alert/Handover

What is it for?
ATMISTER can be used when pre-alerting or handing over.

How do I use it?
With the introduction of the new trauma system all pre-alerts are required to be in the format below.

What does it look like?

A Age and other patient details

T Time of incident

M Mechanism of injury

I Injuries sustained

S Signs and status – HR, RR, BP, GCS, SpO_2

T Treatment given

E Estimated time of arrival

R Requests – e.g., trauma triage tool criteria are met and so the trauma team need to be activated

Refer to: *Trauma Triage Tool, pages 48–49.*

Call Categories

What is it for?

The new call categories have been updated to the Trust's CAD system.

How do I use it?

To respond to emergency calls in the appropriate way.

What does it look like?

New call category	Response required
Red 1	Crew to respond with blue lights and sirens – EMERGENCY CALL
Red 2	Crew to respond with blue lights and sirens – EMERGENCY CALL
Green 1	Crew to respond with blue lights and sirens – EMERGENCY CALL
Pre-alert	Crew to respond with blue lights and sirens – EMERGENCY CALL
Green 2	Crew to respond with blue lights and sirens – EMERGENCY CALL
Green 3	Crew to respond at normal road speed – Emergency call, but no lights and sirens required for response
Green 4	Crew to respond at normal road speed – Emergency call, but no lights and sirens required for response
Urgent/routine calls	Crew to respond at normal road speed – Non-emergency call

ACA

ECA

Q/SAP

TECH

PARA

SP CC

SP PC

Call Categories *continued*

The information sent to crews via the digital radio and in-vehicle MDT systems is as follows:

New call category	Digital radio alert mobile data terminal (MDT) display
Red 1	EMR R1
Red 2	EMR R2
Green 1	EMR HR G1
Pre-alert	EMR PA Pre Alert
Green 2	EMR HR G2
Green 3	EMR CR G3
Green 4	EMR CR G4
Urgent/Routine calls	URG CR URGENT or ROUTINE or Test

ECA

Q/SAP

TECH

PARA

SP CC

SP PC

Cardiac Arrest Checklist

On Arrival	After ALS Initiated	Post-ROSC
• Effective chest compressions (minimise time off the chest)	• Effective and continuous chest compressions on-going (minimise time off the chest)	• ABCDE
• Person performing chest compressions changed every 2 minutes	• Appropriate shocks being delivered	• Stay on scene for a minimum of 10 minutes
• Defibrillator in manual mode	• I-Gel/ET tube in situ	• Respiration rate:
• Assessment of presenting rhythm	• Monitor ETCO$_2$ via capnography	– Consider the use of a ventilator
• Second crew requested and dispatched	– Is there a wave form?	– <10 per min, assist ventilation 1 breath every 6 seconds
• High flow attached to BVM & bag inflated	– Good chest compressions will result in improved ETCO$_2$	– >10 – aim to maintain SpO$_2$ at 94–98%
• Check adequate chest rise with ventilation	– Sudden improvement of ETCO$_2$ may indicate a ROSC	• Aim to optimise ETCO$_2$ between 4.5 & 6.0 (once resp rate and SpO$_2$ 94–98% established)
• If traumatic cardiac arrest, consider enhanced care (helicopter, critical care)	• IV access secured and IV fluids attached	• Obtain and record a full set of vital signs including temperature
	• Cardiac arrest drugs given if required	• 12-lead ECG obtained and interpreted
	• BM measured and recorded	• Is BP < 90 mmHg? If so, administer 250ml normal saline as per JRCALC
	• Reversible causes considered and recorded on PCR	• Symptomatic bradycardia – consider atropine
	• Record working diagnosis on PCR	

If the 12-lead ECG shows a clear STEMI then discuss with the team at the nearest PPCI centre – this also includes ventilated patients with a STEMI. Please do not forget to call the clinical advice line for support 07753 950843

SP PC   SP CC   PARA   TECH   Q/SAP   ECA   ACA   CFR

Cardiac Syncope and Falls

Fall vs Cardiac Syncope

The East of England Ambulance Service policy is shown below:

One third of all neck and femur fractures thought to be caused by a mechanical fall are actually attributed to a cardiac syncope.

Do you routinely perform an ECG after a fall?
- Complete 12-lead ECG.
- Analyse the ECG (10 point and 8 point rules).
  - Regularity, Rate, P Waves and Association to QRS, PR Interval (120–200 MS is normal), QRS and duration (80–120 MS is normal), ST Segment, T Waves, **Check the QT Duration** (If > 450 MS for men or > 470 MS for women then abnormal).
- Obtain Standing and Sitting Blood Pressures.
- Obtain a History of Prodromal Symptoms.
- (symptoms that occur before the full onset of condition, e.g., lightheaded, warm, nausea for syncope).
- Consider transport to hospital if an abnormal ECG or no clear diagnosis of a simple faint.

An elongated QT interval can be a cause of Cardiac Syncope as well as sudden cardiac death.

Remember to refer all falls to SPOC: 0845 602 6856

Effective Communication with Patients who have Learning Disabilities

Communicating with patients and or their carers can be challenging for staff. This Aide-memoire can be used to enhance assessment and communication skills.

Remember, you may have to use a variety of communication tools to ensure that patients can tell you how they are feeling and understand what treatment/assessments you are going to do.

People with learning disabilities may have specific related conditions such as: cardiac problems, different airway anatomy and sensory problems.

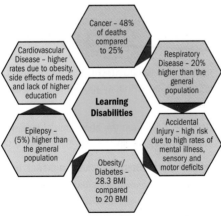

Moseley, J (2012). 'Learning Disabilities', in The Learning and Development Unit's *Operational Mandatory Refresher Workbook 2012/2013*, pp56–61. Norwich: The East of England Ambulance Service Trust.

Effective Communication with Patients who have Learning Disabilities *continued*

1. Beware of missing serious illness. Important medical symptoms can be ignored because they are seen as part of someone's disability.

2. Be more suspicious that the patient may have a serious illness and take action quickly.

3. Find out the best way to communicate. Ask family, friends or support workers for help. Remember that some people use signs and symbols as well as speech.

4. Listen to parents and carers, especially when someone has difficulty communicating. They can tell you which signs and behaviours indicate distress.

5. Don't make assumptions about a person's quality of life. They are likely to be enjoying a fulfilling life.

6. Be clear on the law about capacity and consent. When people lack capacity you are required to act in their best interests.

7. Ask for help. Staff from the community learning disability team can help.

8. Remember the Disability Discrimination Act. It requires you to make 'reasonable adjustments' so you may have to do some things differently to achieve the same health outcomes.

People with learning disabilities will usually have a hospital passport/healthcare plan. Please ensure that this is conveyed with the patient and handed over to the hospital staff along with any medication. This ensures a seamless pathway for the patient.

This is my
Hospital Passport

For people with learning disabilities coming into hospital

My name is:

If I have to go to hospital this book needs to go with me. It gives hospital staff important information about me.

It needs to hang on the end of my bed and a copy should be put in my notes.

This passport belongs to me. Please return it when I am discharged.

Nursing and medical staff please look at my passport before you do any interventions with me.

→ Things you must know about me

→ Things that are important to me

→ My likes and dislikes

Things you must know about me

Religion:
Religious/Spiritual needs:
Ethnicity:
GP:
Address:
Tel No:
Other services/professionals involved with me:

Allergies:
Medical interventions – how to take my blood, give injections, BP ch
Heart
Breathing problems:
Risk of choking, Dysphagia (eating, drinking and swallowing

Date completed   by

Things you must know about me

Name:
Likes to be known as:
NHS number:
Date of Birth:
Address:
Tel No:
How I communicate/What language I speak:
Family contact person, carer or other support:
Relationship e.g. Mum, Dad, Home Manager, Support Worker:
Address:
Tel No:
My support needs and who gives me the most support:
My carer speaks:

Date completed   by

DNA CPR/ADRT

If you are unsure of the validity of any DNA CPR or ADRT, begin CPR until you have gained further advice via the advice line.

DNA CPR/ADRT

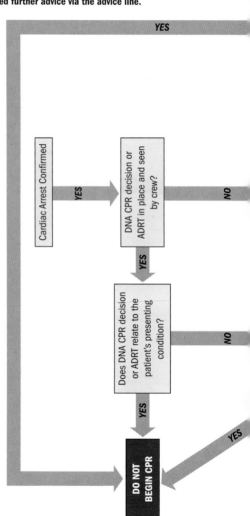

YES

| Cardiac Arrest Confirmed |

YES →

| DNA CPR decision or ADRT in place and seen by crew? |

NO

YES ↓

| Does DNA CPR decision or ADRT relate to the patient's presenting condition? |

NO

YES ↓

DO NOT BEGIN CPR

YES

Providing the clinician has demonstrated a rational process in decision making, EEAST will support the member of staff if this decision is challenged.

The clinician finding a person with no DNA CPR decision or ADRT to refuse CPR, should consider no resuscitation if:

1. The expected outcome of undertaking CPR is no recovery (e.g., it would be inappropriate to start CPR if it will not re-start the heart and maintain breathing).

2. The right to be free from inhuman and degrading treatment (Human Rights Act 1998) outweighs the right to life.

NO

Any condition unequivocally associated with death (as quoted in JRCALC guidelines)?

NO

Begin CPR immediately and in accordance with JRCALC guidance

YES

1. Massive cranial and cerebral destruction
2. Hemicorporectomy
3. Massive truncal injury incompatible with life including decapitation
4. Decomposition/putrefaction
5. Incineration
6. Hypostasis
7. Rigor mortis
8. In a newborn foetus maceration is a contraindication to resuscitation

Refer to: *Resuscitation Policy on EAST 24.*

CFR

ACA

ECA

Q/SAP

TECH

PARA

SP CC

SP PC

13

The incident reporting process

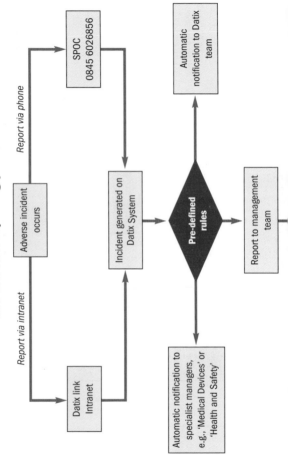

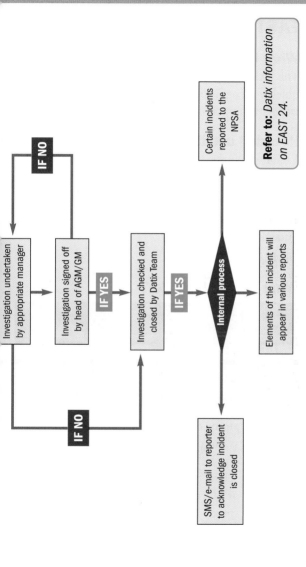

Investigation undertaken by appropriate manager

IF NO

Investigation signed off by head of AGM/GM

IF YES

Investigation checked and closed by Datix Team

IF NO

IF YES

Internal process

Certain incidents reported to the NPSA

Refer to: *Datix information on EAST 24.*

Elements of the incident will appear in various reports

SMS/e-mail to reporter to acknowledge incident is closed

CFR

ACA

ECA

Q/SAP

TECH

PARA

SP CC

SP PC

FAST

What is it for?

The FAST (Face Arms Speech Test) will help you to quickly recognise the key symptoms of a transient ischaemic attack (TIA) or stroke.

How do I use it?

Facial weakness: Can the person smile? Has their mouth or eyelid drooped?

Arm weakness: Can the person raise both arms?

Speech problems: Can the person speak clearly and understand what you say?

TIME TO CALL 999.

What does it look like?

Other symptoms of a TIA or stroke may include:

- Weakness, numbness, clumsiness, or pins and needles on one side of the body – for example, in an arm, leg or the face.
- Loss of or blurred vision in one or both eyes.
- Slurred speech or difficulty finding some words.

Only ever consider TIA when all symptoms have resolved – until then treat as a stroke!

LITE – Manual Handling Assessment Tool

What is it for?

The LITE assessment tool is a quick one minute risk assessment that should be conducted before carrying out any manual handling task, whether lifting and carrying a patient or an inanimate load.

How do I use it?

It is a four step process that assesses all aspects of a lift.

What does it look like?

L is for Load

How heavy is the patient? What is their physical and mental condition? What can they do to help? Did you do a clinical risk assessment?

I is for Individual

That's you! Ask yourself: Am I physically capable of undertaking the task? If the answer is no then don't try.

T is for Task

Stop and think through what you are going to have to do to get the patient into your vehicle. Is there an easier way?

E is for Environment

What hazards will make your job more difficult? Can you move things? Are there any problems on your route from the house or scene to the ambulance?

LITE – Manual Handling
Assessment Tool *continued*

Plan the move

Use your manual handling equipment. Plan with
your colleague and the patient/friends/relatives so
everyone is certain of what they need to do.

Prepare

Clear obstacles, fix open doors and stretch your
back prior to lifting.

Use the correct body mechanics

You should be in a balanced position with your feet
at least shoulder-width apart. You must place your
feet so you can maintain your balanced position
during any lift or transfer.

> **REMEMBER**
> The four principals of lifting are: keep the load close,
> use your legs, keep the spine neutral and do not twist.

Paediatric Emergency Treatment Chart

		CPR ratio	LMA volume	Tidal	RR	HR	SBP
Strength		$\frac{1}{3}$ chest depth					
	Dose	30:2 at puberty	Check wrapper	5-7 ml kg^{-1}			
	Route			Ensure chest rises			
	Notes			ETCO$_2$ aim 4 kPa	Reference – JRCALC guidelines		
Age		100-120 b.p.m.		ml	b.p.m.	b.p.m.	mmHg
<1 month		3:1	1	17-24	30-40	110-160	70-90
1 month		15:2	1	20-28	30-40	110-160	70-90
3 months		15:2	1.5	25-35	30-40	110-160	70-90
6 months		15:2	1.5	35-49	30-40	110-160	70-90
1 year		15:2	1.5	50-70	25-35	110-150	80-95
2 years		15:2	2	60-84	25-30	95-140	80-100
3 years		15:2	2	70-98	25-30	95-140	80-100
4 years		15:2	2	80-112	25-30	95-140	80-100
5 years		15:2	2	90-126	20-25	80-120	90-100
6 years		15:2	2.5	100-140	20-25	80-120	90-110
7 years		15:2	2.5	115-161	20-25	80-120	90-110
8 years		15:2	2.5	130-182	20-25	80-120	90-110
10 years		15:2	3	150-210	20-25	80-120	90-110
12 years		15:2	3	190-266	20-25	80-120	90-110
Adolescent		30:2	3	200-280			

Benzyl penicillin   <1 year 300 mg, 1-9 years 600 mg, >9 years 1200 mg.

Diazemuls   0.3 mg/kg MAX dose if fitting. Do not dilute in saline or water.

Ipratropium   <1 year 0.125 mg, 1-5 years 0.25 mg, >6 years 0.5 mg.

Salbutamol   2.5 mg can be repeated unless side effects become significant.

Glucagon   Birth 0.1 mg, <25 kg, 0.5 mg, >25 kg, >8 years, 1 mg intramuscular.

ECA

Q/SAP

TECH

PARA

SP CC

SP PC

Paediatric Emergency Treatment Chart *continued*

Appearance:
Tone
Interact
Consolable
Look
Speech

Work of breathing:
Sounds
Retractions

Circulation to skin:
Pallor, mottled, cyanosis

Paediatric GCS (E&V as adult) and motor function:

5 = Voice, **4** = Smiles/fixes/follows, **3** = Cries but consolable, **2** = Restless/agitated, **1** = Silent

---

APGAR. Complete at 1 min and 5 min after birth

Clinical sign	0 points	1 point	2 points
Appearance	Blue, pale	Body pink, extremities blue	Completely pink
Pulse	Absent	Below 100	Over 100
Grimace	No response	Grimaces	Cries
Activity	Limp	Some flexion of extremities	Active motion
Respiratory effort	Absent	Slow, irregular	Good, strong cry

Drugs and Treatments

Cardioversion
Synchronised Shock – 0.5–1.0 joules kg^{-1} escalating to 2.0 joules kg^{-1} if unsuccessful.

Amiodarone
5 mg kg^{-1} IV or IO bolus in arrest (0.1 ml kg^{-1} of 150 mg in 3 ml) after 3rd and 5th shocks. Flush line with 0.9% saline or 5% glucose.

Atropine
20 mcg kg^{-1}, minimum dose 100 mcg, maximum dose 600 mcg.

Calcium chloride 10%
0.2 ml kg^{-1} for hypocalcaemia.

Lorazepam
100 mcg kg^{-1} IV or IO for treatment of seizures. Can be repeated after 10 minutes. Maximum single dose 4 mg.

Naloxone
Resuscitation dose for full reversal 100 mcg kg^{-1}. For partial reversal of opiate analgesia 10 mcg kg^{-1} boluses, titrated to effect.

Anaphylaxis
Adrenaline 1:1000 **intramuscularly** (<6 yrs 150 mcg [0.15 ml], 6–12 yrs 300 mcg [0.3 ml], > 12 yrs 500 mcg [0.5 ml]) can be repeated after five minutes. **OR** titrate boluses of 1 mcg kg^{-1} IV **ONLY** if familiar with giving IV adrenaline.

Weights averaged on lean body mass from 50th centile weights for males and females. Drug doses based on Resuscitation Council (UK) Guidelines 2010. Recommendations for tracheal tubes are on full-term neonates.
For newborns, glucose at 2.5 ml kg^{-1} is recommended.

May 2011

Q/SAP

TECH

PARA

SP CC

SP PC

Paediatric Emergency Treatment Chart *continued*

		Adrenaline	Fluid Bolus	Glucose
	STRENGTH	1:10,000	0.9% Saline	10%
	DOSE	10 mcg kg^{-1}	20 ml kg^{-3}	2 ml kg^{-3}
	ROUTE	IV, IO	IV, IO	IV, IO
	NOTES		Consider warmed fluids	For known hypoglycaemia
Age	**Weight kg**	**ml**	**ml**	Recheck glucose after dose **ml**
<1 month	3.5	0.35	70	7
1 month	4	0.4	80	8
3 months	5	0.5	100	10
6 months	7	0.7	140	14
1 year	10	1.0	200	20
2 years	12	1.2	240	24
3 years	14	1.4	280	28
4 years	16	1.6	320	32
5 years	18	1.8	360	36
6 years	20	2.0	400	40
7 years	23	2.3	460	46
8 years	26	2.6	520	52
10 years	30	3.0	600	60
12 years	38	3.8	760	76
Adolescent	>40	10	1000	80

Joint Royal Colleges Ambulance Liaison Committee (2006). *UK Ambulance Service Clinical Practice Guidelines*. Warwick: JRCALC.

Sodium Bicarbonate		Tracheal Tube Cuffed	Tracheal Tube	Defibrillation
4.2%	8.4%			
1 mmol kg^{-1}				4 joules kg^{-1}
IV, IO, UVC	IV, IO			Trans-thoracic
			Monitor cuff pressure	Monophasic or biphasic
m	ml	10 mm	10 mm	Manual
7	–	3.0	–	20
8	–	3.0 – 3.5	3.0	20
10	–	3.5	3.0	20
–	7	3.5	3.0	30
–	10	4.0	3.5	40
–	12	4.5	4.0	50
–	14	4.5 – 5.0	4.0 – 4.5	60
–	16	5.0	4.5	60
–	18	5.0 – 5.5	4.5 – 5.0	70
–	20	5.5	5.0	80
–	23	5.5 – 6.0	5.0 – 5.5	90
–	26	–	6.0 – 6.5	100
–	30	–	7.0	120
–	38	–	7 – 7.5	150
–	50	–	7 – 8	As for adults

Q/SAP

TECH

PARA

SP CC

SP PC

Patient Assessment

Q/SAP

TECH

PARA

SP CC

SP PC

Patient Assessment

cABCDE* Time Critical?

Transport immediately to nearest DGH under emergency conditions with AMISTER pre-alert

Introduce yourself to the patient

Proceed with CSFPPP (see boxes below)

Complaint What seems to be the problem?

Drug History
Drug
Dose
Frequency
Repeat prescriptions
Compliant?
Relevant to PHM

Past Medical History (PMH)
Operations
Hospital admissions
Specific illness enquiry (JAM THREADS*)
Long-term conditions
Lasting problems
Allergies
Immunisation

Family History (FH)
Partner/Single
Other family members
Family medical history
Life within family
Current illness in family
Pets

Social History (SH)
Accommodation
Employment
Smoking/Alcohol/
Illegal Drugs/Eating
Social
Hobbies
Travel

24

*JAM THREADS

Jaundice, anaemia, MI, TB/thyroid, Hypertension, Rheumatic fever, Epilepsy, Asthma, Diabetes, Stroke

Present History (Hx)

Physical examination may be concurrent with gaining present history. Detail of chief complaint then functional enquiry:

General

Unwell lately, tired aches, pains, rash, and lumps. Activities of daily living, wash/toilet etc, SOB OE/AR**

Functional Enquiry

| **Respiratory System (RS)** See separate Aide-memoire (pp. 27–28) | **Cardiovascular System (CVS)** See separate Aide-memoire (pp. 29–30) | **Gastro-Intestinal System (GIS)** See separate Aide-memoire (pp. 31–32) | **Genitourinary system (GUS)** See separate Aide-memoire (p. 33) | **Neurological System (NS)** See separate Aide-memoire (pp. 34–35) | **Mental Health (MH)** See separate Aide-memoire (pp. 36–37) |

* C spine, airway, breathing, circulation, disability, environment

**SOB = shortness of breath; OE = on exertion; AR = at rest

SP PC   SP CC   PARA   TECH   Q/SAP

25

Patient Assessment – Pathology Progression

Type of pathology	Onset of symptoms	Progression of symptoms	Associated symptoms
Infection	Hours	Hours to days	Fevers, localising symptoms, e.g. pleuritic pain and/or cough
Inflammation	Sudden	Weeks to months	Localising symptoms of variable severity, often coming and going
Metabolic	Very variable	Hours to months	Steady progression in severity with no remission
Neoplastic	Gradual	Weeks to months	Weight loss/fatigue
Toxic	Abrupt	Rapid	See SIRS criteria below
Vascular	Sudden	Hours	Rapid development of associated signs
Degenerative	Gradual	Months to years	Gradual worsening interspersed with periods of acute deterioration

Q/SAP

TECH

PARA

SP CC

SP PC

Patient Assessment – Respiratory System (RS)

Observations	Findings
Inspect (but maintain modesty)	• Cyanosis/pallor/respiratory distress/positioning (i.e., tripoding)/medical alert tag • Bruising/breathing asymmetry/flail chest/tracheal shift/scars/chest wall deformities? • Cough/sputum colour (clear, coloured or bloody?) • Rate/rhythm/pattern and depth of respirations?
Palpation	• Assess degree and symmetry of chest expansion • Assess the tracheal position (place two fingers on either side of the trachea and judge the distance of the fingers from the sternomastoid tendons • Palpate for masses, lumps, tenderness subcutaneous emphysema or **tactile fremitus** (vibration of the chest wall during respiration. This is ↑ over areas of **consolidation** and ↓ over areas of **pleural effusion** or **pneumothorax**)

Q/SAP

TECH

PARA

SP CC

SP PC

Patient Assessment
– Respiratory System (RS) *continued*

Observations	Findings
Percussion	• **Hyperresonance** – air in the chest cavity (e.g., pneumothorax, Asthma or COPD) • **Hyporesonance** – consolidation (infection, pleural effusion, pulmonary oedema • **Stony dull** – pleural effusion
Auscultation	• Breath sounds present? Normal, absent or adventitious • Wheezing (lower airway), grunting (usually infants), crackles (fine or coarse), rhonhi (rattling in upper airway), pleural rub (walking in snow) • Always compare one side of the chest with the other • Vocal fremitus • Whispering pectoriloquy

Patient Examination – Cardiovascular System

Test	Observations
Inspect 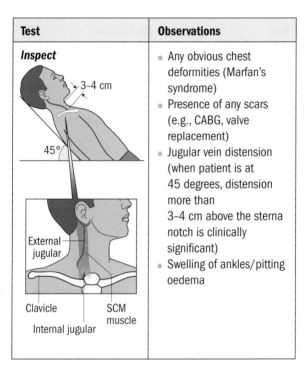	• Any obvious chest deformities (Marfan's syndrome) • Presence of any scars (e.g., CABG, valve replacement) • Jugular vein distension (when patient is at 45 degrees, distension more than 3–4 cm above the sterna notch is clinically significant) • Swelling of ankles/pitting oedema

Patient Examination
– Cardiovascular System *continued*

Test	Observations
Arterial Pulse Points Superficial temporal · External maxillary · Carotid · Brachial · Ulnar · Femoral · Popliteal · Radial · Posterior tibial · Dorsalis pedis	• Radial • Assess the presence and symmetry of each pulse (radial, brachial, femoral, popliteal, dorsalis pedis)
ECG	• 6 point plan – Lead II • 10 rules of normal ECG • Diagnose arrhythmias if present, AF, ectopics, blocks • Infarction? • STEMI

Q/SAP

TECH

PARA

SP CC

SP PC

Patient Examination – Gastro-intestinal System

Test	Observations
Specific questions	• ↓↑ weight change, ↓↑ appetite, D&V, indigestion, haemetesesis flatulence, per rectum bleeding/ irritation or jaundice, constipation, malaena, urination (↑↓ colour) • Any changes in bowel habit? • All women of childbearing age.
Inspect (expose but maintain modesty)	• Expose from the nipples to symphysis pubis • Inspect for: symmetry, abnormal pulsation (AAA), shape (distension – ask the patient!) and scars • Is the patient in obvious pain, comfortable or distressed at rest • Does the patient have pallor or appear jaundiced?
Palpation (watch patient's face for reactions)	• Light palpation (one hand <2.5 cm depth) in a quadrant away from the painful area, then move through all four quadrants • Deep palpation (two-handed – 5 cm depth) of all nine regions • Note any masses (size, shape, pulsatile or location), tenderness (note any rebound tenderness), temperature or presence of guarding

Q/SAP

TECH

PARA

SP CC

SP PC

Patient Assessment
– Gastro-intestinal System *continued*

Test	Observations
Auscultation	• Auscultate each of the four quadrants prior to deciding if bowel sounds are present or absent (silence = sub-acute abdomen)

Elling, B & Elling, K (2003). *Principals of Patient Assessment in EMS,* 1st ed., pp182–97. New York: Thompson Delmar Learning.

Marsh, A (2004). *History and Examination.* 2nd ed., pp120–21. London: Elsevier Limited.

Patient Assessment – Genito-urinary System

Questioning	Possible answers
Specific questions: urination	• Frequency: nocturia • Flow: dribbling, hesitancy, straining, urgency • Colour: clear, cloudy, bloody • Odour: strong suggests infection • Clarity: clear or cloudy • Pain: flank or loin
Universal questions: sexually active	• Contraception used? • Discharge • Pruritus (itching)
Gender specific: males	• Prostate issues
Gender specific: females	• LMP • Potential pregnancy

Marsh, A (2004). *History and Examination*. 2nd ed., pp119–36. London: Elsevier Limited.

Elling, B & Elling, K (2003). *Principals of Patient Assessment in EMS*, pp181–97. New York: Thomson Delmar Learning.

Patient Assessment – Neurological System

Test	Observation
FAST	• **Facial weakness:** Can the person smile? Has their mouth or eyelid drooped? • **Arm weakness:** Can the person raise both arms? • **Speech problems:** Can the person speak clearly and understand what you say? • **Time:** If FAST positive, rapidly assess for thrombolysis/blue light pre-alert criteria; patient should be extricated to ambulance as soon as possible and further assessment carried out en route to hospital.
Functional enquiry	• Headache, visual disturbances, blackout, dizziness, fits, paraesthesia, weaknesses, trauma, any history of TIA.
Check pupils	• Disconjugate gaze: (check light on pupils in same position on each eye) • Pupil size (PEARL). • Accommodation: Hold your finger about 10 cm from the patient's nose, ask them to alternate looking into the distance and at your finger, observe the pupillary response in each eye.
Eye movement	• Check eye movement and nystagmus (H-shaped pattern).

Elling, B & Elling, K (2003). *Principles of Patient Assessment in EMS*. 1st ed. pp167–9. New York: Thompson Delmar Learning.

Q/SAP
TECH
PARA
SP CC
SP PC

Patient Assessment
– Neurological System *continued*

Test	Observation
Eye movement *continued*	• Stand or sit in front of the patient, ask the patient to follow your finger with their eyes without moving their head, check gaze in the six cardinal directions using a cross or 'H' pattern. • Check convergence by moving your finger towards the bridge of the patient's nose.
Field of vision	• Use St Andrews' Cross technique.
Assess all four limbs	• Tone: Normally there is limited resistance through the range of movement. • Movement: Upper limbs push and pull away, lower limbs push and pull feet. • Sensation: Ask patient to close their eyes and touch the patient's skin in the same places on the LHS and RHS of the body; ask the patient to tell you where you are touching and if it is the same pressure on each side.
Assess co-ordination	• Upper limb: Finger-nose test (hold your finger at arm's length from the patient, ask them to rapidly touch their finger and your nose). • Lower limbs: Heel–shin test (ask patient to place the right heel on the left shin and move up and down, and vice-versa). • Assess gait by asking the patient to walk a few steps (if possible).

Q/SAP

TECH

PARA

SP CC

SP PC

Patient Assessment – Mental Health

Observations	Findings
Appearance	• Physical position and posture • Hygiene, dress, age and gender
Affect	• What is the patient feeling?
Behaviour	• What is the patient doing (watch body language cues)?

Cognitive functions	• Level of consciousness:
	  – aware of location and what is happening
	  – long-term memory: check DOB and historical events
	  – short-term memory: what has the patient eaten in the past 24 hours?
	• Sleeping/eating normally?

Speech	• Word choice, content, intonation, clarity and pace
Thought processes	• Is the patient's judgement reasonable given the situation? • Is the patient experiencing visual, auditory or any other sensory phenomena? • Is the patient making rational decisions?

ECA

Q/SAP

TECH

PARA

SP CC

SP PC

Patient Assessment
– Mental Health *continued*

Observations	Findings
Thought processes *continued*	• Self-harm/suicidal thoughts (planned already?) • Enjoying the things that you normally would do? • Insight – do you think there is anything wrong with you?

Non-emergency Service Discharge Checklist and DNA CPR Card

What is it for?

The Flash Card is of credit card size and is made of a similar robust plastic. The card is printed on both sides, one side serving as a General Patient Discharge Check List, whereas the reverse side is specifically for guidance to staff when discharging a patient who carries a DNA CPR Order.

How do I use it?

During the general discharge process, staff will often need to process several pieces of information and hopefully the checklist will ensure all appropriate data are captured.

When a DNA CPR Order is in place for a patient, the card guides both ambulance and hospital staff to follow the correct protocol as outlined in the NHS East of England Integrated Do Not Attempt Cardiopulmonary Resuscitation (DNA CPR) – Policy for Adults. The DNA CPR Order itself is the property of the patient and should travel with the patient following discharge.

Most importantly, the DNA CPR Order itself is the property of the patient and should travel with the patient following discharge. A more detailed explanation of matters that surround this process will be issued to staff on receipt of the card.

What does it look like?

East of England Ambulance Service **NHS**
NHS Trust

DNA CPR

- Is there a DNA CPR Order in place?
- Is the **ORIGINAL** DNA CPR Form with the Patient?
  - If YES – then ensure DNA CPR Form travels with the Patient.
  - If NO – then advise care staff present that resuscitation of patient will be carried out if necessary.
- Have relatives been made aware that a DNA CPR Order is in place?

ACA

General Patient Discharge Check List

Remember to Check:

- Patient's Name & Confirmed Destination Address.
- Any specific Clinical or Moving & Handling Issues.
- Access to property (i.e., Key/Steps).
- Relatives at Home / Care Package in Place.
- TTAs – (Medication).
- Discharge Letter.
- Patient's Personal Belongings / Medical Aids.

Refer to: *For all staff groups other than ACA, see Aide-memoire: DNA CPR, pages 12–13.*

Recognition of Life Extinct (ROLE)

ECA
Q/SAP
TECH
PARA
SP CC
SP PC

Recognition Of Life Extinct (ROLE)

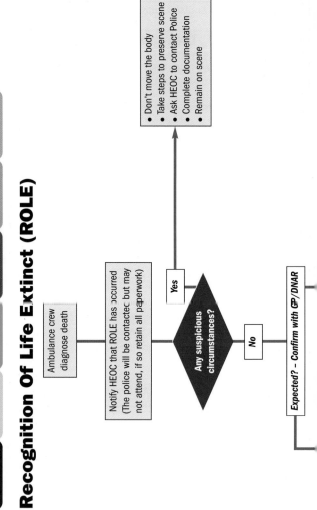

Ambulance crew diagnose death

Notify HEOC that ROLE has occurred (The police will be contacted but may not attend, if so retain all paperwork)

Any suspicious circumstances?

Yes
- Don't move the body
- Take steps to preserve scene
- Ask HEOC to contact Police
- Complete documentation
- Remain on scene

No

Expected? – *Confirm with GP/DNAR*

Death in home or normal place of residence

Death in a public place OR ROLE during transport

Are relatives present?

Yes

- Retrieve all equipment and consumables
- Offer condolences and support documentation
- Inform GP or OOH (if not already done so)

No

- Seek contact details (HEOC may hold some)
- Where *NONE* ask HEOC to contact Police
- Remain on scene until police or other person arrives

Complete documentation

- Complete and sign an ePCR
- Complete a Witness Statement ROLE
- Attach a death label to the patient
- Print two 30-second ECG traces (one for Police one for EOE)

- Remove patient to mortuary (inform prior to transport)
- Request HEOC to inform Police
- Leave documentation with the patient

Under 18

- Transport child's body to the nearest A&E department with parent(s) or guardian(s).
- Children should *NOT* be taken to the mortuary. Only when directed by Police should the body be left at home.

Wherever appropriate a child should be transported to A & E with on-going resuscitation

Joint Royal Colleges Ambulance Liaison Committee (2006). *UK Ambulance Service Clinical Practice Guidelines.* Warwick: JRCALC.

ECA

Q/SAP

TECH

PARA

SP CC

SP PC

41

Sharp's Management

Ensure the sharps bin is correctly assembled according to manufacturer's instructions. Taking care that the lid is secure prior to usage.

To ensure traceability in case of adverse incident, it is **MANDATORY** to complete the sharps bin manufacturers label at the time of assembly with:

- Station of origin
- Date
- Signature.

Safe use of sharps

- Always use sharps containers issued by the Trust.
- Never fill the sharps bin more than ¾ full.
- Under no circumstances must the contents of one sharps container be decanted into another container.
- Never leave a sharp protruding from the bin.
- Always use safe sharp systems where available
- Always wear disposable gloves when handling sharps.
- Sharps bins must be kept out of reach of members of the public. Sharps containers must be located in a safe and secure position in the clinical area.
- When not in use place the lid of the container in the temporary closure position.
- Never leave them for someone else to clear away.
- Always dispose of sharps immediately after use, and at the point of use. Used sharps must never be carried around by hand.

- Never bend or break needles after use.
- Never re-sheath needles.
- Do not disassemble needles from syringes or other devices.
- Never bend, break or manipulate sharps by hand.
- Never pass sharps by hand.

Staff responsibility

The person who uses the sharp has the responsibility for disposing of it safely.

Disposal of sharps bin

- Make sure the sharps bin lid is securely closed before disposal
- Complete the MANDATORY manufacture's label on the front of the sharps bin at the time of disposal with:
  - Date
  - Signature
  - Station ID label across the top (**NOT OVER THE MANUFACTURER'S LABEL**).

The East of England Ambulance Service Trust (2008). *Control and Decontamination Guidelines*. Section 4.4, Sharps Management. July.

Steps 1-2-3

What is it for?

It is used to assess the safety risk of approaching the scene of an accident or incident when the cause is unknown or you have multiple casualties presenting with similar symptoms.

How do I use it?

It is a visual assessment tool, which can be completed from a safe distance without patient contact.

What does it look like?

Step 1-2-3

Step 1 – One casualty
- Approach using normal procedures

Step 2 – Two casualties
- Approach with caution. Consider all options

Step 3 – Three or more
- Do not approach the scene

If possible:
- Withdraw
- Contain
- Report
- If contaminated, isolate yourself
- Send for specialist help.

TIA Assessment

Any patient who presents with FAST symptoms or with a new onset of persistent focal neurological symptoms must be treated as a stroke patient until proved otherwise. TIA assessment should only be considered when there is complete symptom resolution either prior to the ambulance arrival or while en route to the hospital.

What is it for?

ABCD^2 is an evidence-based and NICE-recommended scoring system used to establish an individual's risk of going on to have a full stroke after suffering a TIA. It is not a diagnostic assessment tool to identify TIA.

How do I use it?

If prior to arrival or while at the scene there is complete resolution of the focal neurological symptoms, then it is appropriate to manage the patient as a TIA, and ABCD^2 scoring should be undertaken for the symptoms present at the time of onset.

The scoring is split into low and high risk; any patient with a score of 3 or less is considered low risk and requires specialist follow-up by a stroke specialist within seven days.

Any patient with a score of 4 or above is considered high risk and requires specialist follow-up within 24 hours.

Patients are also considered high risk, irrespective of the ABDC[2] score, if they are prescribed warfarin, have AF or have had a *similar TIA episode* in the past seven days.

Patients identified as high risk should be conveyed to hospital for further assessment.

For patients identified as low risk an appropriate care pathway agreed with a GP is acceptable and the patient does not require conveyance to A&E. A GP appointment must be arranged to be *within the next 24 hours*. However, if this cannot be agreed directly (clinician to clinician) with the patient's GP or OOH GP *then the patient has to be conveyed to A&E*.

Low-risk TIAs should be directly referred to TIA clinics in line with the Trust low-risk TIA pathway.

What does it look like?

	ABCD² Score Variable		Score Given
Age	<60 years	0	
	60 years or above	1	
Blood pressure	Systolic BP >140 mmHg or	1	
	Diastolic BP >90 mmHg		
	BP below these levels	0	
Clinical features (max. score 2) *Assess symptoms present at time of onset*	Any unilateral weakness (face/hand/leg)	2	
	Speech disturbance (without motor weakness)	1	
	Other weakness	0	
Duration of symptoms (from onset to resolution)	>60 minutes	2	
	10-59 minutes	1	
	<10 minutes	0	
		Total Score	

47

ECA

Q/SAP

TECH

PARA

SP CC

SP PC

Trauma Triage Tool (TTT)

What is it for?

The TTT identifies a candidate major trauma patient by looking at the patient's physiological and anatomical parameters. If any of these parameters are triggered, the clinician should consider this patient a candidate major trauma patient.

How do I use it?

The TTT is designed to accompany the patient's primary survey. Upon identifying a candidate major trauma patient, it is imperative that HEOC are informed at the earliest opportunity.

What does it look like?

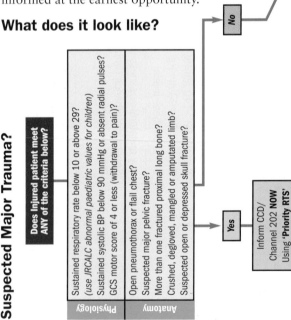

Suspected Major Trauma?

Does Injured patient meet ANY of the criteria below?

No

Physiology
- Sustained respiratory rate below 10 or above 29? (use JRCALC abnormal paediatric values for children)
- Sustained systolic BP below 90 mmHg or absent radial pulses?
- GCS motor score of 4 or less (withdrawal to pain)?

Anatomy
- Open pneumothorax or flail chest?
- Suspected major pelvic fracture?
- More than one fractured proximal long bone?
- Crushed, degloved, mangled or amputated limb?
- Suspected open or depressed skull fracture?

Yes → Inform CCD/Channel 202 NOW Using 'Priority RTS'

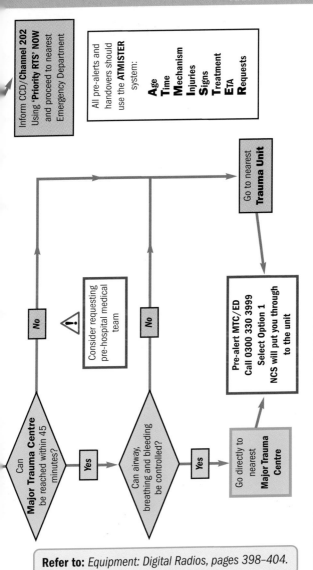

Inform CCD/Channel 202 Using **'Priority RTS' NOW** and proceed to nearest Emergency Department

All pre-alerts and handovers should use the **ATMISTER** system:

Age
Time
Mechanism
Injuries
Signs
Treatment
E**T**A
Requests

Can **Major Trauma Centre** be reached within 45 minutes?

No → Go to nearest **Trauma Unit**

Yes →

Can airway, breathing and bleeding be controlled?

No → Consider requesting pre-hospital medical team

Yes →

Go directly to nearest **Major Trauma Centre**

Pre-alert MTC/ED Call 0300 330 3999 **Select Option 1** NCS will put you through to the unit

Go to nearest **Trauma Unit**

ECA
Q/SAP
TECH
PARA
SP CC
SP PC

Refer to: *Equipment: Digital Radios, pages 398–404.*

49

2

Procedures

Standard Precautions

Standard Precautions, formerly known as universal precautions, are a single set of activities to be used in the care of all patients. Standard precautions aim to break the chain of infection and reduce the transmission of micro-organisms from both known and unknown sources. Use of standard precautions minimises the risk of transmission of infection to both staff and patients.

The key components of standard precautions are:
- Hand hygiene
- Personal Protective Equipment (PPE)
- Safe and appropriate disposal of sharps and clinical waste
- Safe handling of linen
- Decontamination of equipment and the environment
- Aseptic technique.

Hand Hygiene

Hand hygiene is one of the most effective methods to prevent transmission of infection. Hand hygiene should be carried out using the WHO five moments for hand hygiene (illustrated on page 54).

Moments for hand hygiene	Examples of pre-hospital care activity
1. Before touching a patient	• Before any direct contact with a patient
2. Before a clean or aseptic procedure	• Before handling or inserting an invasive device regardless of whether gloves are worn

Moments for hand hygiene	Examples of pre-hospital care activity
	• If moving from a contaminated body site to a clean body site during the care of the same patient
3. After body fluid exposure risk	• After contact with body fluids, excretions, mucous membrane, non-intact skin or wound dressings
	• If moving from a contaminated body site to another body site during the care of the same patient.
	• After removal of gloves
4. After touching a patient	• After any direct contact with the patient
	• After removing gloves
5. After touching patient surroundings	• After contact with surfaces and medical equipment in the immediate vicinity of the patient.
	• After decontaminating any item of equipment used in the care of the patient

All staff should be bare below the elbows as per the uniform policy when performing hand hygiene, this will facilitate thorough cleaning and help prevent recontamination. The correct technique is illustrated in the diagram below.

Your 5 moments for hand hygiene at the point of care

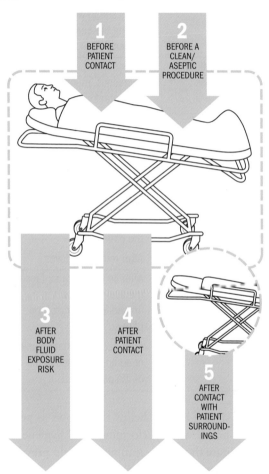

CFR

ACA

ECA

Q/SAP

TECH

PARA

SP CC

SP PC

1 BEFORE PATIENT CONTACT

2 BEFORE A CLEAN/ ASEPTIC PROCEDURE

3 AFTER BODY FLUID EXPOSURE RISK

4 AFTER PATIENT CONTACT

5 AFTER CONTACT WITH PATIENT SURROUND-INGS

Personal Protective Equipment

Personal protective equipment should be guided by risk assessment and the extent of contact anticipated with blood body fluids or pathogens (WHO, 2007)

- Gloves are required if there is a risk of contact with blood, body fluid, mucous membranes and non-intact skin. Gloves are also required for contact with a patient with a known or suspected infection.
- Aprons are required if there is a risk that clothing may be splashed or come into contact with blood body fluids or pathogens. A gown is required where there is risk of extensive contact/splashng with blood or body to the arms and body
- Masks and eye protection are required if there is a risk of splashing to the face. FFP3 masks may also be required when attending a patient with respiratory infections such as TB, SARS or pandemic 'flu.

Remember: personal protective equipment if used correctly can be very effective in reducing the risk of infection however if used incorrectly it becomes a hazard to both patients and staff. Please refer to the IPC safe practice guidelines for further detail.

Hand Cleaning Techniques

How to handrub?
with alcohol handrub

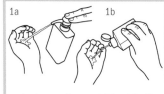

Apply a small amount (about 3 ml) of the product in a cupped hand, covering all surfaces

Rub hands palm to palm

Rub palm to palm with fingers interlaced

Rub tips of fingers in opposite palm in a circular motion

How to handwash?
with soap and water

Wet hands with water

Apply enough soap to cover all hand surfaces

Rub each wrist with opposite hand

Rub back of each hand with the palm of other hand with fingers interlaced

Rub with backs of fingers to opposite palms with fingers interlocked

Rub each thumb clasped in opposite hand using rotational movement

20-30 mins

Once dry, your hands are safe

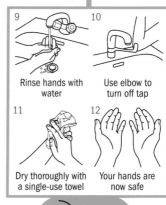

Rinse hands with water

Use elbow to turn off tap

Dry thoroughly with a single-use towel

Your hands are now safe

40-45 mins

Asepsis

The term "aseptic" means "without infection". An aseptic technique is a method used to prevent contamination of wounds and other susceptible body sites or invasive device insertion sites by potentially pathogenic organisms.

All staff performing invasive procedures or managing wounds in the pre-hospital environment should receive appropriate training in the use of aseptic technique.

Aseptic technique is also known as aseptic non-touch technique or sterile technique.

When to use an aseptic technique?

An aseptic technique should be used during any invasive procedure, which breaches the body's natural defences e.g. the skin or mucous membranes, and when handling equipment which will enter a normally sterile area. The principles of asepsis should be applied to:

- Wound management and dressings
- Insertion and manipulation of invasive devices e.g. endotracheal tubes / tracheotomies; urinary catheters; intravenous devices; central lines
- Emergency surgical procedures e.g. tracheotomy insertion or amputation

In the pre-hospital setting it is acknowledged that the wide range of environments in which clinical care is delivered may present challenges when applying aseptic principles. In some circumstances e.g. a road traffic accident the priority must always be to sustain life but where-ever possible, the insertion of invasive devices such as endotracheal tubes, IV cannulae etc. should be undertaken using sterile equipment, appropriate skin preparation and adopting a non-touch technique. Hands should be decontaminated prior to performing any invasive procedure.

When an invasive device has been inserted without application of aseptic technique this must always be recorded in the PCR and hand-over documentation at A&E thus ensuring that devices are replaced at the earliest opportunity to reduce the risk of healthcare associated infection.

The Principles of Asepsis

Action	Rationale
Hand hygiene	Hand washing is the single most important procedure for preventing cross infection. Hand decontamination may be required several times during a procedure. In pre-hospital settings the use of alcohol gel will be the primary method of hand decontamination. More than one application (followed by drying) is required for highly invasive procedures combined with sterile glove use.
Gloves	Disposable gloves should be worn for all contact with mucous membranes or for invasive procedures. Sterile gloves should be worn for high risk invasive procedures e.g. central line insertion, or emergency surgery. Clean, non-sterile gloves are acceptable for other invasive procedures.
Protective clothing	Water repellent plastic aprons will need to be worn to prevent staff clothing from becoming contaminated with bacteria from wounds or invasive devices. It will also protect the wound/invasive device from bacteria that may be present on staff uniform/clothing.
Non-touch technique	The susceptible site should not come into contact with any item that is not sterile.

Action	Rationale
Equipment	All instruments, fluids and materials that come into contact with a wound or during the insertion/manipulation of an invasive device, must be sterile to reduce the risk of contamination. This includes any final dressing(s). The sterility of the device/fluids/materials must be protected from contamination throughout the procedure.
Surface used for procedure	Where appropriate e.g. in an ambulance the surface used for the procedure should be cleaned with a sanitising wipe prior to placing the sterile field. Alternatively, for some procedures, plastic trays may be used. These must be cleaned with a sanitising wipe before and after each use. In an emergency situation e.g. at the road side then every opportunity should be taken to protect the sterility of sterile packs/equipment by providing a sterile field in the vicinity of the casualty.

Further information on Standard Precautions including: Hand Hygiene, PPE and Asepsis is available in the IPC Safe Practice Guidelines

12–Lead Electrocardiogram Placement

1. **Prepare the patient.**
   - Ensure patient dignity and explain the procedure.
   - Remove any clothing from the patient's upper body.
   - Place the patient in a semi-recumbent position with arms and legs uncrossed.
   - Ensure the area for the electrode placement is hair-free, clean and dry.

2. **Attach the limb electrodes to the inside of the upper arm and to the ankles:**
   Red – right wrist;
   Yellow – left wrist;
   Green – left leg;
   Black – right leg.

   If alternative positions are used, note this on the recording. Be aware that there will be changes in the resultant ECG due to voltage differences. Arm electrodes placed on the thorax will lead to significant changes across all leads (including the chest leads because of the altered potential of the central terminal).

3. **Attach chest electrodes.**
   Locate intercostal spaces by starting at the transverse ridge of the angle of Louis and sliding down into the 2nd intercostal space (this avoids mistaking the space between the clavicle and the 1st rib as the 1st intercostal space).

V1: In the fourth intercostal space at the right sternal border.

V2: In the fourth intercostal space at the left sternal border.

V3: Midway between V2 and V4.

V4: In the fifth intercostal space in the mid-clavicular line.

V5: In the left anterior axillary line at the level of V4.

V6: In the left mid-axillary line at the level of V4.

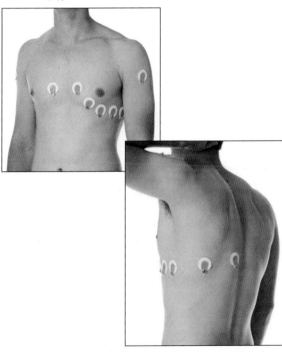

Joint Royal Colleges Ambulance Liaison Committee (2006). *UK Ambulance Service Clinical Practice Guidelines*. Warwick: JRCALC.

Electrodes should be placed under large breasts, not on top – some normal variants may occur in a woman's ECGs due to placement problems.

4. **Enter patient details on the machine.**

   Include:
   - name
   - gender
   - age.

5. **Remind the patient to remain still and quiet until the tracing is recorded.**

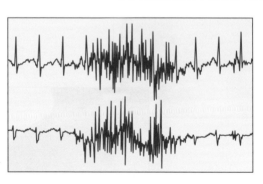

Variation in limb electrode placement can be used in certain circumstances – be sure to record any changes clearly on the paperwork.

6. **Problems?**

   Tremor:
   - interference: remove electrical sources
   - patient: reposition, reassure or move limb
     leads proximally.

   No reading:
   - check electrodes and connections.

   Unexpected readings:
   - check electrode placement.

Manual Airway Manoeuvres

Head tilt–chin lift

- Consider the mechanism of injury, use the head tilt–chin lift technique to manage the airway if you are confident that there is no risk of C-spine injury.
- If positioned on the patient's right side, the clinician's left hand is used to apply pressure to the patient's forehead.
- The tips of the clinician's index and middle fingers on the right hand are used to elevate the patient's mandible to lift the tongue from the posterior pharynx.
- If the clinician is on the patient's left side, use the hands oppositely, but with the same technique.

Jaw thrust

- If there is a possible risk of C-spine injury, use the jaw-thrust technique to manage the airway manually and prevent neck movement.
- The clinician should be positioned at the patient's head, looking down at the patient's face.
- Place the middle fingers of each hand on the angle of the patient's jaw.
- Place the thumbs near the angle of the jaw and ear, and apply an upwards pressure to elevate the mandible to lift the tongue from the posterior pharynx.

CFR

ACA

ECA

Q/SAP

TECH

PARA

SP CC

SP PC

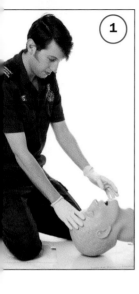

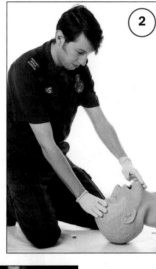

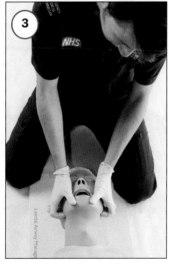

CFR

ACA

ECA

Q/SAP

TECH

PARA

SP CC

SP PC

CFR

ACA

ECA

Q/SAP

TECH

PARA

SP CC

SP PC

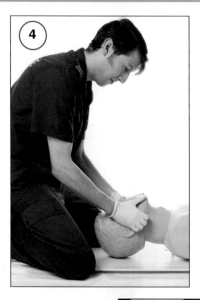

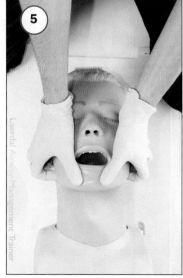

Assessment, diagnosis and treatment

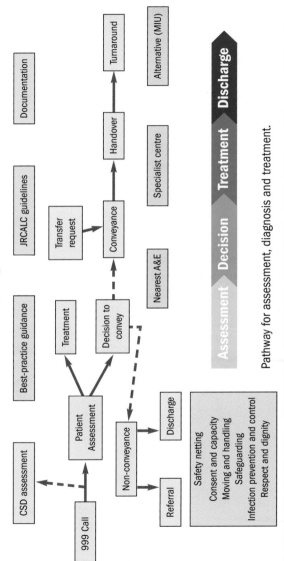

Pathway for assessment, diagnosis and treatment.

CFR

ACA

ECA

Q/SAP

TECH

PARA

SP CC

SP PC

Adult Bag Valve Mask (BVM) Technique

- Use appropriate personnel protective equipment (PPE) and select appropriate size of BVM.
- Attach to high-flow oxygen and ensure the reservoir bag is inflated.
- Apply mask to the face using a thumb/forefinger on the mask, middle/ring finger on the ridge of the mandible and little finger behind the angle of mandible.
- Lift jaw into the mask.
- Gently squeeze the bag and assess the adequacy of ventilation.

A two-handed technique involves using both hands as described above and a second practitioner to squeeze the bag.

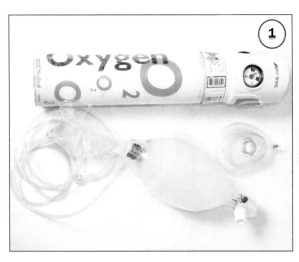

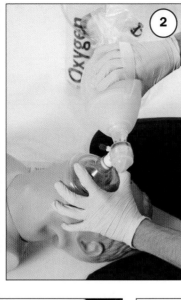

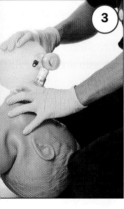

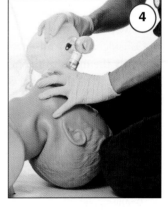

CFR

ACA

ECA

Q/SAP

TECH

PARA

SP CC

SP PC

71

Neonate Bag Valve Mask (BVM) Technique

> **Refer to:** *Procedures: Standard Precautions and Hand-washing pages 52–61.*

- Use standard precautions.
- Select an appropriately sized BVM for the patient – circular masks are more suitable for neonates.
- Attach the BVM to high-flow oxygen and ensure the reservoir bag is inflated.
- Use the appropriate manoeuvres to improve the airway patency.
- Infants have large occiputs that cause natural flexion of the neck (consider padding under the shoulders).
- Do not tilt head beyond a neutral alignment – the 'sniffing' position will kink and obstruct the airway.
- Consider airway adjuncts and suction.
- Apply the mask to the face and gain a good seal.
- Place two or three fingers under the mandible and lift the jaw up.
- Do not grip too hard to avoid causing damage to the soft tissue and oedema, resulting in further obstruction.

REMEMBER

- Gently squeeze the bag until you observe the chest rising – excessive pressure can damage the lungs.
- Finger sweeps to clear an infant's airway are contraindicated.

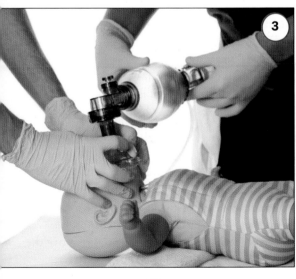

Paediatric Bag Valve Mask (BVM) Technique

- Use standard precautions.

> **Refer to:** *Procedures: Standard Precautions and Hand-washing, pages 52–61.*

- Select an appropriately sized BVM for the patient and attach it to high-flow oxygen – ensure the reservoir bag is inflated.

Use the appropriate manoeuvres to improve airway patency

- Do not tilt the head beyond a neutral alignment (the 'sniffing' position may kink and block the airway).
- Consider using padding under the shoulders to achieve the correct alignment.

Consider airway adjuncts and suction

- NP airways are not generally suitable for infants under 8 years old.
- Use low-pressure suction with extreme caution to avoid stimulating the larynx and causing a vagal reflex response, which could induce apnoea, bradycardia, hypotension and laryngospasm.

Apply the mask to the face and gain a good seal

- Place two or three fingers under the mandible and lift the jaw up.
- The lower jaw support is essential to move the tongue away from the posterior pharynx.

- Do not grip too hard to avoid causing damage to the soft tissue and oedema, which result in further obstruction.

REMEMBER
- Gently squeeze the bag until you observe the chest rising.
- Excessive pressure can damage the lungs in infants.

Bag Valve Mask (BVM) with T Piece Nebuliser

- Select an appropriately sized BVM for patient.
- Circular masks may be more suitable for infants.
- Separate the mask from bag portion of the BVM.
- Attach the straight airway connector to the mask.
- Connect the 'T' adapter to the BVM.
- Assemble the nebuliser mixing chamber, dose with the appropriate drugs for use and connect to the oxygen supply in the usual manner.
- Connect the mask to the end of the reservoir tube.

REMEMBER

- If only one oxygen supply is available, remove the reservoir bag from the BVM to allow a faster filling of the BVM with atmospheric air, or consider connecting a flow meter to the oxygen cylinder to create two outlets.
- If the patient is intubated, remove the mask from the elbow connector and connect the ET tube directly to the elbow connector.

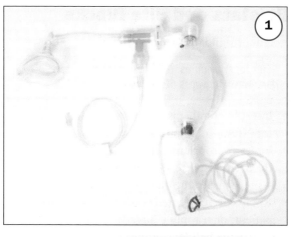

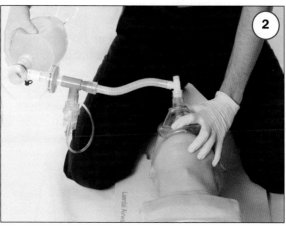

ECA

Q/SAP

TECH

PARA

SP CC

SP PC

Epistats and Bite Blocks

- Adopt standard precautions.

> **Refer to:** *Procedures: Standard Precautions and Hand-washing, pages 52–61.*

- Insert bilateral epistats in the same manner as for NPAs – do not inflate at this stage.
- Insert appropriately sized bite blocks between the molars on each side (either side of ET/LMA) – site as far to the back as possible.
- Apply correctly fitted cervical collar to the patient, or reapply if already in use.
- Inflate the balloons of the epistats with normal saline.
- GREEN valve approx. 20–30 ml (to prevent the epistats being unsited with light traction).
- WHITE valve approx. 10–20 ml until haemorrhage under control.
- Suction catheters can be inserted through the central lumen of the epistats if required.

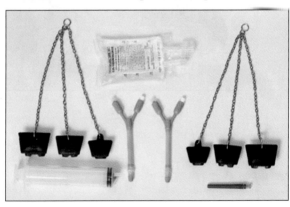

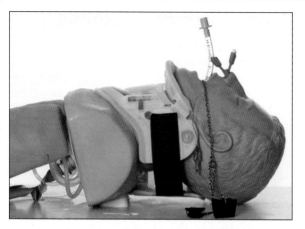

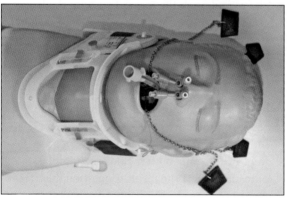

REMEMBER

The use of epistats in isolation may prove detrimental as pushing the mobile maxilla away from the base of the skull will increase the space and allow more room for bleeding to occur.

Transport the patient rapidly to the nearest receiving maxillofacial department.

SP CC

Blood Glucose Monitoring

- Gain consent if possible and explain what you're going to do, how and why. Wash your hands thoroughly or rub alcohol gel into your hands prior to procedure.
- Use the side of a finger in adults and older children or the heel of the foot in young children.
- Clean the area using gauze and saline, making sure to clean any oral glucose on the fingers which may result in a false reading.
- Once the target area is clean and dry, put on gloves and prick the target area with the lancet, apply pressure around the puncture and wipe the first drop of blood away, then squeeze again and place the next drop of blood onto the test strip. Dispose of the lancet into the sharps container.
- Wait for the glucometer to bleep or register the blood sample and make a note of the result. Remove protective gloves as soon as there is no further risk of contamination of blood.
- Repeat if the glucometer finds the sample unreadable or if the result is questionable. Treat the patient per the findings, adhering to JRCALC guidelines.
- Offer the patient a clean piece of gauze to cover the puncture and help cease bleeding.

REMEMBER

Always ensure glucometer has been quality-control checked as part of VDI.

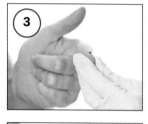

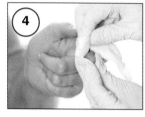

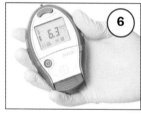

ECA

Q/SAP

TECH

PARA

SP CC

SP PC

Blood Pressure Measuring – Manual/Automatic

- Gain the patient's consent.
- Expose arm to above the bicep muscle, and place a correctly sized cuff approximately 2.5 cm above the elbow.
- Locate the radial and brachial pulses.
- Inflate the cuff until the radial pulse disappears, then inflate by a further 30 mmHg.
- Place stethoscope diaphragm over the brachial pulse.
- Slowly start releasing the pressure from the cuff (approximately 5 points per second).
- Listen for the return of the brachial pulse and note reading – systolic.
- Continue deflating until the pulsating sound disappears and note reading – diastolic.

Automatic

- Wrap the deflated cuff snugly around the upper arm, as for the manual BP procedure
- Ensure that the hose is routed to avoid kinking or compression.

REMEMBER

- Do not place the cuff on same arm as the SpO$_2$ sensor.
- Ensure the cuff is at the same level as the heart and that the artery marker on the cuff is over the artery, pointing towards the hand.

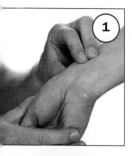

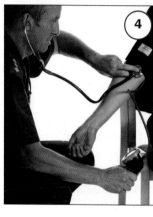

ECA

Q/SAP

TECH

PARA

SP CC

SP PC

Blood Sampling (subject to existence of local agreement)

- Gain patient's fully informed consent for the procedure.
- Adopt standard IPC precautions and perform hand hygiene in accordance with WHO five moments for hand hygiene.

> **Refer to:** *Procedures: Standard Precautions and Hand-washing, pages 52–61.*

- Use an aseptic technique.
- Prepare the required equipment: ChloraPrep, tourniquet, cannula/venepuncture, needle, sample bottles, sharps bin, etc.
- Palpate for a suitable vein to take blood from.
- Clean the selected area with ChloraPrep and air dry for 30 seconds.
- Do not re-palpate after cleaning area.
- Puncture the vein using the venepuncture needle or cannula.

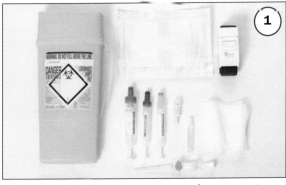

(Equipment for illustrative purposes only, may vary).

- Fill the required bottles/containers with blood and withdraw needle/cannula.
- Apply firm direct pressure to the venepuncture site and cover with a sterile dressing.

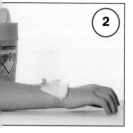

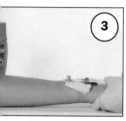

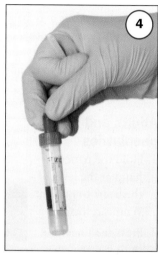

REMEMBER

- If using a cannula, flush through afterwards and attach with a Nicofix™ or similar.
- Drugs can be given via a cannula; however, after a flush no further blood samples can be taken.
- It is important to ensure that the bottles are filled in the correct order to prevent cross-contamination by the additives they contain.
- Clearly label each bottle filled with blood with the patient's full details including the time and date that the sample was taken.
- Hand over the labelled bottles to staff at the receiving hospital with the patient.

Capillary Refill Time

- Capillary refill time (CRT) can be used as part of a cardiopulmonary assessment of patients.
- It should not be used to make clinical decisions in isolation but may be a useful clinical sign in conjunction with other symptoms.
- It can be affected by numerous factors, including age, gender and most notably ambient temperature.

Adults and paediatrics

1. Hold the patient's hand at the level of the heart to prevent venous reflux.*

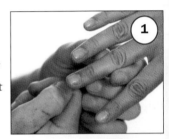

2. Press the fingernail until it turns white (blanching) indicating that blood has been forced from the tissue.

3. Measure the amount of time in seconds taken for the pink colour to return to the tissue.

4. Blanch times >2 seconds may indicate:

- Shock
- Dehydration
- Hypothermia
- Peripheral vascular disease

Infants

1. Press on the sternum (most accurate site, although the forehead or heel can also be used) for 5 seconds with a finger or thumb.*
2. Measure the amount of time in seconds for the pink colour to return to the tissue.
3. Blanch times >3 seconds indicates a possible cardiovascular compromise, as above.

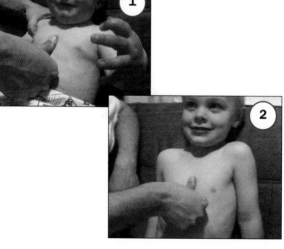

* Consider central and peripheral capillary refill for adults and children to rule out changes caused by the ambient temperature.

Capnography (Zoll™ Sidestream Airway Adaptor Kit)

Select an airway adapter kit based on the patient's size, ET tube diameter and monitoring situation. Airway adapter kits are disposable and single-patient use.

Inserting the sample cell

1. Insert the LoFlo sample cell into its receptacle and ensure that it clicks into place.

2. Ensure that the LoFlo module exhaust tube vents gases away from the module environment.

3. Turn the selector switch on the E Series to MONITOR (ON for AED units).

4. Wait for the CO_2 module to warm up.

Applying a sidestream airway adapter kit

1. Attach the airway adapter kit's sample cell to the sample-cell receptacle on the LoFlo module, and ensure that it clicks into place.

2. Place the airway adaptor assembly at the proximal end of the airway circuit between the catheter mount and the filter. Do NOT place the airway adaptor between the ET tube and the filter as this may contaminate the airway adaptor or the LoFlo module.

3. Check that connections have been made correctly by verifying the presence of a proper capnogram on the E Series display.

Airway Adapter Kit	ET Tube Diameter
Adult/Paediatric Airway Adapter Kit	>4.0 mm
Adult/Paediatric Airway Adapter Kit with Nafion® tubing	
Paediatric/Infant Airway Adapter Kit	≤4.0 mm
Paediatric/Infant Airway Adapter Kit with Nafion® tubing	

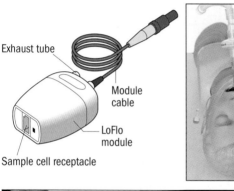

Exhaust tube

Module cable

LoFlo module

Sample cell receptacle

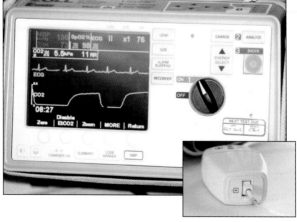

ECA

Q/SAP

TECH

PARA

SP CC

SP PC

89

Emergency Synchronised Electrical Cardioversion

Purpose

The purpose of this Critical Care Guideline (CCG) is to outline the East of England Ambulance Service Trusts policy for Emergency Synchronised Electrical Cardioversion. This CCG is applicable ONLY to those Trust Critical Care and named Trust approved Paramedics that have been signed off to practice this skill by the medical directorate.

Scope

This procedure is only to be performed by those individuals who have successfully completed the required Trust training and sign off package and demonstrated this at a formal assessment conducted by the Trust Medical Director or a nominated approved assessor as part of the CCP syllabus.

Ongoing proficiency is to be assessed every 12 months thereafter and this will be evidenced in the practitioners CPD portfolio.

Background

On occasions a patient will present with a tachyarrhythmia, which requires emergency treatment. Current paramedic practice focuses on providing supportive intervention only and transporting the patient to a hospital for more definitive management. Basic non-invasive techniques such as carotid sinus massage and valsalva manoeuvres in the initial management of narrow complex tachycardia are widely accepted emergency techniques available to paramedics. Ventricular Tachycardia (VT) is treated with Amiodarone in specific circumstances and only with clinical advice.

Resuscitation Council guidelines for the emergency management of tachyarrhythmias, broadly groups patients into categories of broad or narrow complex tachycardias. Stable or unstable. Stable patients usually undergo chemical cardioversion using pharmacological agents, such as Amiodarone. Unstable or compromised patients should be treated using synchronised electrical cardioversion instead.

Indications
- Any tachyarrhythmia which results in haemo-dynamic instability and/or adverse clinical signs characterised by one or more of the following:
  1. Reduced level of consciousness.
  2. Chest pain.
  3. Hypotension (classified as a systolic BP <90 mmHg).
  4. Heart failure.

Contra Indications
- Patients who cannot be safely sedated to facilitate treatment
- Where a patient with capacity refuses to give consent to treatment

Cautions
- Conscious patients will require sedation and analgesia.
- An unsynchronised shock may cause an R on T phenomena which may result in Ventricular Fibrillation.

SP CC

- There is a low risk of causing cardiac arrest even with synchronised DC shocks

Equipment

- A monitor/defibrillator with the facility for synchronised DC cardioversion on which the operator is appropriately trained and authorised to use.
- Procedure

Energy settings

- Broad complex tachycardia or AF – start with a 120–150J biphasic shock (200J monophasic) and increase in increments if this fails.
- Regular narrow complex tachycardia or atrial flutter – start at 70–120J biphasic (100J monophasic) and increase in increments if this fails. (Resuscitation Council UK 2010)

Procedure

- Explain the procedure to the patient and obtain consent where possible
- Apply cardiac monitoring via conventional ECG leads
- Secure IV access
- Apply multi function pads to the patient in the standard defibrillation position.
- Switch the monitor/defibrillator to manual and select 'PADS'.
- Normal defibrillator safety applies.
- Switch the monitor/defibrillator 'sync' mode.
- If the patient is conscious at this point procedural sedation may be required and the necessary steps for this should be taken.
- Administer sedation in accordance with sedation CCG.
- Select the appropriate energy setting.

- Ensure in 'synch' mode and press charge.
- Observe safety steps, ensuring all are clear and deliver shock. The machine will deliver the shock at the appropriate time during the cardiac cycle.
- Check rhythm on the monitor.
- Ensure that this corresponds with a central pulse
- If required repeat shocks up to 3 attempts.

Complications
- Failure to successfully cardiovert to desired rhythm.
- R on T phenomena resulting in VF.
- Pain and discomfort in the conscious patient.
- Minor burns to the chest wall.

Additional Considerations

Ensure receiving hospital staff are made aware and document the procedure on the patient notes/PCR/ePCR. The use of synchronised electrical cardioversion must be handed over to the team leader in the ED even if this has been unsuccessful. Individuals who have performed this procedure autonomously must complete a QA8 case study and submit it to the medical directorate along with a copy of the PRF and patient follow up. Individuals who have performed this skill under direct supervision should consider filling in a DOPS form for their portfolio. All CCPs will be expected to keep an annonomised log book of all the CCP procedures they perform.

Any cardioversion failures that occur and which are attributed to equipment failure should be reported via the EEAST Datix system.

Resuscitation Council (UK) 2010. Peri-arrest arrhythmias. [online] Available at http://www.resus.org.uk/pages/periarst.pdf

SP CC

Manual Handling:
Ferno – Compact 2 Carrying Chair™

To unfold
- Unfold by placing the chair on the ground. With your foot on the chair's foot bar, lift the back up and rearward. Completely unfold by firmly pushing up the back until an audible click is heard.
- Once the chair is locked, move both of the safety rings down over the hinge bracket.

Restraints
- The chair is equipped with two restraints for patient safety. When using the chair, the patient must be secured by the restraints. Assess the patient's condition to determine the optimum strapping procedure.

Blankets
- Blankets may be used with the chair to enhance patient comfort; ensure they are kept clear of any moving parts.

Rolling the patient and chair
- After placing the patient on the chair and fastening the restraints, the attendants move to positions at the front and rear of the chair.
- The rear attendant grasps the chair frame, and then tilts the patient/chair back until the weight is balanced on the chair wheels. The chair can then be rolled without lifting.

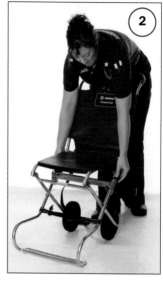

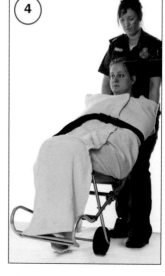

ACA
ECA
Q/SAP
TECH
PARA
SP CC
SP PC

Carrying the patient and chair

- To carry the patient, the same 'tilt/back and balance' procedure is used. The attendants grasp the front and rear carrying handles and lift simultaneously, using the Trust-recommended lifting methods.

GENERAL PRINCIPLES

- When moving patients, always inform them of what you are going to do.
- Always follow good lifting procedures as specified in the current manual's handling regulations and your appropriate training manual.
- Medical advice is beyond the parameters of this manual. It is the user's responsibility to ensure safe practices for the patient and themselves.
- Placement techniques, heavy patients, rough terrain or unusual circumstances may require more attendants.
- Operators must take extra care precautions when operating the chair on uneven ground.
- Extra precautions should be taken to prevent the chair from slipping in adverse, wet or icy weather conditions.
- Stay with the patient at all times and always use the patient restraints provided.

Manual Handling: Carry Sheet

Concertina

- Use if minimal movement of the patient is required:
  - Fold the carry sheet widthways to create a pleated effect.
  - Insert the sheet using the natural hollow under the lumbar region.
  - Extend the sheet towards the patient's head first, and then extend the remainder of the sheet to the patient's feet.
  - Position the patient centrally prior to moving/carrying the patient on the sheet.

Roll method

- Use when the concertina method is not possible:
  - Fold the sheet lengthways into half.
  - Gently roll the patient onto one side and unfold part of the sheet.
  - Place the remaining fold against the patient's back.
  - Roll the patient onto the opposite side and unfold the remainder of the sheet.
  - Position the patient centrally prior to moving/carrying the patient on the sheet.

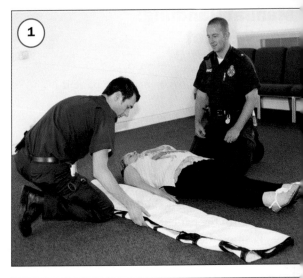

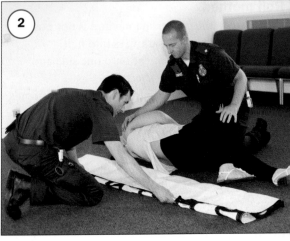

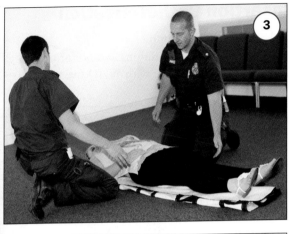

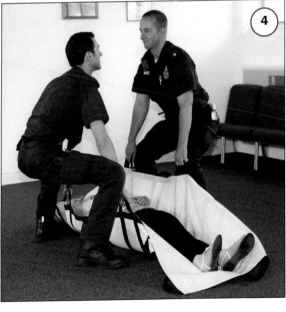

ACA

ECA

Q/SAP

TECH

PARA

SP CC

SP PC

Insertion Catheterisation

- Use an aseptic technique.
- Adopt standard precautions and perform hand hygiene in accordance with WHO five moments for hand hygiene.

> **Refer to:** *Procedures: Standard Precautions and Hand-washing, pages 52–61.*

- Explain the procedure to the patient and ensure privacy.
- Gather and check all the equipment – date, cleanliness and packet integrity: catheter starter pack, Type 2 sterile dressing pack, two units of Instillagel 25 g, 2 × 10 ml ampoule of sterile water, 10 ml syringe, apron, gloves and catheter. Wash hands or use sanitiser and put on gloves.
- The patient needs to be supine for the procedure, with legs spread wide and feet together.
- Check the balloon on the catheter for patency and coat the distal end (2–5 cm) of the catheter with lubricant, maintaining the sterility of the catheter.
- Wash the patient's genitals – anteriorly to posteriorly.
- Connect the catheter to the drainage bag.
- Place drapes in position – leave only the genitals exposed.
- **Males:** Retract the foreskin if possible, instil the gel into the urethra for 3–4 minutes for a local anaesthetic effect.

- **Females:** Separate the labia and instil gel into the urethra for 3–4 minutes.
- When the patient is anaesthetised, insert the catheter gently until 1–2 inches beyond where the urine is noted.
- Allow the urine to drain into the bag and inflate the balloon with an appropriate amount of water for the catheter size. Secure the catheter.
- Measure and test the urine and dispose of all waste in clinical waste bags.

SP PC

Celox™ Haemostatic Application

- Adopt standard precautions.

> **Refer to:** *Procedures: Standard Precautions and Hand-washing, pages 52–61.*

- Prepare the gauze, sufficient packing material and a new dressing pad.
- Feed the gauze into the wound and tightly pack the entire wound space.
- Apply a dressing over the wound and apply pressure over the gauze for a minimum of five minutes.
- Secure the dressing in place and monitor the wound for further bleeding.
- Should a wound start to rebleed (and you believe Celox was put over the bleeding area) then hold the pressure for longer.
- If the bleeding continues, consider restarting the process from the beginning, or additional packs can be used if required.

REMEMBER

- The use of Celox Gauze must be documented on an ePCR, including number of packs used, time and outcome.
- Every use should be recorded on the QA8 form and returned to the Trust Clinical Lead for audit.
- Unsuccessful uses or adverse effects should be reported to the Clinical Lead so they can report the event to the manufacturer.

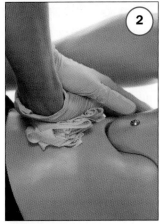

ECA

Q/SAP

TECH

PARA

SP CC

SP

103

Role of Chaperones within the Ambulance Service Trust

Introduction

While many patient contacts and consultations are undertaken completely appropriately in a one-to-one setting, there are clearly circumstances when examinations are more appropriately undertaken in the presence of a chaperone. Complaints related to inappropriate behaviour are a recurring concern and may arise from misunderstandings, misinterpretations or during examinations, especially intimate ones. All clinicians must be aware of such situations (when a patient may feel vulnerable) in which a chaperone might be of value.

Allegations of inappropriate behaviour or allegations that turn out to be malicious are very rare, but when they arise can be exceedingly stressful and embarrassing for all concerned. Guidance provided by the General Medical Council (GMC) is used as the basis for this Clinical Standard Operating Procedure together with the guidance document 'Guidance on the Role and Effective Use of Chaperones in Primary and Community Care settings'. There are two areas in which care is particularly required – when working as a single clinician and during the transport of a patient.

Additionally, we aim to provide practical advice to healthcare professionals working in a variety of locations where the availability of a chaperone may not always be possible.

While it may be recognised that a chaperone is appropriate, consideration needs to be given as to who should undertake the role in a community setting.

General considerations

The designation of the chaperone depends on the role expected of them and on the wishes of the patient. It is useful to consider whether the chaperone is required to carry out an active role, such as participation in the examination or procedure, or to have a passive role, such as providing support to the patient during the procedure.

Informal chaperone

Many patients feel reassured by the presence of a familiar person and in almost all cases this request should be accepted. A situation in which this may not be appropriate is when a child is asked to act as a chaperone for a parent who is undergoing an intimate examination. They may not necessarily be relied upon to act as a witness to the conduct or continuing consent of the procedure. However, if the child is providing comfort to the parent and will not be exposed to unpleasant experiences, it may be acceptable for them to be present. It is inappropriate to expect an informal chaperone to take an active part in the examination or to witness the procedure directly.

Formal chaperone

A formal chaperone implies a clinical health professional, such as a nurse, paramedic or technician, or a specifically trained non-clinical staff member, such as a receptionist. This individual will have a specific role to play in terms of the consultation and this role should be made clear to both the patient and the person undertaking the chaperone role. This may include assisting with undressing or assisting in the procedure being carried out. In these situations staff should have had sufficient training to understand the role expected of them. Common sense dictates that, in most cases, it is not appropriate for a non-clinical member of staff to comment on the appropriateness of the procedure or examination, nor should they feel able to do so.

Protecting the patient from vulnerability and embarrassment means that the chaperone is usually of the same sex as the patient. Therefore, the use of a male chaperone for the examination of a female patient or of a female chaperone when a male patient is being examined could be considered inappropriate.

The patient should always have the opportunity to decline a particular person as a chaperone if that person is not acceptable to them for any reason. In this context it is probably unwise to use an observer to the Service, even if they have the patient's permission to be present within the clinical setting as a chaperone. In all cases where the presence of a chaperone may intrude in a confiding clinician–patient relationship, their presence should be confined to the physical examination. One-to-one

Procedures

CFR
ACA
ECA
Q/SAP
TECH
PARA
SP CC
SP PC

communication should take place after the examination.

Where a chaperone is needed but not available

If the patient has requested a chaperone and none is available at that time, the patient must be given the opportunity to reschedule their appointment within a reasonable timeframe. If the seriousness of the condition dictates that a delay is inappropriate, this should be explained to the patient and recorded in their notes. A decision to continue or otherwise should be reached jointly. In cases where the patient is not competent to make an informed decision, the healthcare professional must use their own clinical judgement, make a record in the patient's notes and be able to justify their course of action.

Issues specific to religion, ethnicity or culture

The ethnic, religious and cultural background of some women can make intimate examinations particularly difficult; for example, Muslim and Hindu women have a strong cultural aversion to being touched by men other than their husbands. Patients undergoing examinations should be allowed the opportunity to limit their degree of nudity by, for example, uncovering only that part of the anatomy that requires investigation or imaging. Wherever possible, particularly in these circumstances, a female healthcare practitioner should perform the procedure.

It is unwise to proceed with any examination if the healthcare professional is unsure whether or not the patient understands the situation because of a language barrier. If an interpreter is available, they may be able to double as an informal chaperone. In life-saving situations every effort should be made to communicate with the patient by whatever means available before proceeding with the examination.

Summary

The relationship between a patient and their clinician is based on trust. A clinician may have no doubts about a patient they have known for a long time, and feel it is not necessary to offer a formal chaperone. However, this should not detract from the fact that any patient is entitled to a chaperone if they feel one is required.

Chaperone guidance is for the protection of both patients and staff and this guidance should always be followed. The key principles of communication and record keeping will ensure that the clinician–patient relationship is maintained and will act as a safeguard against formal complaints or, in extreme cases, legal action.

Single clinician working (based on GMC guidance)

- *Why?* Explain to the patient why an examination is necessary and give the patient an opportunity to ask questions.

- *What?* Explain what the examination will involve in a way that the patient can understand so that they have a clear idea of what to expect, including any pain or discomfort.
- *Consent.* Obtain the patient's consent, recognising the issues related to competence before any examination is undertaken, and be prepared to discontinue the examination if the patient asks you to do so. You must record in the patient records the details of competence and consent.
- *Discussion.* Keep discussion relevant and avoid unnecessary personal comments.
- *Chaperone?* Offer a chaperone and consider who is an appropriate person to undertake this role. This detail should be recorded in the patient's record. If a chaperone is present this should be recorded and a note made of the chaperone's identity. If necessary, be prepared to delay the examination until a chaperone can be arranged.
- *Privacy.* Give the patient privacy to undress and dress, and use drapes to maintain the patient's dignity. Do not assist the patient in removing clothing unless you have clarified with them that your assistance is required.
- *Same sex.* There have been cases when clinicians were accused of inappropriate behaviour by patients of the same sex. If you feel it is necessary, you should ensure a chaperone is present in these situations when intimate examinations are undertaken.

Transportation of patients

The transportation of patients offers particular difficulties and the potential for misunderstandings. Illness and the use of drug treatments can change the mental function of patients such that not only may patients be confused, but also their insight and interpretation of everyday actions may become clouded.

It is essential that explanations are offered and consent is obtained. If during the transportation of a patient there is a need to examine or connect monitoring equipment to the patient, again consent should be obtained.

When dealing with maternity problems, great care is required and, apart from gaining consent for any examination or treatment, the aim should be to have a chaperone present for any form of obstetric examination.

Increasingly, ambulance design and requirements are separating the patient compartment from the cab. Consequently, ambulance staff must be very alert to the consideration of the need for a chaperone in the patient compartment of modern ambulances.

The practical difficulties of achieving this are recognised, but a risk assessment should be undertaken, particularly when children, obstetric patients and patients with mental health issues or who lacking in capacity are being transported.

Do not forget that a contemporaneous note entered on the PRF can be sensible and may prove invaluable should any enquiry be made about the conduct of a patient or staff member.

The use of visual recording in the rear patient compartment is being considered for the protection of both staff and patients.

CFR

ACA

ECA

Q/SAP

TECH

PARA

SP CC

SP PC

Choking – Adult

Patient choking?

Mild

- An airway obstruction with an effective cough.
- Encourage the patient to cough.
- Continue to check for deterioration to an ineffective cough or until the obstruction clears.

Severe

- Airway obstruction with an ineffective cough.
- If the patient is unconscious, start CPR.
- If the patient is conscious give up to five back blows – stand to the side of the patient, support the chest with one hand and lean the patient forwards while using the free hand to 'slap' the patient's back between the shoulder blades.
- Reassess airway after each blow.

- If five back blows fail to relieve the airway obstruction give up to five abdominal thrusts – stand behind the patient, put both your arms around upper part of their abdomen and lean them forwards.
- Clench your fist and place it between the navel and bottom end of the patient's sternum.
- Grasp this hand with the other and pull sharply inwards and upwards

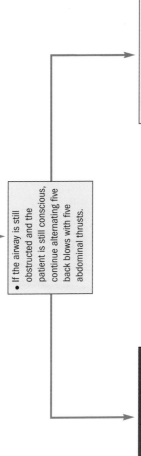

- If the airway is still obstructed and the patient is still conscious, continue alternating five back blows with five abdominal thrusts.

- If the patient remains conscious, but the airway obstruction remains, the patient should still be transferred to the nearest A&E department for further assessment.

- If the patient becomes unconscious, begin CPR.
- (Paramedic grade and above only: consider a laryngoscopy and removal of the obstruction using Magill forceps.)

CFR

ACA

ECA

O/SAP

TECH

PARA

SP CC

SP PC

Choking – Paediatric

CFR

ACA

ECA

Q/SAP

TECH

PARA

SP CC

SP PC

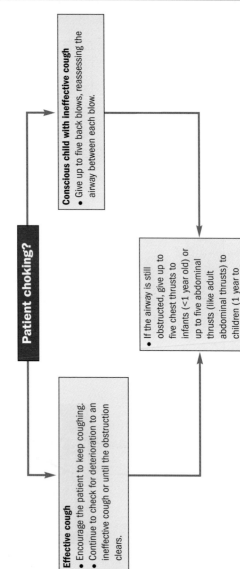

Patient choking?

Effective cough
- Encourage the patient to keep coughing.
- Continue to check for deterioration to an ineffective cough or until the obstruction clears.

Conscious child with ineffective cough
- Give up to five back blows, reassessing the airway between each blow.

- If the airway is still obstructed, give up to five chest thrusts to infants (<1 year old) or up to five abdominal thrusts (like adult abdominal thrusts) to children (1 year to puberty).

- If the patient is unconscious, open the airway and administer five rescue breaths.
- If there is no response, commence CPR.

Paramedic grade and above ONLY
- Consider a laryngoscopy and removal of the obstruction using Magill forceps.

Back blows

Infant
- Support the infant in the prone position, head downwards or over the rescuer's lap.
- Support the head by holding either side of the patient's lower jaw.
- Deliver sharp blows with the heel of one hand in between the shoulder blades.

Child
- As above, although supporting the child in a forwards-leaning position and administering the blows from behind may be preferred.

Chest thrusts – infants

- With the head downwards in a supine position, support the infant down your arm, with the occipital region encircled in your hand.
- Using the landmark for chest compressions, administer thrusts in the same manner, but slower and sharper in nature.

DO NOT USE ABDOMINAL THRUSTS FOR INFANTS

CFR
ACA
ECA
Q/SAP
TECH
PARA
SP CC
SP PC

Clinical Waste Management

Clinical waste is not waste that arises from the normal day-to-day activities of the Trust, such as 'domestic' or 'household waste', or waste categorised as 'no risk'. It is essential that domestic waste and clinical waste be segregated at all times, as otherwise all waste must be treated as clinical waste. The Trust will make special arrangements for the disposal of waste oils, batteries, vehicle parts, IT equipment, fluorescent tubes and other items covered by waste regulations.

Procedure for disposal of clinical waste

Clinical waste should be disposed of as quickly as possible. All healthcare waste, which is any item contaminated with blood or bodily fluids, must be disposed of in a yellow plastic sack or other approved container. In general, when considering the disposal of healthcare waste, staff should not overfill clinical waste sacks (maximum two-thirds full), and should ensure that they are sealed with a tie wrap inscribed with the Trust initials and a station or depot identification label showing the station or depot name and date of disposal.

Storage and disposal at the station or depot

All healthcare practitioners should segregate clinical waste at the point of production and store it securely on the vehicle until the vehicle is returned to the station or depot. On return to the station or depot, all healthcare waste must be disposed of in the approved healthcare waste storage containers, and must carry an identification label showing the station or depot name and date of disposal. These containers can be found in the areas marked with yellow and black tape that are designated for such purposes. All healthcare waste should be segregated at this point so as to avoid waste of different classifications being stored together in the same waste container. Care should be taken to ensure that healthcare waste is not mixed with other deliveries and collections, i.e., laundry, domestic waste and general goods.

CFR
ACA
ECA
Q/SAP
TECH
PARA
SP CC
SP PC

Application of a Collar (Nec-Loc™)

- Adopt standard precautions.

> **Refer to:** *Procedures: Standard Precautions and Hand-washing, pages 52–61.*

- Manage a manual C-spine immobilisation of the patient.
- While maintaining neutral alignment of the C-spine, the second person measures for the correct collar size.
- Measure the distance between the top of the patient's shoulder and tip of their chin.
- Applying the collar:
  - Keeping the head in neutral alignment, slide the front piece of the collar up the chest wall to support the chin.
  - Bring restraining strap around the back of neck. Do not tighten the front piece.
  - Place the back piece around the patient's head.
  - Attach the Velcro straps to the front piece.
- Stabilise the front piece with your fingers while tightening the back piece in an alternating motion.

Ask the patient if they are as comfortable as they can be, check that earrings and other jewellery are not causing the patient discomfort.

Adjustable Collar for Extrication (ACE)

CFR
ACA
ECA
Q/SAP
TECH
PARA
SP CC
SP PC

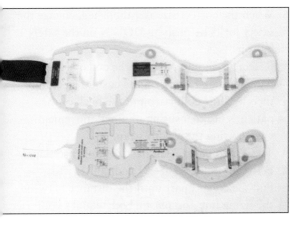

- Rescuer 1 should manually stabilise the patient's head and neck in neutral alignment.
- When head and neck are stabilised, rescuer 2 should apply the Ambu® Perfit ACE to patient.
- The collar must not hyperextend the patient's neck once applied.

Sizing the collar

- Measure the distance between an imaginary plane drawn horizontally and immediately below the patient's chin and a second plane drawn immediately on top of the patient's shoulder.
- Compare this distance with the distance from the collar-sizing line to the lower aspect of the plastic collar body.

- Ambu Perfit ACE is pre-set to neckless size 3; if a larger size is required, disengage the safety locks by pulling UP on the safety buttons.
- When the correct size is established, engage the safety locks by pushing DOWN on the safety buttons.
- Rescuer 2 should position the collar with the patient's chin resting on the cushioned chin rest, then feed the collar around the back of the patient's neck, ensuring minimal movement. Fasten using the Velcro strap.
- The Ambu Perfit ACE has 16 ratchet settings between neckless (size 3) and tall (size 6).
- Pull the collar apart until the distance between the sizing line and plastic body equal's your finger's width.

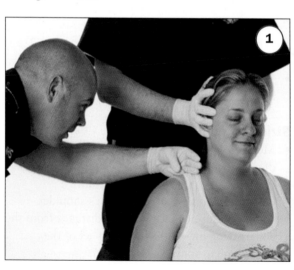

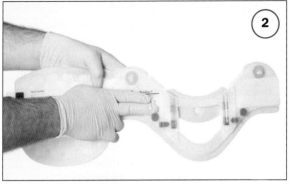

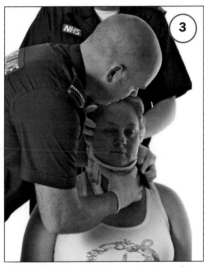

CFR

ACA

ECA

Q/SAP

TECH

PARA

SP CC

SP PC

REMEMBER

If the patient has sustained a head injury be aware of increasing intracranial pressure; once the patient is fully immobilised, the collar can be loosened but DO NOT REMOVE IT.

121

Combat Application Tourniquet™

- Put the self-adhering band around the injured limb and pass the free-running end of the band through the inside slit of the friction adaptor buckle.
- Pass the band through the outside slit of the buckle, utilising the friction adaptor buckle, which will lock the band in place.
- Pull the self-adhering band tight and securely fasten the band back on itself.
- Twist the Windlass Rod™ until the haemorrhage has stopped and lock the rod in place with the Windlass Clip™.
- At this point the haemorrhage should now be under control.
- Secure the Windlass Rod™ by grasping the Windlass Strap™ and pulling it tight, adhering it to the opposite hook on the Windlass Clip™.
- Manage any other injuries as per the local procedures and convey the patient to the most appropriate A&E department.

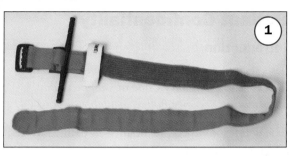

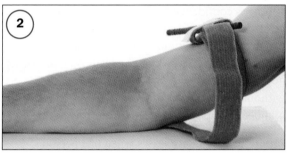

123

Patient Confidentiality

Introduction

This section should be read in conjunction with the Trust's Confidentiality Code of Conduct and Information Security Policy, available on East 24.

The definition of 'confidentiality' as defined by Collins is "private, secret and entrusted with another's confidences". The importance of the healthcare professional (HCP)–patient relationship is reflected in the number of ethical codes and codes of conduct, in which the HCP is under a duty not to disclose information about their patient without the patient's consent. There are, however, a number of important exceptions to this rule.

A duty of confidence arises when one person discloses information to another (e.g., patient to doctor or to HCP) in circumstances where it is reasonable to expect that the information will be held in confidence.

Patients entrust the NHS or allow it to gather sensitive information relating to their health and other matters as part of their seeking treatment. They do so in confidence and they have the legitimate expectation that staff will respect this trust.

It is your duty to uphold patient confidentiality and data protection with respect to patients and colleagues. You are personally accountable for this. Concerns about the Data Protection Act should be notified to the Senior Information Risk Officer and concerns about patient confidentiality to the Caldicott Guardian (normally the Medical Director). Data breaches may be notified to the Information Commissioner and have significant consequences, including police investigation and a large fine.

Any information, data or other forms of information, placed in any article that may be viewed by any person, either electronically (i.e., intranet or internet, such as any of the social networking sites) or on paper, must be very carefully vetted to ensure that all personal information is rendered anonymous and cannot cause distress to individuals or groups unless the information has been seen by the person(s) involved and they have given their explicit permission for such information to be displayed. This permission should be in writing.

Use of social networking sites

The Trust understands that the use of social networking sites has become a part of everyday life and it is important for staff to have the freedom to network in any way they choose in their own time. However, staff must ensure that no comments made are:

- Inappropriate or derogatory to the trust, colleagues or patients.
- Undermine the dignity of their colleagues and/or the reputation, standing and public confidence in the Trust.

Although there is the ability to limit privacy settings on the various networking sites there is still the potential for all and any comments to be viewed by the general public.

Any inappropriate or derogatory comments made relating to the Trust and/or colleagues will be taken seriously and action may be taken under the Disciplinary Policy to ensure the reputation of the Trust and public confidence.

What is Caldicott?

The term Caldicott refers to a review commissioned by the Chief Medical Officer. A review committee, under the chairmanship of Dame Fiona Caldicott, investigated ways in which patient information is used in the NHS.

The review committee also made a number of recommendations aimed at improving the way the NHS handles and protects patient information.

The six Caldicott principles:
1. Justify the purpose(s) of using confidential information.
2. Only use it when absolutely necessary.
3. Use the minimum that is required.
4. Access should be on a strict need-to-know basis.
5. Everyone must understand his or her responsibilities.
6. Understand and comply with the law.

What is the Data Protection Act 1998?

The Data Protection Act 1998 became law in March 2000. It sets standards, which must be satisfied when obtaining, recording, holding, using or disposing of personal data. These are summarised by eight Data Protection Principles:

Personal data must be:
1. Processed fairly and lawfully
2. Processed for specified purposes
3. Adequate, relevant and not excessive
4. Accurate and kept up-to-date
5. Not kept for longer than necessary
6. Processed in accordance with the rights of data subjects
7. Protected by appropriate security (practical and organisational)
8. Not transferred outside the EEA without adequate protection

As well as information held on computers, the Data Protection Act 1998 also covers most manual records, for example:
- health
- personnel
- occupational health
- card indices
- volunteers
- contractors
- suppliers
- finance

Boussignac CPAP System™

CPAP is generally indicated for a patient in moderate-to-severe respiratory distress who is completely alert and maintaining their own airway.

- Select the appropriate-size face mask for your patient:
  - Small adult mask (size 4)
  - Medium adult mask (size 5)
  - Large adult mask (size 6)
- Insert the white end of the Boussignac CPAP into the face mask.
- Connect the funnel end of the green oxygen tubing to an O_2 source capable of delivering flow up to 25 litres/min.
- Set the oxygen flow to deliver CPAP in cmH_2O of water pressure:
  - 15 litres = 5 cmH_2O
  - 20 litres = 7.5 cmH_2O
- Adjust the flow rate to 5–7 cmH_2O.
- Explain to the patient how the Boussignac CPAP will help their breathing.
- Gently hold the mask to the patient's face, ensuring a good face–mask seal.
- Turn the flow control device to the desired litres/min, generally 15 litres/min, to begin the CPAP.
- Gradually adjust the flow to achieve the desired level of CPAP.
- Secure the Boussignac CPAP System to the patient using the head strap.
- Check around the mask for any leaks.
- Adjust the mask and/or head strap accordingly.

- CO_2 can be monitored with either a nasal cannula or an in-line CO_2 adapter.
- Also monitor ECG (4-lead continuous and 12-lead), NIBP, SpO_2.

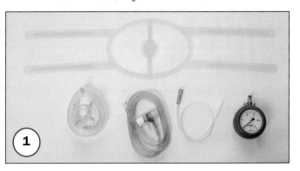

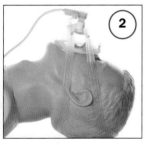

REMEMBER

- CPAP is contraindicated in cases of hypoventilation, reduced level of consciousness and any potential airway compromise.

129

Crash Helmet Removal

- Survey the scene.
- Adopt standard precautions.

> **Refer to:** *Procedures: Standard Precautions and Hand-washing, pages 52–61*

- In the assessment process, quickly identify the need to remove the crash helmet.
- Explain to the patient what you want to do and gain their consent.

Rescuer one

- Manually stabilises the head and helmet into a neutral alignment (unless contraindicated), while maintaining manual C-spine immobilisation.

Rescuer two

- Removes/cuts the chin strap of the helmet and inserts their hands into the correct position either side of the patient's face/head in order to take manual control of the C-spine immobilisation.
- Both rescuers must work as a team to remove the crash helmet.
- When rescuer two has manual control of the C-spine, rescuer one can gently 'pull' each side of the helmet (from the chin area) and ease it up and over, freeing the patient's head.

REMEMBER
- Manage C-spine control at all times throughout this procedure until the patient has been fully immobilised correctly.

ECA

Q/SAP

TECH

PARA

SP CC

SP PC

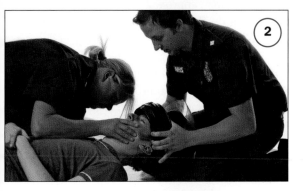

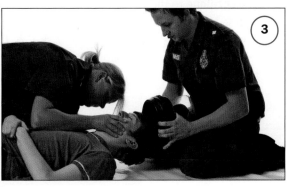

ECA

Q/SAP

TECH

PARA

SP CC

SP PC

Needle Cricothyroidotomy

- Adopt standard precautions and identify the requirement for a needle cricothyroidotomy to be performed.

> **Refer to:** *Procedures: Standard Precautions and Hand-washing, pages 52–61.*

- Position the patient supine, head in a neutral alignment. Manage the C-spine as required.
- Identify the cricothyroid membrane – a palatable recessed area, approx. 2 cm below the 'V'-shaped notch of the thyroid cartilage (Adam's apple).
- Attach a cannula (14 g) to the syringe and insert the cannula at an angle directed midline caudally.
- *Confirm entry into the trachea by aspirating air.*
- Advance the cannula into the trachea, aspirating air to confirm its position.
- Remove the syringe and needle, and secure the cannula in situ with tape.
- Attach the pre-prepared syringe and tubing to the cannula.
- Connect tubing to the oxygen supply at rate of:
  - **adult:** 15 litres/min
  - **paediatric:** 5 litres/min

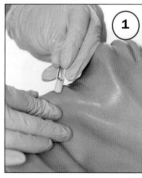

- Allow the oxygen to be applied for 1 second and escape for 4 seconds. Do this by intermittently covering the side hole in the tubing.

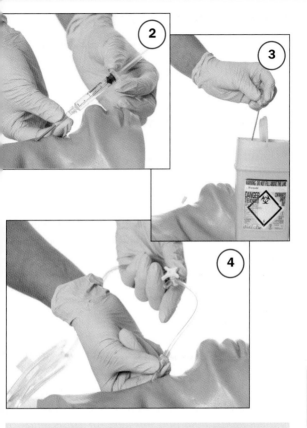

REMEMBER
- Needle cricothyroidotomy should be reserved for situations in which all other attempts to secure a patient's airway have failed and the patient is likely to die from hypoxia.
- This is a temporary emergency solution; rapid transport to the nearest receiving A&E Department must follow.

PARA

SP CC

SP PC

Defibrillation – AED (Adult and Child <8 Years*)

- Assess patient's condition: are they unconscious and pulseless?
- If yes, switch on the AED† and attach the electrodes/pads to the patient in the sternum and apex positions.
- Ensure the pads maintain good contact with the patient's chest.
- Confirm cardiac arrest and commence CPR.
- Follow spoken/visual instructions.
- Allow the AED to analyse the cardiac rhythm periodically.
- If a shock is indicated, give clear instructions to 'Stand Clear' and press the 'SHOCK' button on the AED.
- Continue CPR post-shock.

For staff trained to use the AED on paediatrics, please change to the paediatric pads (CFRs are not authorised to use an AED on a patient <8 years old).

†*Authorised staff only to switch machine into the manual mode, hold two soft keys for 10 seconds and then press the manual soft key.*

REMEMBER
- NEVER shock a patient near an explosive or combustible atmosphere, in water or on a wet patient.
- Check patient's torso for jewellery, piercings, medication patches, pacemakers, wounds or tumours.

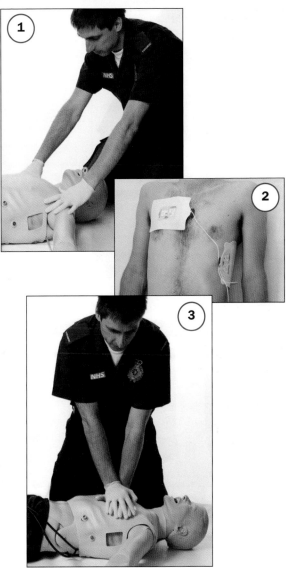

ECA

Q/SAP

TECH

PARA

SP CC

SP PC

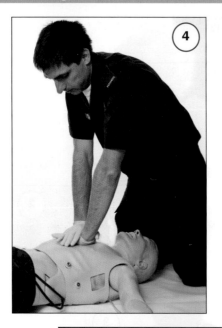

Defibrillation – Manual

- Determine the patient's condition following clinical protocol and verify if the patient is unconscious, not breathing and/or has no pulse.
- Prepare the patient: remove all clothing that covers the chest, and all jewellery and medication patches.
- Dry the skin and remove any excess hair to ensure the pads adhere to the skin.
- Connect the pads to the multifunction cable.
- Open the pad packaging and apply one edge of each pad securely to the apex and sternum.
- Roll the pad smoothly from the secured edge to the other – avoid having any air pockets between the pad and the skin.
- Ensure the pads are making good contact with the patient's skin.
- Hold in the first soft key button and turn the unit on.
- Then select the 'MANUAL' and 'CONFIRM' soft key buttons. The machine is now in manual mode.
- The machine will deliver shocks of 120 J, 150 J and 200 J.
- If the patient is in a shockable rhythm, press the 'CHARGE' button on the front panel (while CPR is still in progress).
- Ensure that all attending persons STAND CLEAR and that oxygen is removed prior to pressing the 'SHOCK' soft key.
- Immediately continue CPR.

CFR

ACA

ECA

Q/SAP

TECH

PARA

SP CC

SP PC

CFR ACA ECA Q/SAP TECH PARA SP CC SP PC

Automated external defibrillator (for use in patients >1 year old)

Notes

Placement of AED pads: one pad on LHS to left of sternum (below clavicle), other pad on RHS at the mid-clavicular line (avoiding breast tissue).

If patient is wet: dry the patient's chest before applying the pads and take all usual precautions not to touch the patient when the shock is delivered.

Supplemental oxygen: although there are no reported cases of a fire, ensure all oxygen sources are moved at least 1 m away before delivering the shock.

Keep interruptions to CPR at a minimum: effective CPR is vital to patient survival, but so is early defibrillation; provide good CPR while the AED is being brought to the patient and while it is being switched on. Then follow all voice prompts.

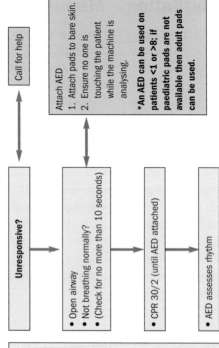

Unresponsive?

↔ Call for help

- Open airway
- Not breathing normally?
- (Check for no more than 10 seconds)

Attach AED
1. Attach pads to bare skin.
2. Ensure no one is touching the patient while the machine is analysing.

*An AED can be used on patients <1 or >8; if paediatric pads are not available then adult pads can be used.

- CPR 30/2 (until AED attached)

- AED assesses rhythm

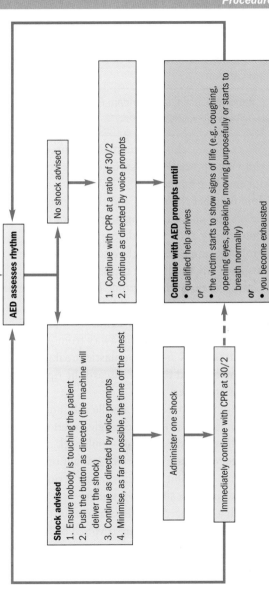

AED assesses rhythm

No shock advised

1. Continue with CPR at a ratio of 30/2
2. Continue as directed by voice prompts

Shock advised

1. Ensure nobody is touching the patient
2. Push the button as directed (the machine will deliver the shock)
3. Continue as directed by voice prompts
4. Minimise, as far as possible, the time off the chest

Administer one shock

Immediately continue with CPR at 30/2

Continue with AED prompts until

• qualified help arrives

or

• the victim starts to show signs of life (e.g., coughing, opening eyes, speaking, moving purposefully or starts to breath normally)

or

• you become exhausted

CFR

ACA

ECA

Q/SAP

TECH

PARA

SP CC

SP PC

Drawing up Drugs

- Adopt aseptic techniques and standard precautions.

> **Refer to:** *Procedures: Standard Precautions and Hand-washing, pages 52–61.*

- Select and check the equipment required: 'blunt' drawing up needle and syringe of the correct size for the drug amount.
- Join together the needle and the syringe,
- Select and check the drug ampoule for the name, dose clarity and expiry date.
- Hold the ampoule upright and tap the tip to displace any fluid in the top section.
- Grasp the tip of the ampoule between your index finger and thumb, and hold the body of the ampoule with your other hand.
- Break off the ampoule top away from you: avoid glass fragments and use a plastic breaking device if available, and then the discard the tip into the sharps container.
- Remove the cap from the needle and, holding the ampoule at a 45 degree angle, insert the needle into the top of the ampoule – pull back on the syringe to aspirate the correct amount of fluid.
- Remove the blunt needle from the syringe and discard it in the sharps container.
- Attach a new needle to the syringe for the administration of the drug (IM/SC) or leave as a syringe for IV administration.

*Please note that ECAs are not authorised to mix any drugs (i.e. Glucagon, Benzopenicillin, etc).

ECA *

Q/SAP

TECH

PARA

SP CC

SP PC

- Some drugs (e.g., glucagon) have all the components required for their administration in their presentation pack.
- The needle and syringe – containing the correct amount of fluid – are already joined.
- Remove the cap from the needle and pierce the top of the ampoule of powder. Insert the fluid and mix together well before aspirating the mixed contents back into the syringe ready for administration.

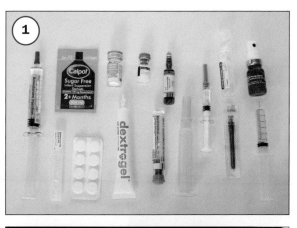

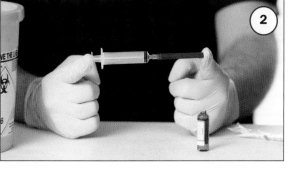

141

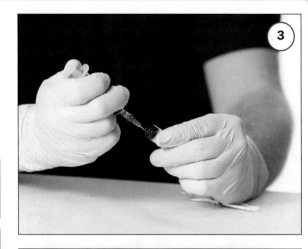

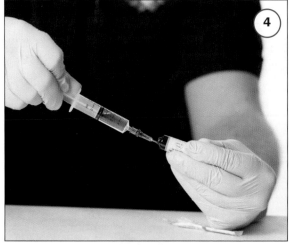

ECA*

Q/SAP

TECH

PARA

SP CC

SP PC

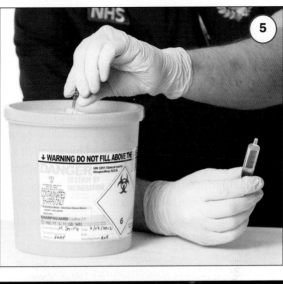

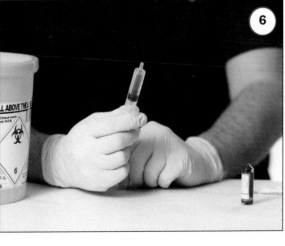

ECA*

Q/SAP

TECH

PARA

SP CC

SP PC

End-of-Life Care

Introduction

End-of-life care includes palliative care. If patients have an incurable illness, palliative care helps make them as comfortable as possible by relieving pain and other distressing symptoms, while also providing psychological, social and spiritual support for them and their family or carers. This is called a holistic approach to care, as it deals with the 'whole' person rather than just one aspect of their care. There has been much effort nationally to improve and co-ordinate end-of-life care. This continues and EEAST contributes to this in many ways.

Types of written information for EOLC

Preferred priorities of care

The PPC is a patient-held, blue and white booklet that the patient fills in themselves with any of their wishes, thoughts and feelings, such as where they want to die, what treatment they want or do not want, even down to who looks after the dog and what they want to be buried, should they wish to do so. This is written by the patient and is not a legal document, but we do try to adhere to it as much as possible.

Liverpool Care Pathway

The Liverpool Care Pathway is used at the bedside to drive a sustained quality of care of the dying during the last days and hours of life. It is a means to transfer the best quality of care of the dying from the hospice movement into other clinical areas, so wherever the person is dying there is an equitable model of care. This is a legal document approximately 11 pages long, which and contains all the wishes of the patient. This is put in place usually within the last 72–48 hours of life. It is signed by a medical doctor and has the patient's name on it. This document overrules anything that has previously been put into place. It should be adhered to wherever possible.

The Gold Standards Framework

The GSF is a systematic evidence-based approach to optimising the care for patients that is delivered by generalist providers. It is concerned with helping people to live well until the end of life and includes care in the final years for people with any end-stage illness in any setting.

DNA CPR

Do Not Attempt Cardiopulmonary Resuscitation (DNA CPR) orders are becoming commonplace. EEAST contributed to the production of the regional form and policy, which are part of the planning process and the recognition that life is coming to an end. It is a futile act to undertake CPR on someone who is expected to die from an incurable illness or if it would lead them to a worse state of health.

Refer to: *Aide-memoire: DNA CPR/ADRT, pages 12–13.*

Common myths

1. DNA CPR orders do not need the agreement of patient and family. They are a clinical decision by the senior clinician that CPR would be a futile act. It is good practice to discuss with the patient and family, but not a legal necessity.

2. DNA CPR orders do not need a review date in all cases. Once signed, most are effective in perpetuity unless a review date is indicated.

3. EEAST will accept any DNA CPR form that is appropriate. Any form is acceptable that shows that a clinical decision was made that CPR would be inappropriate in the circumstances. Use of the regional form is encouraged as this enables consistent decision making.

Advance decision to refuse treatment

Description

An advance decision to refuse treatment (previously known as a living will or advance directive) is a decision that can be made to refuse a specific medical treatment in the circumstances that are stated. This can include the choice to refuse treatment even if doing so might put an individual's life at risk. The advance decision to refuse treatment will not be used if an individual can make their own choices at the time that the treatment is needed and offered.

Key points:
- Making an ADRT is voluntary and should not be made in response to external pressure.
- ADRTs can only be made by a person over the age of 18 years old.
- The person who makes the decision must have the capacity to do so.
- The ADRT must specify exactly what treatment is refused and in what circumstances.
- The decision must be valid.
- The ADRT must be in writing, signed and witnessed.
- The ADRT can only be used to refuse treatment, not to demand treatment or to request treatment that is against the law (e.g., assisted suicide).
- The patient should personally hold a copy and a copy should be held with their patient records.

How do advance decisions relate to other rules about decision-making (e.g., Lasting Power of Attorney, best interests, etc.?)

The Lasting Power of Attorney

A Lasting Power of Attorney (LPA) is a legal document that outlines a person's intentions or decisions about their own finances or personal welfare for a time when they may lose the mental capacity to manage their own finances or make decisions about their personal welfare.

Like the ADRT, it must be made while the person still has mental capacity to do so. The LPA works in the same way as an Ordinary Power of Attorney

CFR

ACA

ECA

Q/SAP

TECH

PARA

SP CC

SP PC

CFR

ACA

ECA

Q/SAP

TECH

PARA

SP CC

SP PC

(OPOA), but will be regarded as still valid if they are deemed to have become mentally incapable. The person can even choose for the LPA not to become valid until after they have been deemed to have lost this capacity.

There are two types of LPA:
- Property and affairs LPA – the attorney is given authority to make decisions about a person's financial affairs.
- Personal welfare LPA – the attorney is given authority to make decisions about a person's health care and personal welfare.

A valid and applicable advance decision to refuse treatment is as effective as a refusal made when a person has capacity.

Therefore, an advance decision overrules:
- The decision of any personal welfare Lasting Power of Attorney (LPA) made before the advance decision was made. So an attorney cannot give consent to treatment that has been refused in an advance decision made after the LPA was signed.
- The decision of any court-appointed deputy (so a deputy cannot give consent to treatment that has been refused in an advance decision which is valid and applicable).
- The provisions of Section 5 of the Mental Capacity Act, which would otherwise allow healthcare professionals to give treatment that they believe is in a person's best interests.

An LPA made after an advance decision will make the advance decision invalid if the LPA gives the attorney the authority to make decisions about the same treatment.

The Court of Protection may make declarations as to the existence, validity and applicability of an advance decision, but it has no power to overrule a valid and applicable advance decision to refuse treatment.

Decisions made in a patient's 'best interests'

Any decision made on behalf of a patient who lacks capacity, and in the absence of either an ADRT or LPA, must be made in that patient's best interest. This applies regardless of who is making the decision or what the decision applies to. The person(s) making the decision for someone who lacks capacity should:

- *Determine that the person does lack the capacity to make a decision.* Assess whether the person might regain capacity (e.g., after medical treatment).
- *Encourage participation.* Always encourage the patient to take part in the decision.
- *Identify all relevant circumstances.* Identify anything the patient may have taken into account if they were able to make the decision for themselves.
- *Find out a person's views.* Consider any wishes or personal preferences that may have been expressed previously, verbally or in writing. Religion and culture should also be considered.

CFR

ACA

ECA

Q/SAP

TECH

PARA

SP CC

SP PC

CFR

ACA

ECA

Q/SAP

TECH

PARA

SP CC

SP PC

- *Avoid discrimination.* Do not discriminate on the basis of someone's age, appearance, condition, etc.
- *Do not make an assumption about the person's quality of life,* nor be motivated in any way by a desire to bring about a person's death.
- *Consult (as time allows) with others for their views about the person's best interests.* This may be a spouse, family or someone previously named by the person.
- *Avoid restricting a person's rights.* Consider if any other options may be less restrictive of the person's rights.

After carefully considering all of the above it is good practice to document clearly what the decision under discussion was, who was consulted, what the outcome of the discussion was and the action taken.

Where an advance decision is being followed, the best-interest principle does not apply. This is because an advance decision reflects the decision of an adult with capacity to do so who has made the decision for themselves. Healthcare professionals must follow a valid and applicable advance decision, even if they think it goes against a person's best interests.

Deciding whether an advance decision is applicable

An advance decision to refuse treatment is not applicable if:

- The patient still has the capacity to make a decision about treatment.
- The treatment refused is not specified.
- Any circumstances specified in the advance decision are absent.
- The present circumstances were not anticipated by the patient when they made the decision and would have affected the patient's decision if they had known about them when they made the advance decision.

> Healthcare professionals should assess whether an advance decision is valid and applicable, and record their determination. That an advance decision contains a statement that it is intended to be binding does not mean that it is binding. It must be assessed in the circumstances existing at the time the decision about treatment needs to be made.

Recognition of the dying phase and associated medical emergencies

It is accepted that there are two stages that a person goes through prior to death, the pre-active and active phase.

Pre-active phase	Active phase
Usually lasting months	Usually lasting days or at the most a few weeks

We are more likely to have contact with terminal patients in the active phase, which in itself creates a number of medical emergencies (Table 1).

CFR

ACA

ECA

Q/SAP

TECH

PARA

SP CC

SP PC

Table 1 Medical emergencies

Clinical emergency	Pathology	Treatment
Breathlessness (physically unable to breath)	No chest pain, no cough or wheeze? • pulmonary embolism • tension pneumothorax • hypovolaemic shock • metabolic acidosis	Assessment
Dyspnoea (sensation of difficulty in breathing)	Central, non-pleuritic chest pain • myocardial infarction • massive pulmonary embolism • pericardial infusion Lateralised pleuritic chest pain • pneumonia • pulmonary infarction • rib fracture • pneumothorax	Treatment pathways, consult CCP/GSF/LCP first (if present), then consider • immediate hospital admission • referral to palliative care team • referral to GP
Nausea and vomiting	Chemotherapy	Assessment

	Movement related (vestibular disorder)	Simple measures
		• make sure the person has access to a large bowl, tissues and water
	Peristaltic failure or gastric stasis – mechanical bowel obstruction, exclude or treat constipation.	• make sure that meals are small and palatable
		• carbohydrate meals are often better tolerated
	Abdominal or pelvic tumour (causing distension, compression, or disturbance of abdominal or pelvic organs)	• offer cool, fizzy drinks (citrus flavours are often preferred)
		• consider parenteral hydration if appropriate
	Anxiety related	• consider relaxation and acupressure bands to relieve symptoms
Pain	Owing to the primary disease, e.g.,	Assessment
	• tumour infiltration	Use the pain score method or Abbey Pain
	• nerve compression	Score as appropriate

CFR

ACA

ECA

Q/SAP

TECH

PARA

SP CC

SP PC

153

Table 1 Medical emergencies *continued*

Clinical emergency	Pathology	Treatment
Pain continued	Associated with treatment, e.g., • diagnostic and staging procedures • surgery Owing to general debilitating disease, e.g., • pressure sores • constipation Unrelated to the primary disease or treatment, e.g., • arthritis • ischaemic heart disease	*Numerical Rating Scale* On a scale of 0 to 10, how strong is your pain? No pain = 0 1 2 3 4 5 6 7 8 9 10 = Worst possible pain *Verbal descriptor scale* Which word best describes your pain? none, mild, moderate, severe Treatment pathways, consult CCP/GSF/LCP first (if present), then consider: • immediate hospital admission • referral to palliative care team – especially if the patient is experiencing 'breakthrough pain' • referral to GP

		...treatment pathways, consult CCP/GSF/LCP first (if present), then consider: • referral to palliative care team • referral to GP
agitation Terminal restlessness is a common symptom at the end of life. Symptoms may include an inability to relax, picking at clothing or sheets, confusion and agitation, and trying to climb out of bed	• opioids • anti-seizure drugs • steroids and anxiolytics • overuse of medications can cause toxicity and underuse can cause pain and discomfort, which can further worsen delirium Untreated physical pain or discomfort Owing to general debilitating disease, e.g., • dehydration • decreased oxygen in the blood/brain • anaemia (decreased red blood cells) • infections and fevers • brain tumours/brain swelling • urinary retention (the inability to void urine could be caused by disease, a kinked urinary catheter or bladder spasms)	

Table 1 Medical emergencies *continued*

Clinical emergency	Pathology	Treatment
Restlessness and agitation continued	• constipation or faecal impaction • cancer treatments • metabolic disturbances (common at the end of life as vital organs begin to shut down) Fear, anxiety, emotional turmoil	
Rattles	End-stage wet respirations occur when secretions build up in the throat and airway. These secretions are perfectly normal and consist of saliva, mucous and any other liquids that are introduced into the patient's mouth (wet sponges, medications, etc.)	Treatment pathways, consult CCP/GSF/LCP first (if present), then consider simple measures: • Change the patient's position – sometimes turning a person from their back to their side is enough clear excess secretions from the airway; you can also try to raising the head of the bed to promote drainage.

CFR

ACA

ECA

Q/SAP

TECH

PARA

SP CC

SP PC

	introduced into the mouth – carers/family will undoubtedly want to keep the patient's lips and oral mucosa moist with wet sponges, but you can minimise the amount of water that will drain down the patient's throat by gently squeezing excess water from the sponge before you moisten their mouth.
	We are likely to be called for catastrophic haemorrhage; although rare, this can occur in terminal patients. If it has been identified as a high risk for this eventuality should be written so do consult the GSF/LCP first. Even if this has been discussed with the patient and their family it is still an extremely distressing event and their wishes may change (e.g., the patient wishes to be conveyed to a hospital).
Bleeding	Local infiltration of blood vessels by tumour Cancer treatments, such as radiotherapy, chemotherapy or surgery Systemic complications of cancer Drug treatments, such as anticoagulants or non-steroidal anti-inflammatory agents Concurrent illness, including infection

CFR ACA ECA Q/SAP TECH PARA SP CC SP PC

Table 1 Medical emergencies *continued*

Clinical emergency	Pathology	Treatment
Bleeding *continued*		If so, then manage the patient as defined by JRCALC guidance and transfer the patient to hospital with a pre-alert
Superior vena cava obstruction	Extrinsic pressure, thrombus or invasion 75% SVCO is in lung carcinoma 15% SVCO is in lymphoma 3% of all patients with lung cancer are affected Benign causes – goitre, thrombus and aneurysm	Symptoms of SVCO depend on the extent and speed of development, and are often worse when lying flat • dyspnoea (50%) • neck and facial swelling (40%) • trunk and arm swelling (40%) • a sensation of choking • a feeling of fullness in the head • headache

CFR
ACA
ECA
Q/SAP
TECH
PARA
SP CC
SP PC

	Usually occurs slowly over weeks or months, but can occur rapidly in days, which is distressing and painful because of venous hypertension; the SVC drains blood from the head, neck, arms and upper thorax into the right atrium.	Physical signs of SVCO • thoracic/neck vein distension (60%) • facial oedema (55%) • tachypnoea (40%) • plethora of the face (15%) • cyanotic/dusky colour (15%) • arm oedema (10%) • vocal cord paresis (3%) If SVCO is suspected, send/transport into hospital
Spinal cord compression (SCC)	3–5% of patients with advanced cancer develop SCC. There is a high risk of failure to recognise SCC, a condition that is often overlooked by clinicians; cancers that metastasise to bone have the potential to invade the vertebrae. 15–41% of patients with cancer develop vertebral metastases.	If recognised early, 70% of patients who were ambulating at the start of treatment retain the ability to walk, 35% of paraparetic patients regain the ability to walk and 5% of completely paraplegic patients improve mobility. If suspected, treat as spinal injury, immobilise and immediate transfer to A&E.

Table 1 Medical emergencies *continued*

Clinical emergency	Pathology	Treatment
Spinal cord compression (SCC) *continued*	4% are from breast, bronchial and prostate (others include kidney/lymphoma). 20% of patients can have more than one level of compression so please be aware of this when diagnosing. 10% cervical, 70% thoracic, 20% lumbar. Presentation of symptoms: • pain, 90% (back/radiating/worse on coughing/feels like a tight band around them • weakness, 75% • sensory-level problems (numbness/pins and needles), 50% • sphincter problems, 40% • progressive functional impairment • saddle anaesthesia (numbness in	

CFR

ACA

ECA

Q/SAP

TECH

PARA

SP CC

SP PC

Hypercalcaemia	A common life-threatening metabolic disorder associated with cancer: • occurs in 10% of cancer patients • 20% in the absence of bony metastasis (humeral) • 80% die within one year (active disease) • more common in myeloma (50%), breast, lung, renal and squamous cell cancer Consider non-malignant causes, e.g., drugs and hyperparathyroidism Common symptoms: • drowsiness/confusion • nausea/vomiting • constipation • thirst • pain	Treatment pathways, consult CCP/GSF/LCP first if present, as a hospital investigation may not be appropriate. If suspected, send/transfer immediately to A&E for IV rehydration and medication.

Table 1 Medical emergencies *continued*

Clinical emergency	Pathology	Treatment
Opioid toxicity	Sometimes patients can accidently overdose (OD) on their opiates if medication has changed (opiate switch) or symptoms in their disease have changed and/or pain has changed; also consider renal failure/impairment (obviously consider stage of condition). Symptoms to look for: • drowsiness • confusion/hallucinations • pinpoint pupils • muscle twitches/jerks • respiratory depression/may rouse to stimulation	***Consider severity of OD*** • Minor (respirations >8 and rousable) reduce medication or cut next dose (Specialist Paramedic (SP)/Nurse/GP only), look at history of patient and symptoms (any change in medication symptoms must be written in the District Nurse notes, not just in our notes; other grades to gain advice from the GP, palliative care team or clinical advice line). • Severe (respirations <8, not rousable) give naloxone, treat as normal OD and take to A&E (consider renal failure).

Seizures	Consider reversible causes, e.g., • glucose, metabolic • anticonvulsant/steroid dose • hypoxia • infection	If not stopping spontaneously: • diazepam 10 mg PR/IV or • midazolam 5–10 mg SC/buccal – can repeat after 10–15 min (only if authorised to give) If the above fails, take the patient to hospital for phenobarbitone 100 mg deep SC
Fractures	Consider as a cause of sudden onset or rapidly escalating bone pain if patient has bone cancer/metastases. With bone metastases the patient only has to stretch and this can cause a fracture so be aware when taking a history of medication, which can be be a major indicator if the patient is on high doses of calcium/osteoporosis drugs,	Immobilise Analgesia If high risk for bone metastases, transfer to A&E for the patient to have an X-ray

External Jugular Vein Cannulation

- Adopt standard precautions, assemble the correct equipment and thoroughly cleanse the insertion site.

> **Refer to:** *Procedures: Standard Precautions and Hand-washing pages 52–61.*

- Use an aseptic technique and perform hand hygiene in accordance with the WHO five moments for hand hygiene.
- Place the patient in a supine, head-down position to fill the jugular vein. Turn the patient's head to the side (feel for a pulse before cannulating to avoid piercing the carotid artery).
- To make the vein more visible, occlude the vessel at the base with the clavicle. Cannulate the vein $\frac{1}{2}$ to $\frac{2}{3}$ of the way from the angle of the jaw to the clavicle with the point aimed towards the shoulder on the side you are cannulating.

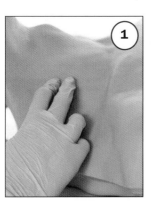 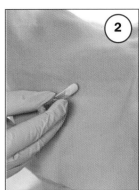

- Aspirate blood using the syringe to confirm placement. DO NOT LET AIR ENTER THE CANNULA ONCE IT IS IN THE VEIN.
- Dispose of sharps as per Trust policy.
- Apply a suitable non-circumferential dressing, e.g., Niko-Fix.
- Attach pre-prepared giving set and fluid.

REMEMBER

You should try all other means of cannulating a peripheral vein before attempting this procedure. The risks associated with this procedure are:

- Puncture of the carotid artery
- Potential massive haematoma if infiltration occurs
- Air embolism

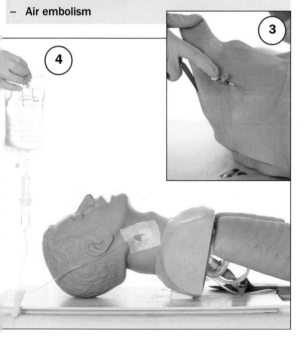

PARA

SP CC

SP PC

Gas Management and Cylinder Safety

- Compressed medical O_2 cylinders should be:
  - Stored under cover, inside, kept dry and clean and not exposed to extremes of temperatures, and away from stocks of combustible material.
  - Stored separately from industrial and other non-medical cylinders.
  - Stored so as to maintain separation between full and empty cylinders.
  - Used in strict rotation so that cylinders with the earliest filling date are used first.
  - Stored separately from other medical cylinders within the storage area.
  - F size and larger cylinders should be stored vertically, E size and smaller should be stored horizontally.

- To prepare the cylinder for use, remove the tamper-evident seal and the valve-outlet protection cap.
- Do not remove and discard any batch labels fitted to the cylinder.
- Ensure the correct compressed medical oxygen regulator is selected for connection to the cylinder.
- Ensure the connecting face on the regulator is clean and the fitted sealing washer is in good working condition.
- Connect the regulator, using moderate force only, and connect the tubing to the regulator/flow meter outlet.
- Only the appropriate regulator should be used for the particular gas concerned.
- Open the cylinder valve slowly and check for any leaks.
- Cylinders and any associated equipment must never be lubricated and must be kept free from oil and grease.
- Cylinders used with a pressure regulator:
  - Having connected the regulator or manifold yoke to the cylinder, check the connections for leaks.
  - Should leaks occur this will usually be evident by a hissing noise.
  - Should a leak occur between the valve outlet and the regulator or manifold yoke, depressurise and remove the fitting, and fit an approved sealing washer.
  - Reconnect the fitting to the valve with

moderate force only, fitting a replacement regulator or manifold tailpipe as required.

– Sealing or jointing compounds must never be used to cure a leak.
– Never use excessive force when connecting equipment to cylinders.
– If leaks persist, label the cylinder and return it to the supplier.
• When the compressed medical oxygen cylinder is empty ensure that the:
– Cylinder valve is closed, using moderate force only, and the pressure in the regulator or tailpipe is released.
– Valve outlet cap, where fitted, is replaced.
– Empty cylinders are immediately returned to the empty cylinder store for return to the supplier.

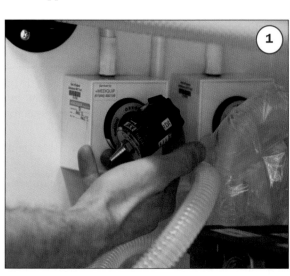

CFR

ACA

ECA

Q/SAP

TECH

PARA

SP CC

SP PC

Glucogel for Emergency Care Assistants and Community First Responders

Conscious with signs of reduced blood sugar

- The patient may well be able to indicate that they think they have a reduced blood-sugar level. They may describe the way they feel as similar to previous 'hypo episodes'.
- The clinical signs of a hypo include feeling clammy, sweaty, faint, hungry or confused (acting strangely).
- In these settings the patient should be given oral sugar to drink.

Altered level of consciousness

- Again, it is essential that you assess the ABCs and, where appropriate, give first aid. You may, for instance, place the patient in the recovery position.
- In this setting it is appropriate to give Glucogel following closely the method of administration.

Method of administration

- Glucogel comes as a clear tube that contains 23 g of 40% dextrose. The tube is opened by twisting the top.
- The contents can be sucked and swallowed if the patient is conscious.

- However, if the patient is compromised (unwilling or unable to co-operate) in any way, the gel can be applied to the patient's gums. It is possible to rub small amounts of the gel onto the inside of the patient's cheek, but take care not to cause any choking. The patient should be in the recovery position.
- It is expected that the beneficial effects of Glucogel should be noticed within a few minutes.
- It should never be necessary to use two tubes. The patient should stop acting strangely, the sweating should reduce and, if unconscious, the level of consciousness should begin to improve as the blood sugar rises.
- Some patients who have reduced blood sugar levels can act strangely and may require reassurance that they are safe.

Records

- If Glucogel is used it is essential that this is recorded on the CFR report form and that the ambulance crew clearly understand that Glucogel was used. If Glucogel is used by an ECA it must be recorded on the Ambulance Trust's official ePCR.

CONTRAINDICATIONS

Glucogel should not be used:

– on anyone under two years of age

– if the blood-sugar level is known to be high.

Note: This guidance is for Emergency Care Assistants and Community First Responders <u>only</u>. All other staff should refer to the JRCALC guidance.

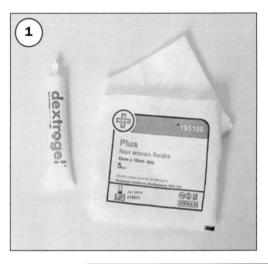

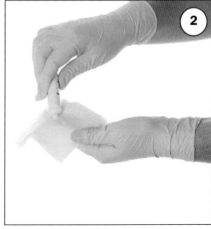

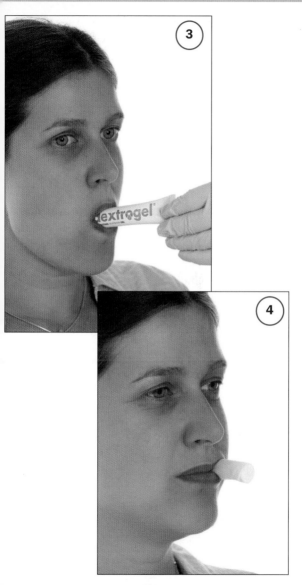

Manual Handling: Manual Handling Belts

- From sitting to standing:
  - Place the belt around the patient's hips and fasten the belt firmly to prevent the belt from riding up to the patient's armpits.
  - Encourage the patient to move to the edge of the chair/bed and have their feet firmly on the floor.
  - Allow the patient to move at their own pace, and provide support and assistance as required.
  - One operator should stand on one side of the patient and the other operator on the other side.
  - Taking a handle on the belt, manoeuvre the patient using clear instructions to assist them to stand.
- Recumbent to sitting manoeuvre:
  - Place the belt behind the patient's shoulders – avoid putting pressure on the patient's neck.
  - Kneel alongside the patient holding the belt with your nearside hand only, with your palm facing outwards.
  - Both operators should sit back on their heels using their body weight to sit the patient up.
  - Allow the patient to steady themselves once sat up.

REMEMBER

- Always consider any underlying conditions that may cause injuries.

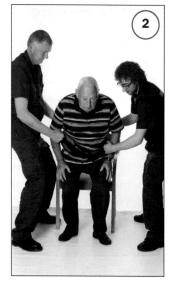

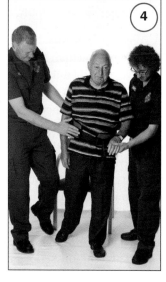

ACA

ECA

Q/SAP

TECH

PARA

SP CC

SP PC

IABP Transfers

Introduction

The *Intra-aortic balloon pump* (IABP) is a mechanical device that increases myocardial oxygen perfusion, while at the same time increasing cardiac output. Increasing cardiac output increases coronary blood flow and therefore myocardial oxygen delivery. It consists of a cylindrical polyethylene balloon that sits in the aorta, approximately 2 cm (0.79 inches) from the left subclavian artery, and counter pulsates. That is, it actively deflates in systole, increasing the forwards blood flow by reducing the after-load. It actively inflates in diastole, increasing the blood flow to the coronary arteries. These actions combine to decrease myocardial oxygen demand and increase myocardial oxygen supply.

A computer-controlled mechanism inflates the balloon with helium from a cylinder during diastole, usually linked to either an electrocardiogram or a pressure transducer at the distal tip of the catheter; some IABPs, such as the Datascope System 98XT, allow asynchronous counter pulsation at a set rate, although this setting is rarely used. Helium is used because its low viscosity allows it to travel quickly through the long connecting tubes, and it has a lower risk of causing an embolism should the balloon rupture.

Owing to the critical nature of this type of transfer, and to prevent any serious incidents, the vehicle deployed must have a 240 volt power supply to ensure that the IABP battery is not relied upon during the transfer. The 240 volt vehicle will also have a tail lift that is capable of lifting the patient, trolley and IABP; the IABP does not therefore need to be disconnected from the patient during this manoeuvre.

Vehicle inverter operator guide

Refer to the Procedure 'Vehicle Inverter Operation'. Safe operating procedure fixing instructions for an IABP using a generic vehicle.

On being advised of an IABP transfer to another hospital, the following procedure should be followed:

1. Ensure that the vehicle you are driving has a 500 kg tail lift and a 240 volt power supply. If it does not, advise HEOC who will deploy a vehicle appropriate for an IABP transfer, referring immediately to the HEOC IABP pack.
2. Ensure that there is sufficient fuel in the vehicle for the journey.
3. Ensure that all loose equipment is stored appropriately to avoid any trip hazards.
4. On arrival at the dispatching hospital:
   i.   Remove the stretcher from the vehicle and take it to the appropriate area of the hospital, as advised by HEOC, ready for the patient.
   ii. Locate the IABP fixing bracket and ensure that it is not damaged in any way (*Figure 1*).

5. Owing to the bracket's weight, use a hospital trolley to take it to the vehicle.

6. Ensure that the rear seat is in its closed position with the seat facing the stretcher (*Figure 2*).

7. If the fixing is OK, fix the bracket securely to the rear seat pillar. Ensure that the bottom plate fits over the floor seat, and locate the front bolts and strengthening webs on the pillar support (*Figure 3*).

8. Check that the clamp is firmly secured around the pillar (*Figure 4*).

9. Once you are happy that the clamp is fitted correctly, return to pick up the patient and the IABP.

10. Transfer the patient to the trolley using the appropriate lifting aids and, where necessary, ask for additional assistance. This is likely to be a co-ordinated movement because of the medical devices attached to the patient. The responsibility for this lift is the responsibility of the medical team at the hospital.

11. Ensure that the IABP is removed from its carry frame (*Figure 5*). It is possible that the hospital clinical team ask that the carry frame remains on until the very last minute. This is acceptable; however, the carry frame must not be conveyed into the ambulance during the transfer. The IABP weighs 72 kg so it must be pulled or pushed along using the carry handle and wheels provided.

12. Moving the patient needs to be done in a controlled manner because of the connection

between the patient and the IABP. Where possible, the stretcher should be moved with staff at the side of the trolley and the person moving the IABP should be at the rear centre of the trolley. The person at the rear should take control of the move as they can see the patient and tubing, and ensure that no snagging or pulling of the piping occurs.

13. Once the lift is level with the bed of the vehicle, the IABP should be moved off the lift.
14. The pump now needs to be stowed safely in the bracket fitted earlier to the rear seat pillar.
15. Using two people, place the pump between the 'U'-shaped bracket. Ensure that the carry handle is stowed away prior to moving the pump to its final position for travelling. This is done by pressing the button on the slide of the carry handle and pushing the handle down.
16. Move the pump back as far as possible into the bracket.
17. Using the straps provided, secure the front of the pump first (*Figure 6*).
18. Ask the escort clinical team to remove the monitor from the pump so that the top securing straps can be positioned.
19. Tighten all the straps so that the unit is secure for travel.
20. Ask the escort clinical team to replace the monitor if necessary.
21. The crew members secure the vehicle for travel and transport the patient to their intended destination.

ECA

Q/SAP

TECH

PARA

SP CC

SP PC

22. As there are only two positions in the rear of the vehicle, both crew members travel in the cab.

23. On arrival at the receiving hospital, the reverse procedure, from 26 to 13, must be followed.

24. The crew must wait at the hospital, to transport the clinical team, trolley and the pump back to the dispatching hospital.

25. Ensure that the pump is secure, as described above, for this move.

26. Once back at the originating hospital, remove the bracket and return it to the designated storage area. This can be done either by the acute clinical staff or the ambulance crew.

27. Prior to storing the bracket, the acute trust clinical staff must inspect it for any damage and report this to the crew. The ambulance crew should report any defects via the HEOC (and the Cardiac Clinical Lead for Essex).

28. Advise HEOC that you are now back on duty.

Figure 1
Fixing bracket for a triangular-based chair.

Figure 2
The rear seat folded up.

The triangular shape of the bracket fits into the shape of the seat base.

Figure 3
The fixing bracket in position. Prior to sliding it in, ensure that the lugs at the end of the triangular section are folded in.

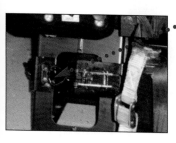

Figure 4
Once in position, ensure that the barrel clamps are firmly closed.

ECA

Q/SAP

TECH

PARA

SP CC

SP PC

181

Figure 5
The IABP removed from its carrier ready to be loaded onto the ambulance.

• Button to release handle ready for pulling.

• Once loaded onto the ambulance, the IABP monitor (indicated) needs to be removed by the clinical team so that the pump can be secured.

Figure 6
Ensure that the monitor is removed prior to strapping. Fix in the following order: Strap 1 (indicated) and then straps 2 and 3. Tighten all the straps to ensure that the IABP is firmly fixed into the bracket.

• Straps 2, 3
• Strap 1

ECA
Q/SAP
TECH
PARA
SP CC
SP PC

Figure 7
Ancillary battery
strap.

Responsibilities of the ambulance staff transporting the patient

The East of England Ambulance Service Trust (EEAST) recommends that the best practice is to transfer the IABP and patient on a critical-care trolley, which is purpose built for this type of transportation, or an EEAST trolley depending on how unwell the patient is. EEAST will not refuse other transfers, but EEAST will not be held responsible for any incidents that happen en route because hospital equipment is insecure in the vehicle.

Ambulance staff will go to the agreed pick-up point at the hospital, where they will be met by a member of the hospital staff who informs them of the IABP transfer and the ward the patient is on. *It is the responsibility of the hospital trust staff to ensure that the IABP equipment is charged and ready to go, along with all of the necessary transfer equipment.*

ECA

Q/SAP

TECH

PARA

SP CC

SP PC

The vehicle to be used for this type of transfer is a newer model; the IABP bracket that is compatible has a triangular fixing and so can fit into a triangular chair base. A tail-lift vehicle is essential as the IABP unit and batteries weigh in excess of 80 kg. *Please make HEOC aware if your vehicle is not suitable so that another resource can be allocated.*

Ambulance staff collect the triangular bracket from the ward on a hospital trolley and fix it to the vehicle as outlined above. The patient can be transferred to the ambulance with the IABP by the hospital staff. *Owing to the weight of the bracket, it must be transported from the ward to the ambulance using a hospital trolley.*

Establish whether the transfer will be carried out using a critical-care trolley or an EEAST trolley.

It is the ambulance staff's responsibility, with the support of the accompanying hospital staff, to ensure that the transfer of the patient onto the ambulance is safe. It is also the ambulance staff's responsibility to ensure that the journey is undertaken swiftly and safely. *Owing to the weight of the balloon pump and to comply with 'Best Practice' for CEN compliance, only two staff from the acute trust can travel with the patient during this transfer.*

In *exceptional circumstances* that require three hospital staff for the transfer, this must be communicated when initially requesting the

ECA

Q/SAP

TECH

PARA

SP CC

SP PC

transfer. Under certain circumstances, arrangements may be put in place for an ambulance car containing personnel to act as a second crew member, if needed, to escort the ambulance.

If you are advised by the HEOC to take an alternative route because of an incident further along your route, you must inform the clinical staff accompanying the patient and discuss any necessary measures.

Any medical care required during the journey will be provided by the acute trust clinical staff. The ambulance staff will support and assist the clinical staff and vice-versa. *Ambulance staff are not authorised to operate the IABP under any circumstances.*

If there are any adverse traffic problems en route that would affect the ETA at the receiving hospital, on discussion with the clinical staff a police escort can be considered and requested through HEOC.

The patient will then be taken into the hospital. The escort clinical staff will complete the handover to the receiving hospital staff.

In the event of a cardiac arrest, the ambulance will be stopped safely on the road and the ambulance crew will assist the hospital clinical staff. Any decision to divert to another hospital rests with the clinical staff from the hospital. If

ECA

Q/SAP

TECH

PARA

SP CC

SP PC

the patient dies during the journey and death is confirmed by the escorting clinical staff, then the patient is taken back to the originating hospital. The acute trust clinical staff will arrange for the patient to be taken to the hospital mortuary.

In the event of a breakdown of the transfer vehicle, another vehicle suitable for an IABP transfer must be dispatched as a matter of urgency.

This transfer is to be undertaken as an emergency transfer using blue lights and sirens. It has been agreed that the vehicle will return the IABP and hospital staff to the appropriate acute trust.

The return journey – responsibilities of all key personnel involved

The ambulance crew recover the IABP and locate it back into its travel bracket. Together with the clinical staff they will endeavour to return promptly to the originating hospital. While on the return journey the ambulance may be deployed to make a first response or to attend a Red 1 or Red 2 call.

For a Red 1/2 call, or if the ambulance comes across an incident, then there may be a need to transport a patient to the nearest hospital. It has to be recognised that the IABP and escort staff will make movement in the back of the ambulance more difficult. The journey back to the originating hospital will be completed *after* such

ECA

Q/SAP

TECH

PARA

SP CC

SP PC

an incident. Once the IABP and the fixing bracket have been removed they will be given back to the hospital staff.

Such a transfer may take 3–4 hours to complete.

ECA

Q/SAP

TECH

PARA

SP CC

SP PC

Manual Handling: IBEX Tran-Seat 700H Stair Chair™

- Remove the chair from its holder.
- Position the chair in an upright position, ensuring that all locking mechanisms are secure.
- Use of the IBEX chair is a two-person task: operator 1 stands behind the chair and grips the handles firmly, while the patient is assisted by operator 2 into a sitting position.
- Rest the patient's feet comfortably on the foot plate.
- Secure the patient with a seat belt around the upper torso, with their arms inside the belt.
- Leg restraints should also be used.
- If descending stairs, operator 1 should extend the handles to chest height prior to the descent.
- Operator 2 takes position on the stairs, and holds the handles on the foot plate.
- When both operators agree, they move the chair towards the stairs, and tilt the chair back in line with the angle of descent.
- Operator 2 firmly presses the chair against the stairs, allowing the tracks to grip during the descent.
- Both operators must communicate throughout to maintain a controlled descent.

ACA

ECA

Q/SAP

TECH

PARA

SP CC

SP PC

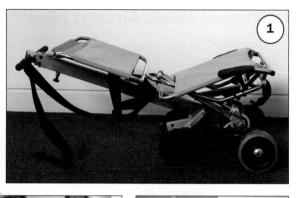

ACA

ECA

Q/SAP

TECH

PARA

SP CC

SP PC

REMEMBER

- Both operators should do a dynamic risk assessment regarding TILE – TASK, INDIVIDUAL, LOAD, ENVIRONMENT – prior to using the chair.

Laryngeal Mask Airway: I-Gel™

- Adopt standard precautions.

> **Refer to:** *Procedures: Standard Precautions and Hand-washing, pages 52–61.*

- Open the I-Gel package and take out the pack containing the device. In the last minute of pre-oxygenating the patient, transfer the device into the lid of the cage.
- Place a small bolus of water-based lubricant onto the smooth inner surface of the device ready for use.
- Grasp the I-Gel along the integral bite block and lubricate the back, sides and front of the cuff.
- After lubrication, ensure that no bolus of lubricant remains in the bowl of the cuff or elsewhere on the device.
- Avoid touching the cuff with your hands and place the I-Gel back into the cage pack.
- Introduce the leading soft tip into the patient's mouth in the direction of the hard palate.
- Glide the device downwards and backwards along the hard palate with gentle, continuous pushing until a definitive resistance is felt.
- The incisors should rest on the integral bite-block.
- Position the device so that the I-Gel cuff outlet faces towards the patient's chin.
- The I-Gel should be taped down from the maxilla to the maxilla.
- Insertion of the I-Gel should take less than 5 seconds.

Size	Age	Weight
3	Small adult	30–60 kg
4	Medium adult	50–90 kg
5	Large adult	90 kg+

Above are the sizes to use for I-Gel.

REMEMBER
- Do not use the silicone-based lubricant of the I-Gel device.

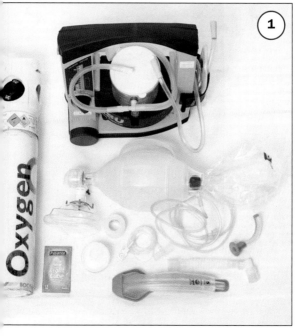

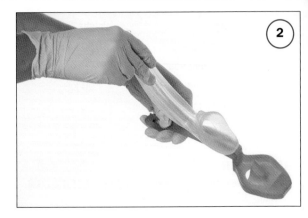

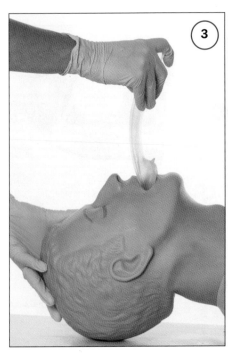

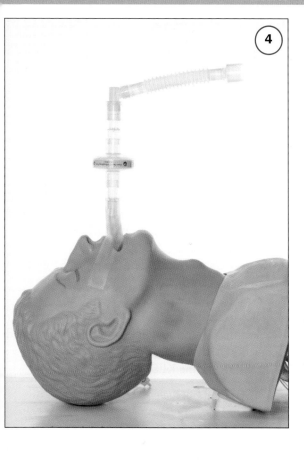

④

Q/SAP

TECH

PARA

SP CC

SP PC

Immobilisation

CFR

- Consider personal safety and adopt standard precautions.

  > **Refer to:** *Procedures: Standard Precautions and Hand-washing, pages 52–61.*

ACA

- Ascertain the mechanism of injury where possible.

ECA

- Rescuer 1 should apply manual immobilisation to the head and neck by placing one hand either side of the patient's head with fingertips towards the patient's chin/face, taking care not to cover the patient's ears.

Q/SAP

- Rescuer 2 should complete the primary survey and treat accordingly.
- Rescuer 2 should then apply a correctly sized collar to the patient's neck.

TECH

- Select the appropriate immobilisation device and position it on the patient:
  - KED – see the KED procedure.

    > **Refer to:** *Procedures: KED Procedure, pages 220–221.*

PARA

  - Spinal board – see the relevant procedure.

    > **Refer to:** *Procedures: Spinal Board, pages 324–327.*

SP CC

  - Orthopaedic stretcher – see relevant procedure.

    > **Refer to:** *Procedures: Orthopaedic Stretcher, pages 260–261.*

SP PC

- Rescuer 1 should only release manual immobilisation when the patient is appropriately secured and immobilised, and ready for transport.

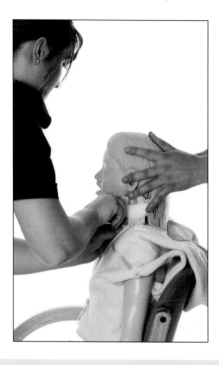

REMEMBER

Do not proceed with the neutral alignment of the patient's head and neck if there is:

- Increase of pain.
- New or increased neurological signs or symptoms.
- Increase in muscle spasm.
- Compromise of the airway.
- Resistance to movement.

Setting up an Infusion

- Adopt standard precautions.

> **Refer to:** *Procedures: Standard Precautions and Hand-washing, pages 52–61.*

- Use an aseptic technique and perform hand hygiene inaccordance with the WHO five moments for hand hygiene.
- Gather and check the equipment:
  - Fluid bag as prescribed – check that the name and dose are correct, the packaging is intact and that it's in date.
  - Giving set – check the packaging is intact and that it's in date.
- Remove the packaging from the fluid bag and giving set, and remove the cover from the port on the fluid bag – twist to break it off.
- Insert the spike of the giving set to the port of the drug bag – do not touch or contaminate it. Use a twisting motion and some force as it may be stiff.

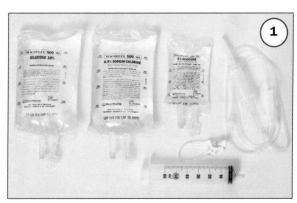

- Half fill the chamber of the giving set by squeezing the bag.
- Run fluids through the giving set – ensure that no bubbles are left in the giving set.
- Connect the Leur connector to the cannula in situ.
- Set the infusion rate by adjusting the roller in the flow-control portion of the giving set.
- Ensure aseptic techniques are used throughout and dispose of sharps as per Trust Policy.

Intramuscular Injection

- Adopt standard precautions.

  > **Refer to:** *Procedures: Standard Precautions and Hand-washing, pages 52–61.*

- Use an aseptic technique and perform hand hygiene inaccordance with the WHO five moments for hand hygiene.
- Explain the procedure to the patient, or parent/carer of the patient in cases of minors/vulnerable adults, and gain informed consent.
- Select the appropriate drug – check with a colleague (if present) the name of the drug, that it is in date, clarity and container integrity.
- Select the injection site: the deltoid muscle, the upper outer quadrant of the buttock or outer aspect of the thigh.
- Position the patient to expose the injection site and clean the area.
- Prepare drug accordingly.
- Some drugs – benzyl penicillin – need to be mixed prior to injection: draw up the required amount of water for the injection, inject into the powder container and mix the two constituents.
- Other drugs are 'ready' and require the clinician to snap the vial, draw up the fluid, replace the drawing up needle with an appropriate size needle for injection (21 g or 23 g).
- Warn the patient, remove the needle guard, pull the skin taut and to one side, and pierce the skin at a 90 degree angle.

Q/SAP

TECH

PARA

SP CC

SP PC

- Draw back the piston of the syringe – if there is no blood, administer the drug slowly.
- Release the tension on the skin, remove the needle and apply firm pressure to the site.
- Dispose of sharps appropriately.

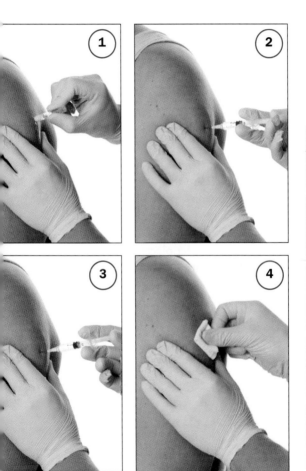

Intraosseous Infusion (Manual Needle)

- Adopt standard precautions.

> **Refer to:** *Procedures: Standard Precautions and Hand-washing, pages 52–61.*

- Use an aseptic technique and perform hand hygiene inaccordance with the WHO five moments for hand hygiene.
- Locate the correct anatomical site for the IO puncture.
- Palpate the tibial tuberosity and medial border of the tibia.
- Thoroughly cleanse the insertion site, which is 1–2 cm distal to the tuberosity.
- Holding the base plate of the needle cannula, remove the trocar by turning the handle anticlockwise.
- Confirm a correct placement by attaching a syringe to aspirate the blood and bone particles.
- Dispose of the needle in the sharps.
- Place a support behind the knee.
- Insert the needle at a 90-degree angle to the leg, advance the needle with a twisting motion until a 'pop' is felt.

- Secure the needle and initiate the infusion –
  reassess the flow and check for signs of
  subcutaneous extravasation.

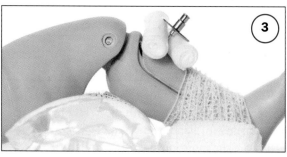

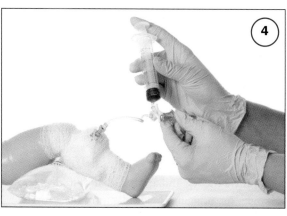

PARA

SP CC

SP PC

EZ-IO® Procedure

Use EZ-IO when attempts at gaining peripheral access have been made on the upper/lower limbs and failed.

EZ-IO can be used on conscious patients as the pain response is such that local anaesthetic can be applied.

EZ-IO can be used in patients of any age who require fluid/medications during on-going resuscitation.

- Adopt standard precautions.

> **Refer to:** *Procedures: Standard Precautions and Hand-washing, pages 52-61.*

- Use an aseptic technique and perform hand hygiene inaccordance with the WHO five moments for hand hygiene.
- Locate the insertion site using landmarks (patella, tibial tuberosity and tibial plateau) and clean the site.
- Adult (>40 kg): directly medial to the tuberosity on the flat aspect of the tibial plateau.
- Children (3–39 kg): 1 cm distal to the tuberosity and medial onto the flat aspect of the tibial plateau.
- Prepare the driver set with the appropriately coloured cartridge: RED 3–39 kg and BLUE >40 kg.
- Stabilise the leg and approach at a 90 degree angle, introducing the needle into the skin. Push

PARA

SP CC

SP PC

through the skin to the bone, but not into the bone at this point.

- Ensure the 5 mm mark is visible and continue insertion with a steady, even pressure on the driver.
- Power the needle until the flange of the needle hub rests against the skin or until a decrease of resistance is felt – stop when you feel a 'pop'.
- Remove the driver from the needle set and secure the hub and IV line. Ensure the wristband is placed on the patient's wrist – same side as the IO insertion.
- Remove the stylet from the needle – rotate it counter clockwise while holding the catheter hub – and dispose as per sharps policy.
- Confirm the placement – blood is observed from the catheter, and blood or marrow is aspirated from the catheter.
- Attach the primed EZ connect system to a three-way tap and IV giving set with fluids to the IO, and ensure the flow rate using either a pressure cuff or syringe.
- Adminster 2% lidocaine and then flush the IO catheter with 10 ml saline/water for injection and monitor for extravasation.

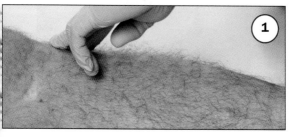

PARA

SP CC

SP PC

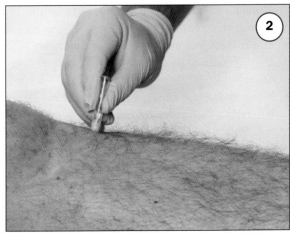

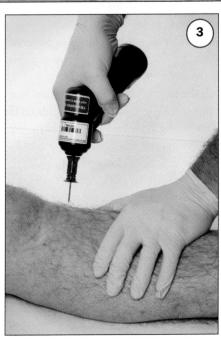

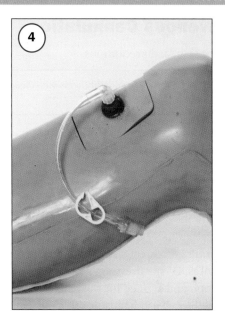

REMEMBER
DO NOT USE IO PROCEDURE WHEN:
There are fractures of the tibia or femur on the side to be used, the patient has had previous knee replacement, there is an infection over the insertion site, the extremity is compromised by an underlying medical condition (such as tumour or vascular disease) or there is excessive tissue over the site such that the needle will be unable to penetrate the bone.

PARA

SP CC

SP PC

Intravenous Cannulation

- Adopt standard precautions.

> **Refer to:** *Procedures: Standard Precautions and Hand-washing, pages 52–61.*

- Use an aseptic technique and perform hand hygiene inaccordance with the WHO five moments for hand hygiene.
- Explain the procedure to the patient and gain their consent.
- Prepare the required equipment and check the date, cleanliness and packaging: tourniquet, ChloraPrep, correct size cannula for indented purposes, IV site dressing, ampoule of water for injection and syringe for flushing cannula, sharps box. Wash hands or use hand sanitiser and don gloves.
- Select the venepuncture site: dorsum of hand, forearm or antecubital fossa.
- Use the most distal vein suitable – look and feel for a vein. Apply the tourniquet to the upper arm to allow the veins to engorge with blood.
- Clean the chosen site with ChloraPrep for 30 and allow to dry for 30 seconds. Do not re-palpate the skin after cleaning.
- Apply tension to the skin distal to the site and insert the needle–cannula assembly through the skin.
- Once the skin is penetrated, redirect the needle to enter the vein and advance it.

PARA

SP CC

SP PC

- As the needle advances into the vein a 'flashback' of blood will appear in the cannula hub, which confirms vein penetration.
- Pull back on the needle inside the cannula tip. When the needle is totally within the cannula, advance the cannula and needle by its full length into the vein.
- When the cannula is fully advanced, release the tourniquet and place a finger over the top of the cannula.
- Remove the needle and dispose of it in the sharps box, cap the end of the cannula and secure with a sterile IV dressing prior to flushing.

REMEMBER

Indications for IV cannulation:

- Provide access for drug administration
- Deliver IV fluids

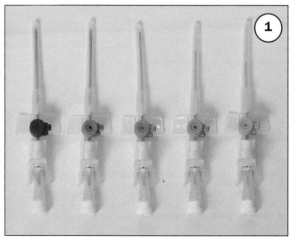

PARA

SP CC

SP PC

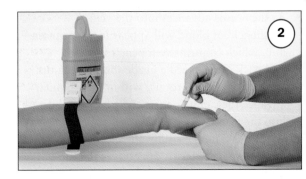

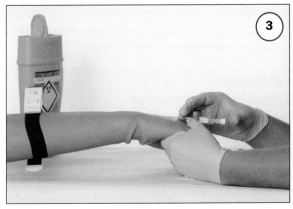

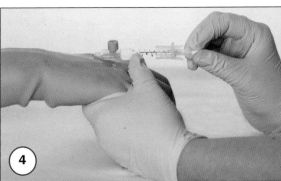

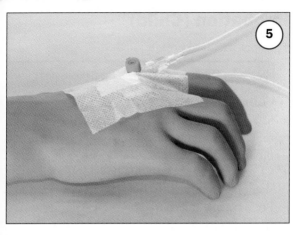

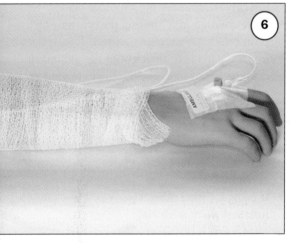

PARA

SP CC

SP PC

Intubation (Child)

- Adopt standard precautions.

> **Refer to:** *Procedures: Standard Precautions and Hand-washing, pages 52–61.*

- Select correct size of equipment: suction, ET tube, laryngoscope blade and handle, catheter mount and BVM.
- Clear any obstruction from the visible airway – suction as required.
- Pre-oxygenate the patient.
- Place infants in a neutral position with a towel/blanket under the shoulder blades.
- Place children in a 'sniffing the morning air' position.
- Insert the blade to the right of the midline, move it to the left to push the tongue to the left and out of view.
- Identify the epiglottis and slide the tip of the blade over and beyond the vallecula.
- Raise the blade and epiglottis and pass the ET tube through the vocal cords by 2–4 cm.
- If using a cuffed tube, inflate the cuff with air until a seal is obtained.
- Securely fit the catheter mount to the ET tube – not for infants – and ventilate the patient with

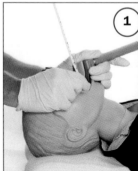

PARA

SP CC

SP PC

oxygen (ensure a bilateral chest movement is achieved). Check breath sounds using a stethoscope and capnography.

REMEMBER
The position of the larynx and large epiglottis means it is usually easier to use a straight-bladed laryngoscope in infants.

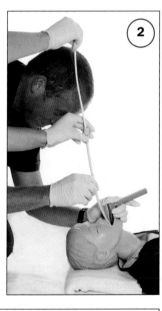

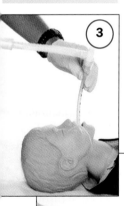

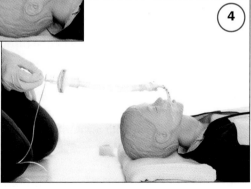

PARA

SP CC

SP PC

211

Adult Intubation

- Adopt standard precautions.

> **Refer to:** *Procedures: Standard Precautions and Hand-washing, pages 52-61.*

- Select the equipment required: bougie, suction, ET tube, laryngoscope blade and handle, tube tie, catheter mount and BVM.
- Clear any obstruction from the visible airway – suction as required.
- Pre-oxygenate the patient.
- Position the patient so they are supine and 'sniffing the morning air'.
- Insert the blade to the right of the midline, move it to the left, pushing the tongue to the left and out of view.
- Identify the epiglottis and slide the blade tip into the vallecula.
- Raise the blade and epiglottis, place the bougie into the larynx and hold the bougie at the lips.
- The assistant threads the lubricated ET tube over the bougie and then holds the bougie stable at the distal end.
- The clinician then passes the ET tube through the vocal cords until the cuff passes just below the cords.
- The assistant then removes the bougie while the clinician inflates the cuff.
- The cuff is inflated with air until a seal is obtained.

PARA

SP CC

SP PC

- Attach the catheter mount and ventilate the patient with oxygen – ensure a bilateral chest movement is achieved. Check the breath sounds using a stethoscope and capnography.
- Connect the patient up to the ventilator.

REMEMBER

- Do not attempt to introduce an ET tube if the patient has a gag reflex.
- Take care on insertion of the blade and tube not to cause trauma to the soft tissues and teeth.
- Consider C-spine immobilisation throughout and maintain as required.
- Ensure adequate ventilation throughout the whole procedure.

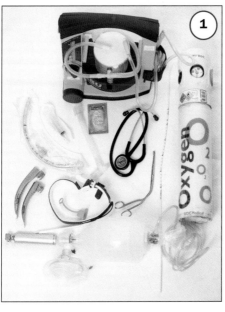

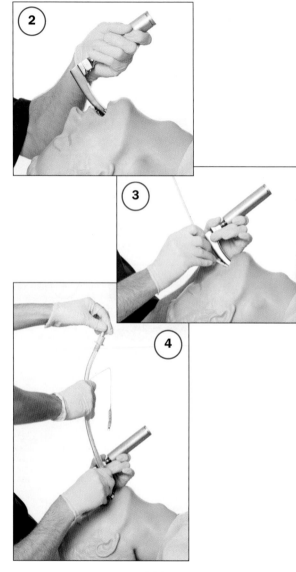

PARA

SP CC

SP PC

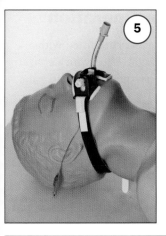

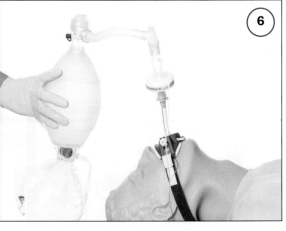

PARA

SP CC

SP PC

Vehicle Inverter Operation

The new Mercedes ambulances are fitted with a device called an electrical converter, which converts the vehicle's 12-volt battery supply into 240 volts (like you have at home).

This then allows crews to plug in infusion pumps and monitoring equipment to use on inter-hospital transfers without having to rely on the equipment's batteries.

1. Ensure the vehicle engine is running (not on run lock).

2. Press the 'INVERTER' button on the carnation panel in the vehicle saloon (this alone will not activate the inverter).

3. Switch in the 'SINE WAVE INVERTER' (black panel above the heater controls).

4. This will then engage the vehicle inverter and the sine wave panel will display a reading showing the inverter is working.

5. A 240-volt device can now be plugged in and operated.

ECA

Q/SAP

TECH

PARA

SP CC

SP PC

Trauma Jaw Thrust

- Adopt standard precautions.

> **Refer to:** *Procedures: Standard Precautions and Hand-washing, pages 52–61.*

- If the patient is in the supine position, kneel behind the patient, resting your elbows on the surface the patient is lying on.
- From above the patient's head, position your hands on each side of the patient's head, pointing them towards the patient's feet, with your thumbs supported against the patient's cheekbones.
- Spread your fingers upwards around the angle of the patient's mandible.
- Apply gentle equal pressure with these fingers to move the mandible.
- The patient's mouth should be open – if necessary, use your thumb to open the patient's lower lip.

If the patient is upright

- Ensure that a person is available to provide manual immobilisation.
- Face the patient.
- Pointing your fingers slightly upwards, place your thumbs on the patient's cheekbones.
- Spread your fingers around the angle of the patient's mandible.
- Apply gentle equal pressure with these fingers to move the patient's mandible anteriorly.

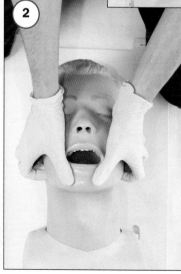

Kendrick Extrication Device™

- Access the scene and carry out a primary survey.
- Maintain a manual C-spine immobilisation.
- Examine the patient's neck and apply a rigid cervical collar before application of the KED.
- Ease the casualty forwards briefly, still maintaining C-spine control, and slide the KED between the casualty and the seat.

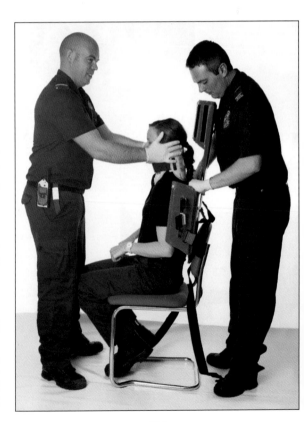

- Check the KED is correctly aligned and the wings are fitting correctly under the armpits and around the torso.
- Fasten straps in the following order: Yellow (middle strap), Red (bottom strap), Green (top strap).
- Ensure there is no gap between the patient's head/neck and the KED. Use the pad provided to fill any gap to ensure a neutral alignment and reduce any movement.

- Check and tighten all the straps.
- Apply and tighten the leg straps.
- To lift the patient, only use the lifting handles at the top and sides of the KED.

Ferno-Washington, Inc. (2001). '4.5 Torso Straps'. In: *Ferno-Washington, Inc. Users' Manual*, p11. Wilmington: Ferno-Washington, Inc.

Kendrick Traction Device

- Apply the ankle hitch around the injured leg, slightly above the ankle bone, and tighten the stirrup by pulling the GREEN tabbed strap until snug under the heel.
- Apply the upper thigh strap by sliding the male buckle under the knee, see-saw the strap upwards until it rests in the crotch area.
- Engage the buckle by clicking the straps together.
- Tighten the strap until the traction-pole receptacle is positioned at the belt line of the pelvic crest.
- Snap out the traction pole, ensuring each joint is securely seated.
- Place the traction pole alongside the injured leg with one section of the pole extended past the foot.
- Adjust the length as required and place the pole ends in the traction-pole receptacle.
- Secure the elastic strap around the knee.
- Place the YELLOW tab over the dart end of the pole, below the foot, and apply traction by pulling the RED tab.
- Traction should be applied by grasping the strap on each side and simultaneously pulling and feeding with equal pressure.
- Finish packaging the limb by applying the upper thigh and lower leg elastic straps.

REMEMBER

- As a guide, apply approximately 10% of the patient's body weight – to a maximum of 15 lb of tension – to the traction.

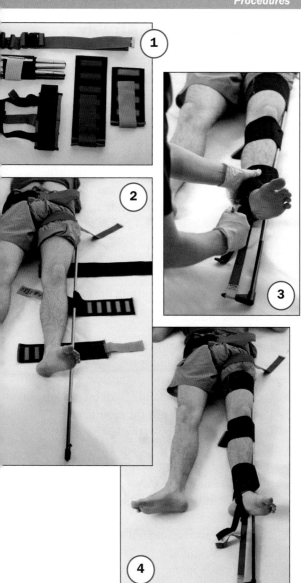

223

Laryngeal Mask Airway (Cuffed Tube)

- Adopt standard precautions.

> **Refer to:** *Procedures: Standard Precautions and Hand-washing, pages 52–61.*

- Prepare the equipment required: check the cuff of the LMA – inflate with 50% more air than required for that airway size, and then deflate the cuff completely so that no folds appear at the tip.
- Lubricate the base of the LMA ready for insertion.
- Pre-oxygenate the patient using a BVM and oxygen – ventilation should not be interrupted for >30 sec to accomplish LMA insertion.
- Position the patient: 'sniffing the morning air' for adults, and head in a neutral alignment for paediatrics.
- Insert your finger between the cuff and the tube, and place the index finger of your dominant hand in the notch between the tube and the cuff.
- Open the patient's mouth, and insert a lubricated LMA along the roof of the mouth.
- Use your finger to push the LMA against the hard palate.
- Inflate the cuff with the amount of air required for the size of the LMA used.
- Attach the tube of the LMA to a BVM and ventilate the patient.
- Confirm chest rise and fall and auscultate for equal breath sounds.
- Continuously monitor the patient.

- For transportation, the patient may be connected to a ventilator and capnography.

Size	Age range	Air (ml)
1	Neonate >5 kg	4
1.5	Child 5-10 kg	7
2	Child 10-20 kg	10
2.5	Child 20-30 kg	14
3	Child/small adult (30-50 kg)	20
4	Small/normal adult	30
5	Normal/large adult	40

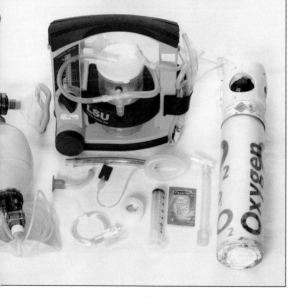

ECA

Q/SAP

TECH

PARA

SP CC

SP PC

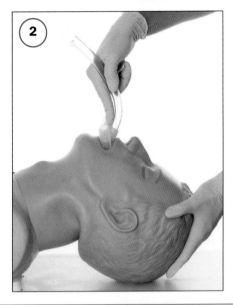

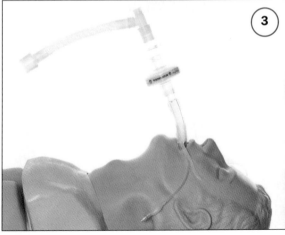

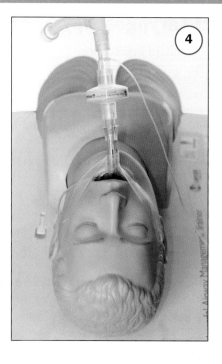

ECA

Q/SAP

TECH

PARA

SP CC

SP PC

227

Direct Laryngoscopy

- Adopt standard precautions.

> **Refer to:** *Procedures: Standard Precautions and Hand-washing, pages 52-61.*

- Assemble and prepare equipment: laryngoscope blade and handle.
- Pre-oxygenate the patient for 2–3 minutes using BVM and oxygen.
- *Adults:* Place the patient's head in the 'sniffing the morning air' position.
- *Children:* Place the patient's head in neutral alignment. Consider the use of padding under the shoulders.
- Hold the laryngoscope in your left hand.
- Insert the blade into the right side of the patient's mouth and move the tongue towards the left-hand side.
- Move the blade towards the midline and advance until the distal end is located:
  - for adults, in the vallecula,
  - for children, over the vallecula.
- Lift the laryngoscope handle slightly upwards and towards the patient's feet, without levering on the teeth or gums, until you can visualise the glottis opening and vocal cords.
- If required, use Sellick's manoeuvre to assist with the visualisation.

> **Refer to:** *Procedures: Sellick's Manoeuvre, page 314.*

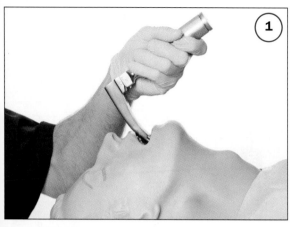

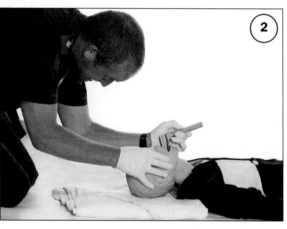

PARA

SP CC

SP PC

Adult basic life support

Unresponsive

NO
- Assess for illness/injury
- Call for help/treat as appropriate

YES

- Open airway
- Breathing normally?*
- (Check for no more than 10 seconds)

YES
- Move into recovery position
- Call for help/treat as appropriate
- If unsure begin CPR

NO
- Place one hand in the middle of the patient's chest, place heal of the other hand on top and interlock fingers
- Start chest compressions at a rate of 100–120 per minute and at a depth of 5–6 cm
- Compression and release should take the same amount of time

* In the first few minutes after cardiac arrest, a victim may barely be breathing, or may be taking infrequent, noisy, gasps. This is often termed agonal breathing and must not be confused with normal breathing.

If in any doubt, act as if not breathing.

CFR ACA ECA Q/SAP TECH PARA SP CC SP PC

230

If the chest doesn't rise:

1. Check the victim's mouth and remove any visible obstruction
2. Recheck that there is adequate head tilt and chin lift
3. Do not attempt more than two breaths each time before returning to chest compressions

If you are not trained or unwilling to perform mouth to mouth:

1. Give chest compressions only
2. If only chest compressions are given, these should be continuous at a rate of 100–120 per minute

- After 30 compressions open the airway using a head-tilt chin lift
- Pinch the soft part of the nose and seal lips around patient's mouth
- Blow steadily into the patient's mouth, watching for chest rise
- Repeat then continue chest compression/rescue breaths at a ratio of 30/2

Notes

1. If there is more than one rescuer present, another should take over CPR about every 1-2 minutes to prevent fatigue. Ensure the minimum of delay during the changeover of rescuers, and do not interrupt chest compressions.

2. Continue resuscitation until qualified help arrives and takes over or the victim starts to show signs of regaining consciousness (such as coughing, opening of eyes, speaking or moving purposefully and starting to breathe normally) or you become exhausted.

CFR

ACA

ECA

Q/SAP

TECH

PARA

SP CC

SP PC

Advanced adult life support

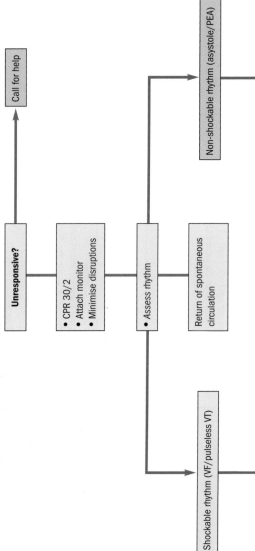

Unresponsive?

Call for help

- CPR 30/2
- Attach monitor
- Minimise disruptions

- Assess rhythm

Shockable rhythm (VF/pulseless VT)

Return of spontaneous circulation

Non-shockable rhythm (asystole/PEA)

- Administer one shock of 120 J, 150 J or 200 J
- *Chest compressions to continue whilst defibrillator is charging*

- Immediately continue with CPR at 30:2 for 2 minutes
- Minimise interruptions

- Give adrenalin every 3–5 minutes as soon as IV access is gained

- Immediately continue with CPR at 30/2 for two minutes
- Minimise interruptions

Post-arrest treatment

- Manage using ABCD approach
- Manage oxygenation and ventilation (aim for 94–98% SpO2 to prevent hyperoxaemia)
- 12-lead ECG – transfer to Papworth if appropriate (see guidance on PPCI transfer)
- Remain on scene for at least 10 minutes post-arrest to ensure patient is stable

Reversible causes (4Hs and 4Ts)

- hypoxia
- hypovolaemia
- hypo/hyperkalaemia/metabolic
- hypothermia
- thrombosis – coronary or pulmonary
- tamponade cardiac
- toxins
- tension pneumothorax

During CPR

- High quality CPR is vital; ensure minimal disruption and good rate, depth and recoil
- Oxygenate well
- LMA (rather than ET) should be used to minimise disruption to CPR (unless it is clinically indicated to use ET)
- Continuous chest compressions, ventilation and capnography when advanced airway in place
- Vascular access (IV or IO)
- Give adrenalin every 3–5 minutes (after third shock)
- Give amiodarone (also after third shock) for persistent VF/VT
- **Do not interrupt chest compressions to give drugs**
- Consider the 4Hs and 4Ts (reversible causes)

PARA

SP CC

SP PC

Loading a Patient onto the Vehicle (with Stretchers)

- One crew member will be at the front of the stretcher to pull, and the other will be at the bottom end to push.
- One crew member should raise the stretcher to the maximum as this is the optimum position for pushing.
- The two handholds under the foot section of the stretcher can be used for pushing.

Loading the stretcher onto the vehicle

- The crew must align the stretcher with the bottom of the ramp and, on 'READY, SET, GO', push/pull and walk onto the ramp on tail-lift vehicles or, on non-tail-lift vehicles, walk up the ramp until the stretcher is inside the vehicle.

Unloading the stretcher from the vehicle

- One crew member walks down the ramp/off the tail-lift ahead of the stretcher, holding the stretcher at waist height.
- The other holds the pulling handle in its short position, acting as a breaking force to control the descent of the stretcher.
- Prior to exiting the ramp, raise the stretcher to waist height.

These instructions apply to loading stretchers onto both tail-lift and non-tail-lift vehicles.

ACA

ECA

Q/SAP

TECH

PARA

SP CC

SP PC

Manual Handling: Mangar ELK

- Unroll the folded-over edge of the ELK, replace the stability bar and refit the cap end.
- Connect the four hoses (colour coded and numbered) from the hand control to the connectors on the ELK.
- Position the Airflo compressor at the side of the ELK and connect the input hose from the hand control to the air-outlet socket on the Airflo compressor and select 'AUTO' function.
- Assist the patient onto the ELK cushion, preferably in a sitting position.
- Position yourself behind and at the side of the patient to provide support throughout.
- Explain to the patient what will happen.
- Operate the number '1' button on the hand control and steady the patient as the ELK lifts.
- Stop inflation when the first (bottom) compartment of the cushion becomes hard and the compressor stops. Support the patient at all times.
- Operate buttons '2', '3' and '4' *in sequence* in the same manner.
- When all four compartments are inflated, help the patient to stand or transfer from the cushion.
- To deflate, disconnect each air hose by pushing the release collar on the connector away from the hose and pull the hose clear of the connector.
- Clean and roll up the cushion ready for next use.

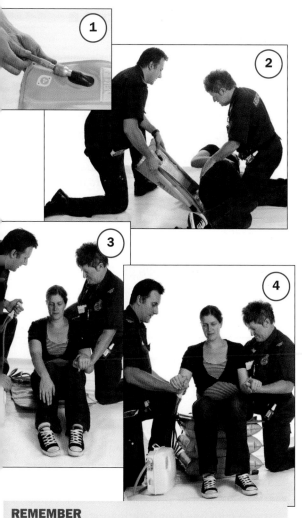

ECA

Q/SAP

TECH

PARA

SP CC

SP PC

REMEMBER

– Always inflate the cushion from the bottom up.
– The ELK will lift up to 450 kg, (70 stone/980 lb).

Moving a Patient from a Property

- In the ambulance service, lifting cannot always be avoided.
- Carry out a thorough patient assessment and establish the patient's clinical condition.

> **Refer to:** *Aide-memoire: Patient Assessment, pages 24–25.*

- *Consideration should be given to allowing the patient to move themselves and must be balanced against what is practical versus their clinical condition.*
- If you do have to lift a patient then, before you do, stop and think using the *LITE one-minute assessment tool.*

> **Refer to:** *LITE Manual Handling Assessment Tool, pages 17–18.*

Walking

- It is advised to always use a manual handling belt when walking with a patient. Walk slightly behind with a hand on the belt.
- If the patient loses balance then stop and let them regain control before walking on.
- If the patient starts to fall, encourage them to stand as upright as possible.
- If a fall cannot be prevented: assume a broad stance with one foot slightly forward, grasp the patient's body firmly at the waist or under the axilla and allow him to slide down against your

leg. Ease the patient slowly to the floor using your body as an incline. Lower your body along with the patient, if necessary.

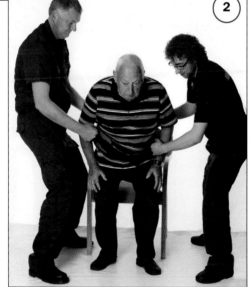

CFR

ACA

ECA

Q/SAP

TECH

PARA

SP CC

SP PC

To move a patient from a bed to a carry chair

Refer to: *Procedures: Manual Handling: Slide Sheet, pages 318–321.*

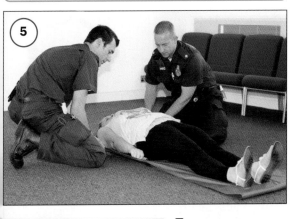

To carry a patient down the stairs using a carry chair

Refer to:
Procedures: Manual Handling: Carry Chair, pages 94–95 or Manual Handling: IBEX Chair, pages 188–189.

CFR

ACA

ECA

Q/SAP

TECH

PARA

SP CC

SP PC

To carry a patient down the stairs using a carry chair

Refer to: *Procedures: Manual Handling: Carry Chair, pages 94–95 or Manual Handling: IBEX Chair, pages 188–189.*

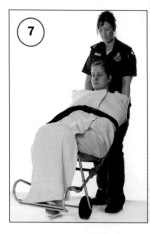

To move a patient in a wheelchair

Refer to: *Procedures: Manual Handling: Wheelchair Up/Down Kerb, pages 372–373, or Manual Handling: Wheelchair onto Ramp, pages 370–371.*

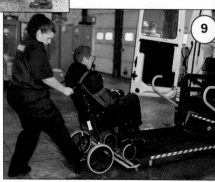

To move a patient from a bed to a stretcher

> **Refer to:** *Procedures: Manual Handling: Slide Sheet, pages 318–321.*

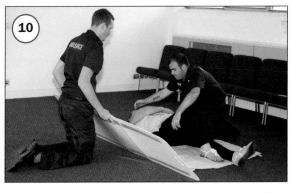

To move a stretcher onto a ramp/tail-lift

> **Refer to:** *Procedures: Manual Handling: Wheelchair onto Ramp, pages 370–371, or Loading Patient onto the Vehicle (with Stretchers), pages 234–235.*

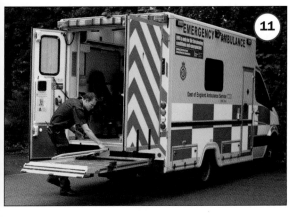

CFR

ACA

ECA

Q/SAP

TECH

PARA

SP CC

SP PC

Nasogastric Tube

Indications

Nasogastric tubes are indicated in the unconscious patient where stomach decompression and/or control of gastric contents are required.

CONTRAINDICATIONS

Nasogastric tubes are contraindicated in patients with severe maxillofacial trauma. Orogastric tube insertion may be approved in these patients at the direction of further clinical advice. No drugs or fluids may be given down nasogastric or orogastric tubes by EEAST staff.

Cautions

Careful consideration must be given to patients falling in the following categories:

- Suspected basilar skull fracture due to the risk of intracranial insertion (insert orally instead)
- Recent sino-nasal surgery (insert orally instead)
- Coagulation abnormality (for example, cases where coagulopathy coexists with other conditions – for instance, oesophageal varices)
- Oesophageal varices or strictures
- Gastric bypass surgery
- Alkaline ingestion (such as bleach, drain cleaner)
- Nasal polyps (insert orally instead). Nasogastric insertion may not be appropriate in these patients. Orogastric tube placement may be approved at the direction of further clinical advice.

Equipment

- Nasogastric tube (the trust uses the Ryles tube rather than the fine bore nasogastric tubes where aspiration would be difficult).
- Lubricating jelly.
- Magill forceps.
- Laryngoscope with appropriate sized blade.
- Micropore tape or commercially available tube holder.
- Laerdal Suction Unit (LSU) with yankeur catheter.

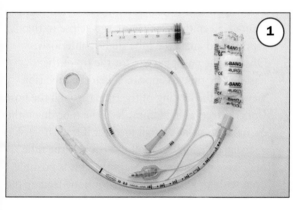

Procedure

Use standard procedures.

> **Refer to:** *Procedures: Standard Precautions and Hand-washing, pages 52–61.*

1. Prepare patient. Ensure adequate access for direct laryngoscopy and position patient accordingly. Check patient's nostrils for signs of trauma or physical abnormalities.

2. Prepare equipment. Remove equipment from sterile packaging.
3. Measure tube length against patient. Place the distal end of the tube slightly inferior to the xiphoid process. Run the tube along the patient's sternum, around the back of the ear and to the patient's nasal septum, taking note of the measurement marking at the septum.
4. Liberally lubricate distal end of the nasogastric tube.
5. Gently insert the tube along the floor of the nose, below the inferior turbinate, to cause minimum trauma. Keep the nasogastric tube close to the septum and angle the tube slightly inferiorly.
6. Observe the nasopharynx for the tip of the nasogastric tube to appear. When the tube is in view, halt the feeding of the tube through the nose.
7. Under direct laryngoscopy, feed the tube down the oesophagus using Magill forceps. If the patient has a strong cough reflex, halt insertion as the tube may have passed into the larynx. This is possible even with an ET tube in situ. Continue feeding the tube into the oesophagus until the pre-noted measurement marker arrives at the nasal septum.
8. Secure the tube at the patient's head with micropore tape.
9. If the patient starts coughing or showing any other signs of respiratory distress, stop advancing the nasogastric tube and withdraw immediately as it may have entered the trachea.
10. Connect the proximal end of the nasogastric tube to an appropriate sized yankeur catheter attached to an LSU and gently aspirate.

DO NOT pass anything down the NG tube. The
pre-hospital applications of an NG tube are for
decompression and control of stomach contents only.

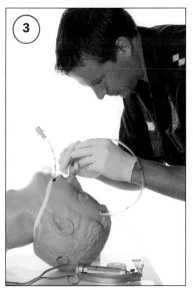

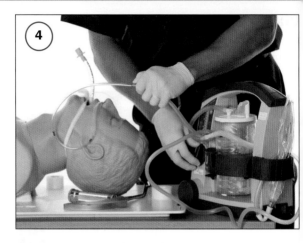

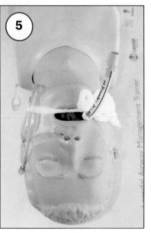

Additional Considerations

Ensure receiving hospital staff are made aware (if appropriate) and document the procedure on the patient notes/ PCR/ePCR.

Nasopharyngeal Airway

- Adopt standard precautions.

> **Refer to:** *Procedures: Standard Precautions and Hand-washing, pages 52–61.*

- Identify the appropriate use of the NP airway, i.e., for patients who will not tolerate an oropharyngeal airway or if trismus is present.
- The current evidence advises that an average-sized female requires a size 6 airway and an average-sized male requires a size 7 airway.
- If present, check that the safety pin is in situ on the wide, flange end of the tube.
- Lubricate with KY jelly or other appropriate lubricant used by the Trust.
- Select the widest nostril.
- Insert gently with the NP airway pointing posteriorly along the floor of the nose (90 degrees to the patient's face).
- If resistance is felt, stop – do not force.
- Gently rotate clockwise and anticlockwise 45 degrees while continuing to insert.
- If further resistance is felt, relubricate and try the other nostril or a smaller airway.

Q/SAP

TECH

PARA

SP CC

SP PC

CONTRAINDICATIONS
Under 12 years old

CAUTIONS
- Severe maxillofacial injury and suspected basal skull fracture.
- Insertion of the tube may cause epistaxis from localised trauma, potentially leading to airway obstruction.

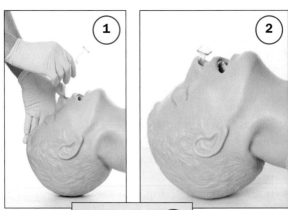

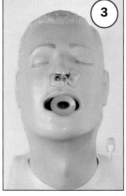

Nebulisation

- Adopt standard precautions.

> **Refer to:** *Procedures: Standard Precautions and Hand-washing, pages 52–61.*

- Identify the need for intervention after fully assessing the patient's respiratory status, and note the patient's chest sounds.
- Obtain a peak flow reading – best of three readings if the patient is able.
- Reassure the patient and explain the procedure to gain informed consent.
- Prepare the equipment.
- Check the drug(s) – name, dose and date – with a colleague (if present).
- Empty the drug contents into the nebuliser turret.
- Attach the nebuliser to the oxygen and adjust the flow.
- Position the mask/mouthpiece on the patient and adjust for comfort (image 3).
- Administer the nebulised drugs (image 4).
- Reassure the patient and monitor throughout, observing for any side effects.
- Completely re-assess ABCs post-nebulisation.
- If possible, gain a peak-flow reading post-nebulisation, confirm if the wheeze is still present or not, identify the appropriate referral pathways and handover to the receiving health professional.

Q/SAP

TECH

PARA

SP CC

SP PC

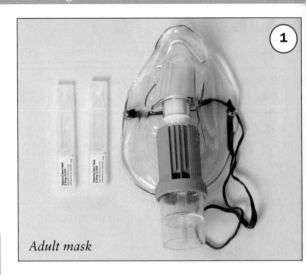

Adult mask

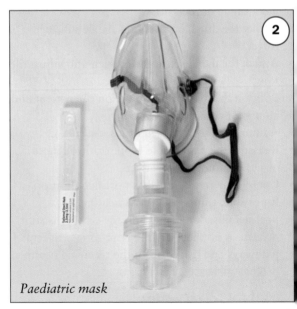

Paediatric mask

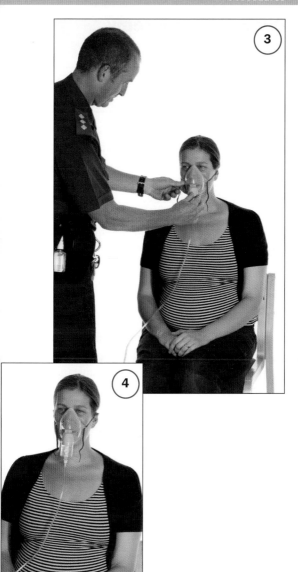

Open Thoracostomy

- Adopt standard precautions.

> **Refer to:** *Procedures: Standard Precautions and Hand-washing, pages 52-61.*

- Secure the airway using an ET tube and verify the correct placement using capnography.
- Observe the chest for symmetry and auscultate to confirm if air entry is equal and rule out tension pneumothorax.
- If the ventilation is compromised or there is a high index of suspicion, proceed with the thoracostomy.
- Position the patient supine (preferably on a trolley), with the arm (procedure side) abducted to 90 degrees.
- Identify the 4th or 5th intercostal space in the mid-axillary line – in men, ensure the incision line is above the line of the nipple.
- Apply betadine spray if the circumstances permit.
- Using a 22 blade scalpel, make a 4–5 cm incision through the skin and subcutaneous fat, down to the intercostal muscles.
- Using 8 inch Spencer Well's forceps, perform a blunt dissection through the intercostal muscles to enter the pleural space – aim towards the top of the 6th rib to avoid the neurovascular bundle.
- Insert your finger through the hole and perform a 'finger sweep' to ensure the parietal pleura has been breached, and feel for lung expansion.

- Remove your finger and reapply betadine.
- Repeat for the opposite side and dispose of scalpels in a sharps box.
- If resuscitation is successful and leads to spontaneous breathing, occlude the wounds with Ashermann Chest Seals.

REMEMBER
- Open thoracostomy is intended to relieve tension pneumothorax; if haemothorax is revealed at the pre-hospital stage, the clinician should insert and secure a chest drain.
- When plugging the hole with a dressing be aware of the risk of a re-tension.

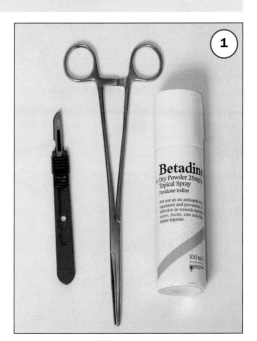

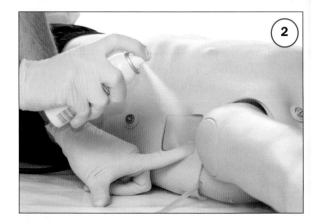

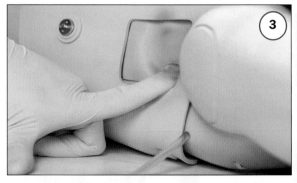

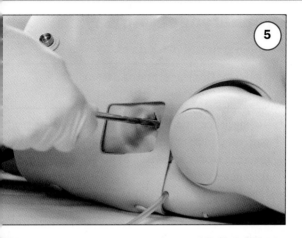

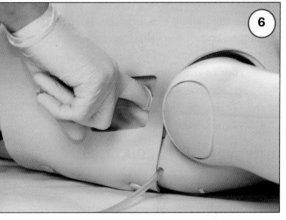

Oropharyngeal Airway

- Adopt standard precautions.

> **Refer to:** Procedures: Standard Precautions and Hand-washing, pages 52–61.

- To check the appropriate size of airway for the patient, compare the length of airway with the distance from the middle of the incisor teeth to the angle of the jaw.
- Ensure the visible airway is clear – use suction if required.

Insert airway – ADULT

- Open the patient's mouth and, holding the flanged end of the OP-airway, insert 'upside down' so the curved surface faces upwards to the roof of the mouth.
- Insert approximately half of its length and rotate the OP airway, advancing it until the flanged end rests outside the patient's lips.

Insert airway – PAEDIATRICS

- Correctly size the OP airway as above, but insert the airway the correct way round – by depressing the tongue – and slip the airway into position.

REMEMBER

- Using an **OP** airway is contraindicated when the patient has a gag reflex.
- Once the OP is inserted, maintain close observation of the patient for signs of obstruction of the lumen of the OP airway – clear with suction if required.

REMEMBER

- The OP airway will not protect the patient's airway from aspiration of fluids.

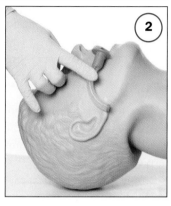

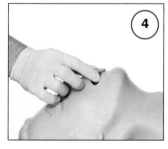

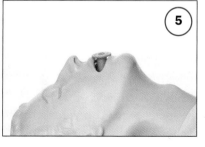

ECA

Q/SAP

TECH

PARA

SP CC

SP PC

Orthopaedic Stretcher

- Explain the procedure to the patient.
- Ensure the stretcher is complete with straps and in good working order.
- Place the stretcher alongside the patient and adjust it for the correct length.
- Separate the stretcher – press the buttons at either end of the stretcher and place one-half on either side of the patient.
- Ease the stretcher halves under the patient – ensure the patient's head and legs are supported.
- Clip each end together simultaneously, where possible.
- Apply the stretcher straps: chest first, then the waist and then a figure of eight around the legs.
- Apply the straps firmly to limit movement.
- Apply the head blocks and straps prior to loading the patient for transport if required.
- Lift the patient with a person at each end, one at the head end and the other at the foot end.
- Lift the patient simultaneously and lower the patient onto a stretcher to avoid pinching the patient.
- Remove the orthopaedic stretcher if necessary: remove straps and blocks (maintain C-spine immobilisation) and press the buttons at either end of the stretcher to separate it.
- Clean the stretcher and re-secure in storage.

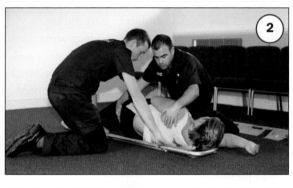

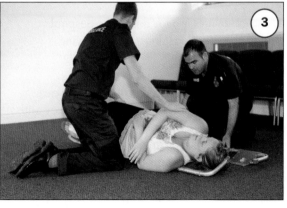

Oxygen Therapy

Principles of care

- Oxygen is essential for cell metabolism, and therefore patients who are acutely hypoxic from any cause will suffer organ damage and death unless supplemental oxygen is administered and delivered to the cells.
- Under certain circumstances excessive oxygen therapy has been shown to be harmful by reducing the minute volume and increasing acidosis, or by inducing vasoconstriction.
- The need for oxygen therapy should be assessed and oxygen prescribed to meet a target oxygen-saturation level.
- Oxygen saturation does not guarantee satisfactory breathing, so respiratory rate, blood pressure and heart rate must also be monitored.

These guidelines are for use in pre-hospital emergency situations under the following conditions:

- adult patient
- 1:1 care and monitoring from a healthcare professional who should obtain a history and use an ABCDE approach
- continuous monitoring of respiratory rate, heart rate and oxygen saturation by pulse oximetry (SpO_2)
- blood-pressure monitoring
- disease-specific monitoring (e.g., pre- and post-nebuliser peak flows)

CFR
ACA
ECA
Q/SAP
TECH
PARA
SP CC
SP PC

100% oxygen via a non-rebreathing mask or bag valve mask should be given to patients in the following circumstances:

– cardiac arrest or undergoing resuscitation
– carbon monoxide poisoning
– major trauma
– anaphylaxis
– sepsis or shock
– active convulsions
– hypothermia
– where the patient is acutely unwell and oximetry is not available or functioning
– severe LVF
– pulmonary embolism
– lung fibrosis
– severe pneumonia
– lung collapse

COPD patients

Some (not all) COPD patients need a certain amount of hypoxia to drive respiration. Excess oxygenation in these patients can lead to Type 2 respiratory failure, in that removing their 'hypoxic drive' causes an abnormally low respiratory rate, retention of carbon dioxide and eventual loss of consciousness. It is therefore very important to monitor respiratory rate closely.

- Known COPD patients should initially be given 28% oxygen with a target saturation of 88–92%.
- Some COPD patients may carry an alert card that warns to avoid excess oxygen and advises a target saturation.

CFR

ACA

ECA

Q/SAP

TECH

PARA

SP CC

SP PC

- For patients who are not known to have COPD, or it is unclear, suspect COPD if the patient is over 50 years of age, has no history of asthma, is a long-term smoker or ex-smoker, or has a history of longstanding breathlessness on exertion.
- Patients with COPD who are critically ill should receive the same treatment as other critically ill patients (JRCALC Table 1), pending a blood-gas result in hospital – the rationale should be documented.
- Where available, air-driven nebulisers are recommended for COPD patients.

Conditions not automatically requiring oxygen UNLESS HYPOXAEMIC

- Myocardial infarction.
- Acute coronary syndrome.
- Stroke (NICE advice is to give O_2 if SaO_2 <95%).
- Pregnancy and obstetric emergencies.
- Hyperventilation.
- Poisoning and drug overdose.
- Metabolic and renal disorders.

Contraindications to oxygen therapy

- Paraquat poisoning (not an absolute contraindication if hypoxaemic).
- Explosive environment and/or fire hazard (including defibrillation).

Ambulances carry two sizes of cylinders:

- 'D' size = 340 litres
- 'F' size = 1360 litres

REMEMBER
- O_2 cylinders are safe in the absence of sources of ignition, smoke and static electricity.
- They are pressurised and may explode if exposed to heat.

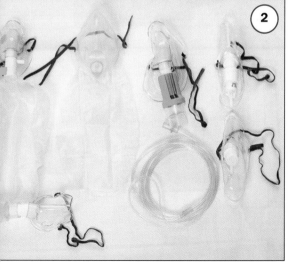

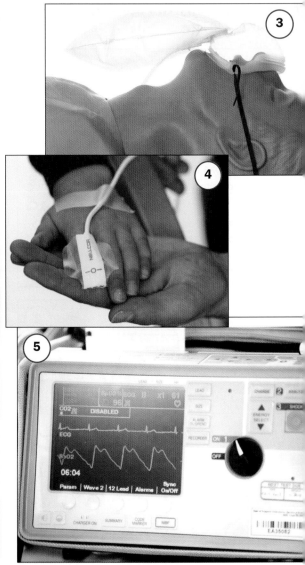

Transcutaneous Cardiac Pacing

- Identify the need for pacing: symptomatic bradycardia or complete heart block.
- Ensure the patient's chest is free from hair, moisture, jewellery, medication patches and wounds.

Applying the electrodes

- Apply cardiac monitoring via conventional ECG leads.
- Apply multi-function pads – anterior/posterior.
- Set to 'Pacing' mode; set pacer rate at 80bpm and current to Ohm.
- Slowly increase pacing current until capture is seen.
- Confirm mechanical capture by palpation of central pulse.
- It is advisable to set current to 10mA above the level needed to maintain capture.
- Monitor settings and be prepared to adjust either pacing rate or current in order to maintain capture and effective cardiac output.

Manual Handling:
PATSLIDE™

- A minimum of two people are required for this manoeuvre.
- Explain the intention to the patient and, where possible, gain their consent.
- The PATSLIDE can be used to transfer conscious and unconscious patients.
- Using the sheet on the patient's bed, operator 1 grips the sheet at the patient's hip and shoulder furthest away.
- Operator 1 rolls the patient towards themselves until the patient is lying on their side, while operator 2 positions the PATSLIDE in between the patient and the bed.
- Operator 1 then lowers the patient back to the supine position while operator 2 supports the slide.
- Ensure the patient's feet are on the lower end of the sheet.
- Lay the patient supine – or as supine as is comfortable for them – maintaining their dignity and modesty at all times.
- Position the trolley cot alongside the patient's bed so that the two are at the same height.
- Adjust, where possible, to prevent overstretching.
- Both operators, gripping the sheet at the patient's hip and shoulder level, simultaneously slide the patient across the board and onto the trolley cot.

- Position the patient centrally, roll them to one side and remove the PATSLIDE.
- Secure the trolley straps around the patient for safe transport.

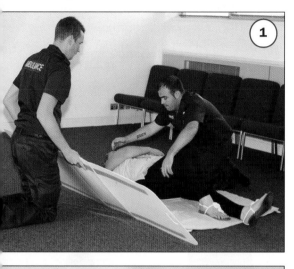

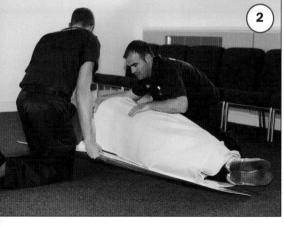

ACA

ECA

Q/SAP

TECH

PARA

SP CC

SP PC

269

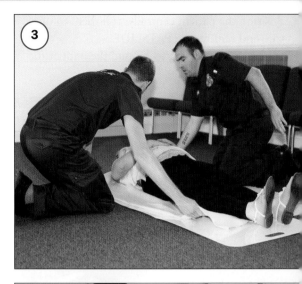

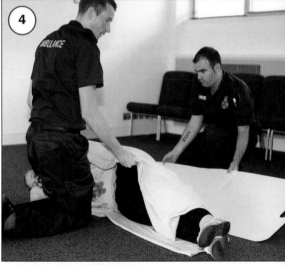

Peak Expiratory Flow Rate (PEFR)

- Adopt standard precautions.

> **Refer to:** *Procedures: Standard Precautions and Hand-washing, pages 52–61.*

- Identify the need to assess the patient's peak flow.
- Explain to the patient and gain their consent.
- Select the appropriate peak flow meter.
- Position the patient, sitting or standing, and make sure they are comfortable.
- Securely attach the mouthpiece to the meter and ensure the pointer is set at zero.
- Get the patient to hold the meter without obstructing the pointer's movement.
- Ask the patient to take a short, sharp breath and blow into the mouthpiece.
- Ask the patient to perform the process twice more (unless the patient is very breathless).
- Record the highest of the three readings.
- Dispose of the used mouthpiece appropriately.

REMEMBER

– If the patient has their own peak flow meter, ask them if they would mind using that one as it will allow comparison with the previous readings recorded.

ECA

Q/SAP

TECH

PARA

SP CC

SP PC

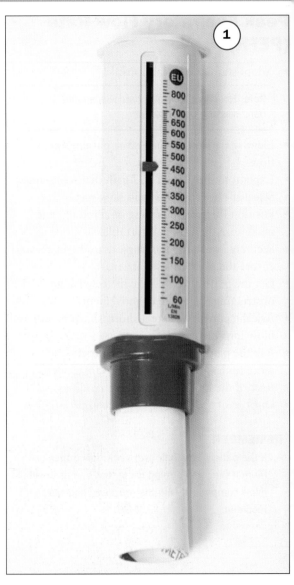

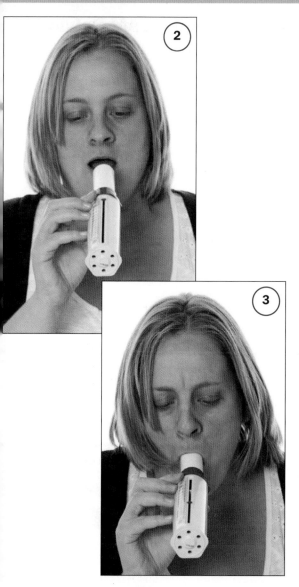

ECA

Q/SAP

TECH

PARA

SP CC

SP PC

Pelvic Splint – SAM Pelvic Sling™ II

- Adopt standard precautions.

> **Refer to:** *Procedures: Standard Precautions and Hand-washing, pages 52–61.*

- Use appropriate PPE as required.
- Inform the patient of your intended actions to use the pelvic splint.
- Remove the patient's outer clothing so that the splint is against the skin, where appropriate.
- Place the splint into the correct position with minimal movement of the pelvis.
- Placement should be over the greater trochanters.
- Pass the black Velcro strap through the orange buckle.
- Using equal pressure, tighten the splint by pulling on the orange strap and black Velcro strap simultaneously until a 'click' is heard.
- Avoid over-tightening.
- Fasten the Velcro straps to secure the splint.

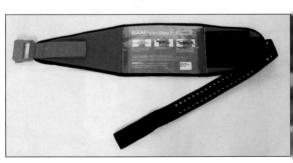

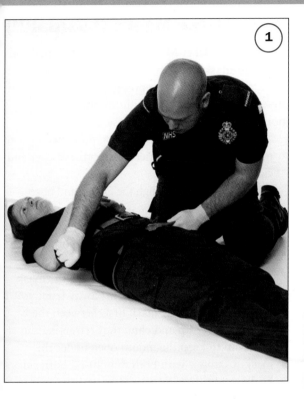

ECA

Q/SAP

TECH

PARA

SP CC

SP PC

275

Pocket Face Masks (Laerdal™)

The Laerdal Pocket Mask is primarily designed for mouth-to-mask ventilation of a non-breathing adult, child or infant. It represents an often-preferred alternative to mouth-to-mouth or mouth-to-nose breathing because its use:

- helps overcome rescuer hesitation prompted by fear
- provides a physical barrier between the rescuer and victim
- allows ventilation through the mouth and nose simultaneously
- helps provide an open airway with only a moderate backwards head tilt, which may be important for trauma victims
- If using a one-way valve, mount it on the mask port. Direct the exhalation port away from you.
- Apply the rim of the mask first, between the victim's lower lip and chin, thus retracting the lower lip to keep the mouth open under the mask. Clamp it with both thumbs on both sides of the mask. The index, middle and ring fingers grasp the lower jaw just in front of the ear lobes, above the angles of the jaw, and forcibly pull upwards. Open the airway by tilting the head moderately backwards.
- Blow into the mask every four seconds. Maintain an open airway at all times.
- For airway control and mouth-to-mask breathing alone, work from the top of the head.

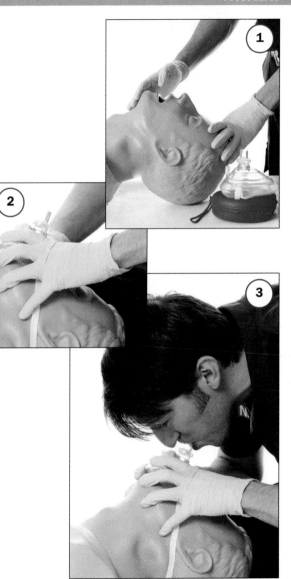

Procedural Sedation (General Overview)

Procedural sedation and analgesia should only be undertaken following clinical advice. It is used to:
- facilitate the management and movement of patients by providing pain relief;
- facilitate orthopaedic manipulations in adults and children to:
  - alleviate pain
  - reduce possible neurovascular complications
  - reduce possible skin damage over an injured joint

Inclusion criteria
- Adults and children over 6 months old who have been physically injured and who are no longer trapped.
- A minimum of two staff competent in advanced airway-management skills must be available.

Route/method
Intravenous
- The intravenous dose should be administered over a period of 30–60 seconds. More rapid administration may result in transient respiratory depression or apnoea, and enhanced pressor response.
- IV access is preferred, particularly for adults, because in the event of a clinically important unpleasant recovery reaction (e.g., occasional combativeness), *midazolam can be administered promptly* (emergence phenomena –

misinterpreted sensory stimuli can cause patients
to have a frightening recovery, unpleasant
dreams can occur for up to 24 hours afterwards
– less frequent in children).

> **Refer to:** *Procedures: Intravenous Cannulation, pages
> 206–209.*

Intramuscular
• Note-the IM route is associated with a higher
  rate of vomiting and a longer recovery period.

> **Refer to:** *Procedures: Intramuscular Injection, pages
> 198–199.*

Name, form and strength of medicine
Ketamine injection 10 mg/ml, 20 ml ampoule.
Ketamine injection 50 mg/ml, 10 ml ampoule.
Check strength carefully before administering.

ROUTE OF ADMINISTRATION	
IV	**IM**
Initial dose Adult: 10 mg/kg (over 30–60 seconds) Child: 1.5-2.0 mg/kg (over 30–60 seconds)	***Initial dose*** Adult: 4-5 mg/kg Child: 4-5 mg/kg
Repeat dose Adult: 0.5 mg/kg every 5–15 minutes as required Child: 0.5-1.0 mg/kg every 5–15 minutes as required	***Repeat dose*** Adult and Child: 2–4 mg/kg 10 minutes after the initial dose if required

SP CC

Interventions required pre-, during and post-procedure

- Pre-treatment – topical anaesthetic for IV cannula insertion if indicated.
- Commence ECG and SpO_2 monitoring – avoid frequent BP monitoring.
- Airway maintenance.
- O_2 supplementation only if clinically indicated (SATS drop).
- Assess adequacy of sedation (eye glazing/nystagmus) – action as above.
- Commence procedure – duration no longer than 30 minutes.
- Recover patient in quiet, appropriately staffed area with SpO_2/HR monitoring – minimal stimulation.
- Patient must be monitored fully throughout and en route to hospital. Must be accompanied by a doctor or paramedic authorised to work within the PGD that covers this procedure.

Taking a Pulse

- A pulse is usually felt at the wrist – use two fingers, not your thumb, and firmly press the tips of your fingers on the inner side of the patient's wrist, close to the radius.
- Note its:
  rate – beats/min
  strength – strong, normal or weak
  regularity – regular or irregular
- If the patient is in shock or hypothermic, it may be difficult to find a pulse at the wrist; instead feel for a carotid pulse at the neck.
- When taking a pulse in paediatrics, feel in the brachial area – inner side of the upper arm.
- Pulse oximeters and ECG monitors can also show pulse rates.
- Note any changes in the patient's pulse.

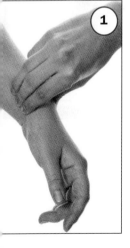
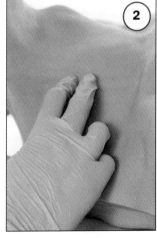

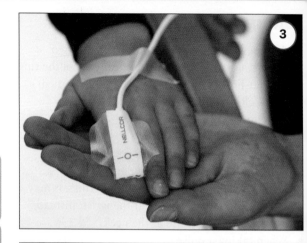

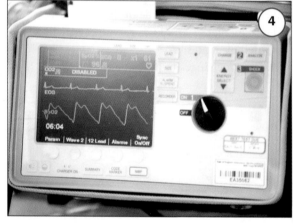

Pulse Oximetry (Adult)

- Attach the pulse oximeter probe to a finger or toe – ensure the sensor cable runs over the top of the patient's hand or foot.
- The fleshiest part of the finger/toe should cover the lower detector window, and the tip of the finger touches or passes the raised digit stop inside the sensor.
- Wait a few seconds to allow the reading to register. The probe should have a constant red light.
- Note the reading given.
- Ensure the probe is not affected by:

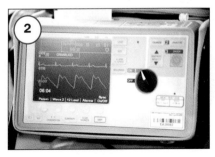

  - strong ambient light
  - nail varnish
  - dirt/bodily fluids
  - cold extremities
  - excessive movements
  - NIBP on the same extremity
  - partial coverage of the detector window
- These may affect the accuracy of the reading given.

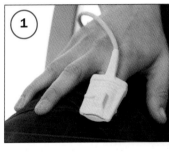

Pulse Oximetry (Paediatric)

- Adopt standard precautions.

> **Refer to:** *Procedures: Standard Precautions and Hand-washing, pages 52–61.*

- Ensure the sensor site is not subject to excessive motion and is free of debris, bodily fluids, etc.
- Open the pouch and remove the sensor.
- Hold the sensor with the printed side downwards, bend the sensor backwards and remove the backing material from the sensor.
- Attach the digit to the detector side of the sensor first – ensure full coverage of the detector.
- Fold over the emitter part of the sensor around the digit and secure the wings.
- *Ensure the sensor is not wrapped too tightly around the digit.*
- When positioned properly, the cable should run on the top side of the digit used.
- Ensure the sensor is not lower than heart level.

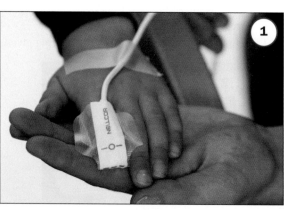

REMEMBER

– The Zoll oximeter can also show the waveform to confirm the strength of the signal. This can be shown by pressing MANUAL, CONFIRM, WAVE 2, then WAVE 2 again.

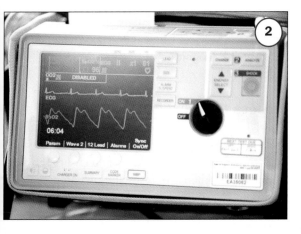

ZOLL Medical Corporation (2005). *ZOLL E SERIES OPERATOR'S GUIDE: Pulse Oximetry (SpO₂)*, pp5–6. USA: ZOLL Medical Corporation.

Action to be Taken after Recognition of Life Extinct

Introduction

Qualified ambulance staff are able to confirm or recognise death; registered medical practitioners are able to certify death. This is set out in the Joint Royal College Ambulance Liaison Committee UK Ambulance Services Clinical Practice Guidelines as part of the Recognition of Life Extinct (ROLE) procedure (*Figure 1*).

Process following ROLE

- Advise relatives on the scene that the patient has died, and offer condolences.
- Remove any equipment used and ensure the area is safe for others. All resuscitation equipment should be removed from the body and surrounding area, including all consumables.
- Notify the Health Emergency Operations Control (HEOC) that ROLE has occurred.
- Contact the patient's GP, advise the GP of the circumstances and ascertain if the death was expected. Most deaths the ambulance service attend are not expected. GP out-of-hours (OOH) services should be informed when appropriate.
- If the death was not expected (by the patient's doctor) or there is any uncertainty about this, request the attendance of the Police via HEOC. It is up to the Police to decide whether to attend.
- Complete and attach the Trust's Recognition of Death Body Label to the wrist or ankle of the

body. Include the clinician's employment number or name on the label and note on the electronic Patient Care Record (ePCR) that a body label has been used.

- Complete a Witness Statement (ROLE) (Appendix 1) form using the following guidance. Give the original copy of the Witness Statement to the attending Police. The duplicate copy of the Witness Statement should be submitted to the Trust.
- Handover to the attending Police, including giving them the original copy of the completed Witness Statement (ROLE). If the Police do not attend, complete the Witness Statement, but retain both copies (it may be requested by the Police later).
- Complete and sign an ePCR. This should include the history, examination and reasons why death was recognised. No copy of the ePCR should be left on the scene. Requests for copies of patient documentation should be made in writing to the Trust. If an ePCR is not available then a scannable paper PCR should be completed, applying the same guidance as for the ePCR, with the exception that the second copy can be left with the police if they are on the scene.
- When appropriate, leave the relatives the available 'dealing with death' support documentation.

Q/SAP

TECH

PARA

SP CC

SP PC

Transportation

- Deceased patients in their usual place of residence are not normally transported by the ambulance service; instead, relatives or the Police should arrange transport with an undertaker. The exception to this is children (under 18 years of age), who should normally be transported (see 'ROLE of children' below).

- When ROLE has occurred with the patient in a public place, ambulance clinicians may be requested to remove the body. On such occasions the body should be transported to the nearest mortuary. HEOC should be informed of this prior to transportation and HEOC should inform the receiving mortuary (note that not all mortuaries are open 24 hours a day).

- If ROLE occurs during transportation of the patient, the body should be taken to the mortuary of the nearest hospital. HEOC should be informed of this prior to transportation and HEOC should inform the receiving hospital. Failure to communicate may cause a delay in the hospital being able to accept the body.

- On arrival at the mortuary, the mortuary attendant will need to sign the ePCR. Once finalised, the Toughbook needs to be docked at the hospital's Accident and Emergency (A&E) department and a paper copy printed out. This then needs to be returned to the mortuary prior to the crew booking the trolley clear. Should a paper PCR be used instead of an ePCR, the top copy should be left following its signature.

If there are suspicious circumstances associated with the death

- Clinicians should consider at each death whether the circumstances appear suspicious and if foul play is possible.
- The Police should always be called when the circumstances appear suspicious. Wait on the scene to handover to the Police.
- Take care throughout to try not to disturb or corrupt any potential evidence.
- Do not move the body unless directed to do so by the Police.
- Do not remove any invasive equipment used to resuscitate the patient.

Different religious and cultural backgrounds

- The Trust procedure will not normally cause any problem with any specific group of people; however, clinicians should be mindful of differences in the way different religious and cultural groups deal with death.

ROLE of children

- A child is defined as any person under the age of 18 years of age.
- Whenever appropriate, transport the child to the nearest hospital A&E department with on-going resuscitation.
- The Police should always be informed when a child is seriously injured or has suffered a cardiac arrest.

- When ROLE occurs after an unexpected death, the child's body should be transported to the nearest hospital A&E department, accompanied by the child's parent(s) or guardian(s). This is to allow the multiprofessional rapid response collaboration to occur in line with government guidelines. Children should not be taken to a mortuary. When directed by the Police to do so, the body should be left on scene.

Patient Care Record

- An ePCR must be completed for every patient, which includes all patients assessed as dead. In cases of obvious death, there may be little assessment and treatment to record; however, the other elements of the ePCR should be recorded as completely as possible. If it is not possible to use the ePCR, then a paper PCR should be used.

Completion of Witness Statement (ROLE)

- The form was originally designed with Coroners and Constabularies to ensure that it conformed to requirements and regulations.
- This form should be completed fully, ensuring everything recorded is factual and legible.
- Age – Draw a circle around 'Over 18' (cross the box on the scannable version).
- Dated – State the date, record the month in words in full, record the year in full (e.g., '10th January 2012').

- Signature – The clinician completing the form should sign at this point.
- Name – Record the first name and surname of the clinician completing the document.
- Grade – Record the clinical grade of the clinician completing the form (e.g., 'Paramedic').
- Years of duty – Record in figures the number of years the clinician has been employed as an NHS emergency ambulance crew member (e.g., '11').
- Time/date – Record the time and date the clinician arrived at the scene. Use the format hh:mm dd/mm/yyyy (e.g., 'at 13:05 on 03/06/2012').
- Location – Record the address of the incident.
- Gender – Record the gender of the deceased; give 'Unknown' if appropriate.
- Description of body – Record a brief description of the deceased to help identification (e.g., 'Elderly white man with grey hair, of large build').
- Position of body – Record the position in which the body was found and any injuries found. Remember to report only the facts, so if an internal injury is suspected ensure to record 'suspected' (e.g., 'Recumbent on bed under bedding. No injuries found').
- History – Record a brief history as stated by bystanders. Remember to report only the facts (e.g., 'Patient called out to wife from another room. Wife went through to find patient unresponsive).

- Treatment – Record the treatment given. If no resuscitation was attempted, state this, along with the reason. When full resuscitation was started, a statement such as 'Advanced life support treatment given as in Resuscitation Guidelines 2010' is appropriate.
- Time/date – Record the time and date the clinician declared ROLE. Use the format hh:mm dd/mm/yyyy (e.g., 'at 13:05 on 03/06/2012').
- Additional information – Record anything else that may help an investigation of the death.
- ePCR number – Record the unique ePCR number, including any prefix (e.g., 'ES 000123').
- Incident number – Record the unique CAD incident number, including any prefix (e.g., '10012009-0124').
- Signature – The clinician completing the form should sign here.
- Witness – Ask someone to witness that the statement was written by the clinician at that time. Record the name of the witness and ask them to sign the form.

WITNESS STATEMENT
(Recognition of Life Extinct (ROLE))
(CJ Act 1967, s.9; MC Act 1980, ss. 5A (3) (a) and 5B; Criminal Procedure Rules 2005, Rule 27.1)

Statement of (ID Number)

I am (name) and I am employed by

the East of England Ambulance Service NHS Trust as a (grade of clinician)

and based at I have worked for years

on front line duties and have received training which allows me to recognise death.

At (time) on (date) / / 2 0 I attended at

(location/address)

Where I saw the body of a ☐ Male ☐ Female

(add any other descriptive and relevant details including approximate age of the body)

I also saw the body (position of the body and any injuries)

I was informed that (if appropriate give a brief history)

I carried out an examination according to the Trust's guidelines giving the following treatment

At (time) on (date) / / 2 0 I recognised that death had occurred.

Additional Information

This statement (consisting of ONE page signed by me) is true to the best of my knowledge and belief and I make it knowing that if it is intended in evidence I shall be liable to prosecution if I wilfully stated in it anything which I know to be false or do not believe to be true.

Date / / 2 0 Signature

Signature witnessed by (name)

Patient Care Record Number Ambulance Incident Number

DEACTIVATED

Q/SAP

TECH

PARA

SP CC

SP PC

293

Q/SAP

TECH

PARA

SP CC

SP PC

Action to be taken once ROLE is confirmed

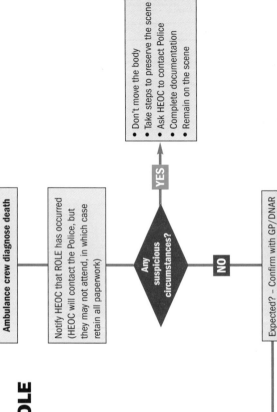

Ambulance crew diagnose death

Notify HEOC that ROLE has occurred (HEOC will contact the Police, but they may not attend, in which case retain all paperwork)

Any suspicious circumstances?

YES

- Don't move the body
- Take steps to preserve the scene
- Ask HEOC to contact Police
- Complete documentation
- Remain on the scene

NO

Expected? – Confirm with GP/DNAR

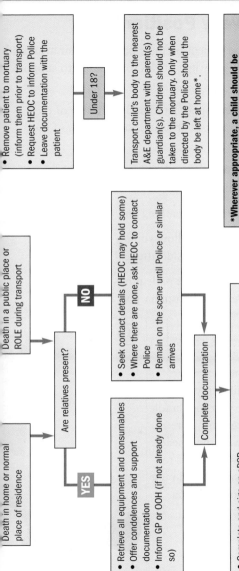

Figure 1 Action to be taken after ROLE

Death in home or normal place of residence

Death in a public place or ROLE during transport

Are relatives present?

YES
- Retrieve all equipment and consumables
- Offer condolences and support documentation
- Inform GP or OOH (if not already done so)

NO
- Seek contact details (HEOC may hold some)
- Where there are none, ask HEOC to contact Police
- Remain on the scene until Police or similar arrives

Complete documentation

- Complete and sign an ePCR
- Complete a Witness Statement (ROLE)
- Attach a death label to the patient
- Print two 30-second ECG traces (one for the Police and one for EOE)

Under 18?

- Remove patient to mortuary (inform them prior to transport)
- Request HEOC to inform Police
- Leave documentation with the patient

Transport child's body to the nearest A&E department with parent(s) or guardian(s). Children should not be taken to the mortuary. Only when directed by the Police should the body be left at home*.

*Wherever appropriate, a child should be transported to A&E with on-going resuscitation

Q/SAP

TECH

PARA

SP CC

SP PC

295

Recovery Position

1. Roll the patient on their side with their arms and upper leg at right angles to the body to support them.

2. Tuck their upper hand under the side of their head so that their head is on the back of the hand.

3. Open their airway by tilting the head back and lifting the chin.

4. Monitor their breathing and pulse continuously.

5. If their injuries allow you to, turn the patient onto their other side after 30 minutes.

6. If you suspect the patient has a spinal injury, then perform a Trauma Jaw Thrust.

> **Refer to:**
> *Procedures, pages 66–68.*

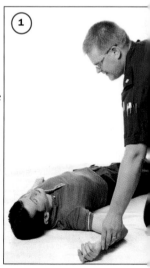

7. For children younger than 1 year old, cradle the infant in your arms with their head tilted downwards to make sure they do not vomit or choke on their tongue.

CFR

ACA

ECA

Q/SAP

TECH

PARA

SP CC

SP PC

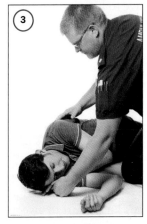

297

Removal of Patient from a House (Walking)

- In the ambulance service, lifting cannot always be avoided.
- Carry out a thorough patient assessment and establish the patient's clinical condition.

> **Refer to:** *Aide-memoire: Patient assessment, pages 27–37.*

- *Only allow the patient to move themselves if it will not be detrimental to their clinical condition.*
- If you do have to lift a patient, before you do, *stop and think* using the *LITE one-minute assessment tool.*

> **Refer to:** *Aide-memoire: LITE, pages 17–18.*

Walking

- It is advised to always use a transfer belt when walking with a patient. Walk slightly behind with a hand on the belt.
- If the patient loses their balance then stop and let them regain control before walking on.
- If the patient's knees start to give way sharply say 'STAND UP' to make them stand tall again and prevent them from falling.

To move a patient from a bed to a carry chair

> **Refer to:** *Procedures: Manual Handling: Slide Sheet, pages 318–321.*

ACA

ECA

Q/SAP

TECH

PARA

SP CC

SP PC

To carry a patient down the stairs using a carry chair

Refer to: *Procedures: Manual Handling: Carrying Chair, pages 94–95 or Manual Handling: IBEX Chair, pages 188–189.*

To move a patient in a wheelchair

Refer to: *Procedures: Manual Handling: Wheelchair Up/Down Kerb, pages 372–373 or Manual Handling: Wheelchair onto Ramp, pages 370–371.*

To move a patient in a wheelchair to a vehicle chair

Refer to: *Procedures: Manual Handling: Handling Belts, pages 174–175 or Manual Handling: Transfer Board, pages 354–355.*

To move a patient from a bed to a stretcher

Refer to: *Procedures: Manual Handling: Slide Sheet, pages 318–321.*

To move a stretcher onto a ramp/tail lift

Refer to: *Procedures: Manual Handling: Wheelchair onto Ramp, pages 370–371 or Manual Handling: Loading Patient onto the Vehicle (with Stretchers), pages 234–235.*

ACA

ECA

Q/SAP

TECH

PARA

SP CC

SP PC

Checking the respiratory rate

For adults: count the number of breaths in 30 seconds – if difficult to count, place your hand on their chest and count the rise and fall. Multiply by two to get breaths/min.

For paediatrics: Count the number of breaths in 60 seconds.

- Note the rate – normal, fast, slow or non-existent.
- Note the respiratory rhythm – regular or irregular.
- Evaluate the depth of breathing – excessively shallow or deep breathing may indicate injury or illness.

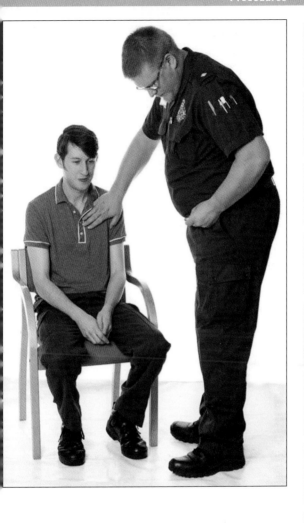

CFR

ACA

ECA

Q/SAP

TECH

PARA

SP CC

SP PC

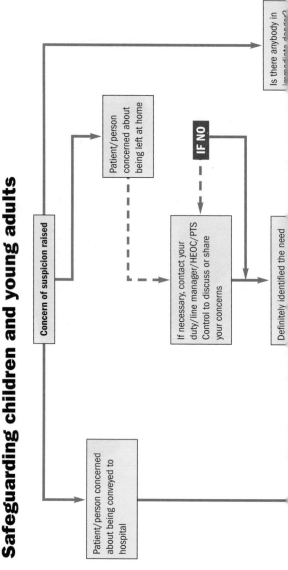

CFR

ACA

ECA

Q/SAP

TECH

PARA

SP CC

SP PC

Safeguarding children and young adults

Concern of suspicion raised

Patient/person concerned about being left at home

Patient/person concerned about being conveyed to hospital

If necessary, contact your duty/line manager/HEOC/PTS Control to discuss or share your concerns

IF NO

Is there anybody in immediate danger?

Definitely identified the need

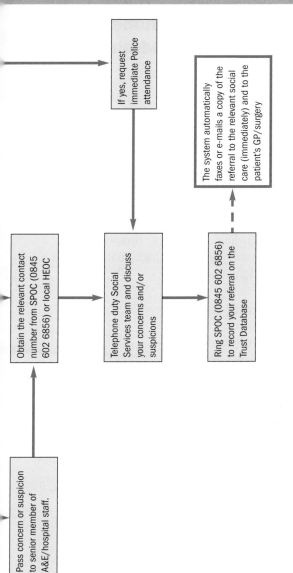

Pass concern or suspicion to senior member of A&E/hospital staff.

Obtain the relevant contact number from SPOC (0845 602 6856) or local HEOC

Telephone duty Social Services team and discuss your concerns and/or suspicions

If yes, request immediate Police attendance

Ring SPOC (0845 602 6856) to record your referral on the Trust Database

The system automatically faxes or e-mails a copy of the referral to the relevant social care (immediately) and to the patient's GP/surgery

CFR

ACA

ECA

Q/SAP

TECH

PARA

SP CC

SP PC

303

Safeguarding Vulnerable Adults and Children

Introduction

All staff employed by the East of England Ambulance Service NHS Trust have a responsibility for the safety and well-being of their patients and colleagues.

Living a life free from harm and abuse is a fundamental human right of every person and an essential requirement for health and well-being.

Safeguarding is integral to complying with legislation, regulations, high-quality patient care and safety (*Table 1*).

Referring patients

Children

All child cases (anyone under the age of 18 years old) are safeguarding concerns and must go through to the local authority.

If children are involved in any way in the referral, they must take priority over the other individuals involved. If you have concerns for a family, you must refer the children and adults separately.

Call social services in the area that the child lives and then call SPOC on 0845 602 6856.

Adults

If the patient is an adult, then the system is split into safeguarding issues and vulnerability needs;

CFR

you will need to work out what the priorities for referral are.

Safeguarding (to social care) issues

Patients who have been abused, even if taken to a hospital, are a safeguarding concern. Crews must tell Social Services about these patients; if you cannot get through or there is no one to take your message, then go directly back to SPOC, quote the number you tried to call and make the referral via the call handler, telling them the information you wanted to tell social care. *Do not delay in returning to SPOC.*

Table 1 Safeguarding issues fall into one of these types of abuse.

Type of abuse	Definition
Financial or material	Any person being exploited for financial gain or material wealth – can be by family, care staff, rogue traders or burglars. Most at risk are elderly patients and those with learning disabilities in independent living.
Discriminatory	A breach of a person's Human and Civil Rights by any other person or persons; this is a criminal act that contravenes many Acts within the law.
Forced marriage	When a male or female is forced into marriage without consent, which can happen to children as young as seven; these marriages are often difficult and

ACA

ECA

Q/SAP

TECH

PARA

SP CC

SP PC

Type of abuse	Definition
Forced marriage *continued*	domestic abuse can be a factor in such relationships – any sexual contact is rape or sexual assault as it is not considered consensual.
Hate crime	This agenda focuses around community cohesion and people perpetrating acts of violence or harassment on members of their local community; examples of this are 'happy slapping', racially motivated criminal acts or acts of violence against disabled people.
Concealed pregnancy	Any female who does not know she is pregnant and/or has not engaged with the midwifery services prior to the birth of her child.
Domestic abuse/ violence	Where two or more people reside in the same dwelling and perpetrate psychological, physical, emotional, sexual or neglectful behaviour towards each other – this can often escalate to such levels of violence that death can occur.
Institutional	When professional or paid individuals are in a position of care and support over another or many people, it is possible that in this position of trust they may be seen to abuse people who are, in theory, under care. This can be anyone of the listed forms of abuse. Often others working with this person

CFR

ACA

ECA

Q/SAP

TECH

PARA

SP CC

SP PC

Type of abuse	Definition
Institutional *continued*	know this information and they choose to perpetuate the abuse by not whistle blowing and telling others. Examples of this can be found in care homes, residential homes, hospitals, children's homes, disabled-care facilitates, etc.
Physical	Hitting, throwing, burning, scalding, shaking, slapping, etc., where the perpetrator has left a physical injury on the person suffering.
Fabricated induced illness	Where a person will perpetrate physical harm on another by, for example, poisoning, or emotionally influencing the person suffering into performing acts; the perpetrator will behave in this way to get gratification from the medical services.
Emotional	Emotionally bullying someone when in a position where you are calling for another. An example of this is telling someone that they are worthless, unloved, a nuisance, etc. - the psychological harassment of one person by another.
Neglect	When someone in a position of trust is not fulfilling his or her duty of care for a person, which includes a failure to meet basic human needs such as food, water, shelter, warmth, love, care, medical treatment, dental care, clothing, etc.

CFR

ACA

ECA

Q/SAP

TECH

PARA

SP CC

SP PC

Type of abuse	Definition
Self-neglect	Where a patient is deemed to be a risk to themselves or others and has, could or will continue to perpetuate risk-taking behaviour, which could be drugs, alcohol, self-harm, not taking medication, not eating, etc.
Internet	The internet can be a dangerous place for vulnerable and impressionable minds, a place where anyone can access vulnerable minds and groom them to participate in inappropriate behaviour.
Human trafficking	Many people move voluntarily from one country to another, but there is a growing trade in the buying and selling of human life (trafficking), which is now big business, with males and females being moved across borders to undertake forced work to profit another – the most common industries are domestic servitude, labourers, sexual exploitation and forced organ donation.
Violent extremisms	Individuals who are targeted by people with extremist views and then groomed into perpetrating violent acts or terrorist attacks.
Tissue viability	Not identifying pressure sores, moisture lesions, infected wounds and poorly managed bandages where infection is evident, not identifying that a person is suffering and neglectful in caring for their needs.

Vulnerability and GP need

A person who is a vulnerable adult could be someone who resides in their own home and does not cause any concerns to you about being abused or mistreated by anyone they come into contact with. This person just needs extra care packages, walking aids or a visit from the GP, etc. The crew needs to contact SPOC to give them all the patient details, and then SPOC will send this referral through to the GP.

Trust procedures for consent and capacity should be followed where appropriate and indicated.

> **Refer to:** *Policies: Safeguarding children and young adults, and Safeguarding vulnerable adults, available on EAST 24.*

All patients should consent to be referred, and a discussion regarding the holistic care for the patient and what you want to achieve from the vulnerable person referral should be had prior to referring through to SPOC.

SPOC questions are not meant for third-party callers and so it would be very difficult for you to make the referral for anyone else.

Please contact the Safeguarding team at Cambourne if you have any questions regarding safeguarding:

Tel: 01954 712436

Fax: 01954 712448

Eoeasnt.eoe-safeguarding@nhs.net

What to do if you are concerned that an adult is vulnerable, but not at risk of significant harm and therefore not in need of urgent safeguarding?

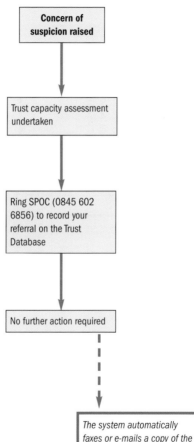

CFR

ACA

ECA

Q/SAP

TECH

PARA

SP CC

SP PC

CFR

ACA

ECA

Q/SAP

TECH

PARA

SP CC

SP PC

What to do if you are concerned that a child or vulnerable adult is being abused or neglected?

Concern of suspicion raised

Patient/person concerned about being left at home

Patient/person concerned about being conveyed to hospital

If necessary, contact your duty/line manager/HEOC/PTS Control to discuss or share your concern

IF NO

Is there anybody in immediate danger?

Definitely identified the need to contact social services

Pass concern or suspicion to a senior member of A&E/hospital staff

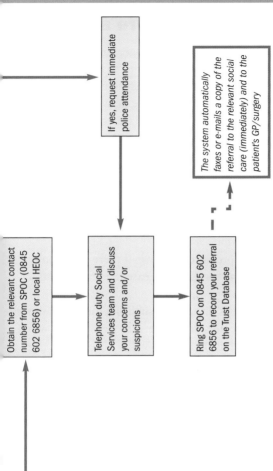

If yes, request immediate police attendance

Obtain the relevant contact number from SPOC (0845 602 6856) or local HEOC

Telephone duty Social Services team and discuss your concerns and/or suspicions

Ring SPOC on 0845 602 6856 to record your referral on the Trust Database

The system automatically faxes or e-mails a copy of the referral to the relevant social care (immediately) and to the patient's GP/surgery

CFR

ACA

ECA

Q/SAP

TECH

PARA

SP CC

SP PC

313

Sellick Manoeuvre and BURP

- Locate the cricoid cartilage, larynx, trachea and hyoid bone by palpation to ensure that pressure is applied to the correct structure.
- Hold the cricoid cartilage between your thumb and middle finger, and place your index finger on the cricoid cartilage.
- Push down gently but firmly. If the patient is conscious or there is a risk of spinal injury, use less pressure.
- Cricoid pressure can be used to move the larynx posteriorly to aid visualisation during intubation.
- Apply pressure as above; if there is difficulty inserting the ET tube, ease the pressure off a little.
- If there is difficulty visualising the cords, move the cricoid side to side – the oesophagus won't move, but the trachea will.
- If the blade is inserted too deeply you'll feel the larynx being lifted.
- You'll be able to confirm the correct placement of the ET introducer or ET tube when you feel it pass through the cricoid rings.

BURP: Backwards, Upwards, Rightwards Pressure

- This is used with children, although it can be useful with adults also.
- Apply your fingers as described above, apply backwards pressure and push the cartilage towards the patient's chin and move it to the patient's right.
- This technique is useful when the trachea is located in an anterior anatomical position, as in small children.

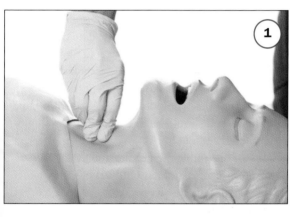

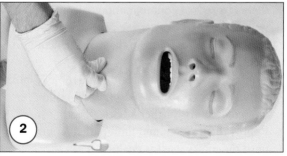

Sharps Management

- A sharp is defined as 'any article that can cut or puncture the skin'; this includes needles, glass ampoules, giving sets and safety cannulation devices.
- All sharps must be disposed of in approved yellow sharps bins that conform to B57320:1990/U N3291.
- Never fill a sharps container by more than two-thirds full, and always ensure they are fully closed and the label is completed prior to disposal.
- The label must state the station of origin at the time of opening/first use, and the date of disposal is to be written on it before the container is placed in an approved yellow clinical waste bin.
- Handling of sharps should be kept to a minimum; they should not be passed from hand to hand and should be discarded using a single-handed technique.
- Do not dissemble the needles and syringes or re-sheath needles/cannulas, and *never* empty a sharps container of its contents.
- In event of a needle stick/sharps injury where there is a risk of contamination, encourage the wound to bleed – never suck the wound.
- Seek medical advice from the management and A&E Department.
- Contact Occupational Health on 01638 718439 (office hours) or 07740 610899 (24 hours) immediately for further advice.
- Report the incident and limit patient contact until the injury itself is dealt with.

Procedures

CFR

ACA

ECA

Q/SAP

TECH

PARA

SP CC

SP PC

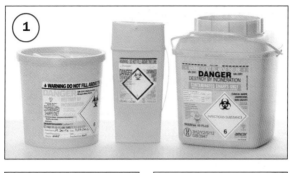

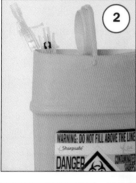

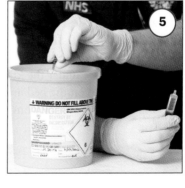

Manual Handling: Slide Sheet

Patient fallen in a confined space

- Get the patient onto a carry sheet.
- Place a large slide sheet on the floor, under the carry sheet.
- The slide sheet reduces friction by up to 50%.
- Pull the patient out into a larger space where more equipment can be used to get the patient up.
- Hold a corner of the carry sheet so you can pull between the mid-thigh and hip level.
- Make sure you are in the power position.

Bed to carry chair with two manual handling belts and a slide sheet

- Roll the patient onto their side and place a large slide sheet between their shoulders and feet.
- Fit one belt under the thighs and one around the waste.
- On 'READY, SET, SIT', help the patient to sit.
- One crew member supports the patient from behind and one under the knees.
- With one knee on the bed and the other on the floor, move the patient from the bed to the chair.

Bed to stretcher with a large slide sheet

- Roll the patient and place a large slide sheet under the patient's bed sheet.
- Place the stretcher as close to and as high as the bed as possible. Put the stretcher breaks on.
- Fill any gap between the bed and the stretcher using a blanket.
- Both crew members stand behind the stretcher and hold the bed sheet.
- On 'READY, SET, PULL', they pull the sheet towards them and the patient slides onto the stretcher.
- If required, a PATSLIDE™ can be used under the slide sheet to aid the transfer; however, a third person on the side opposite to the crew must help to transfer the patient.

> **Refer to:** *Procedures: Manual Handling: PATSLIDE™, pages 268–270.*

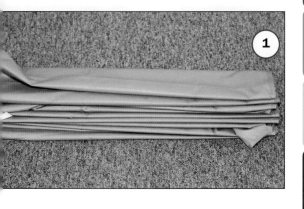

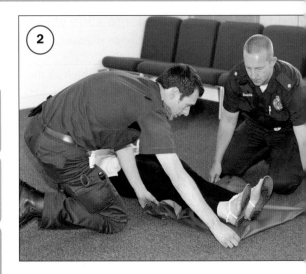

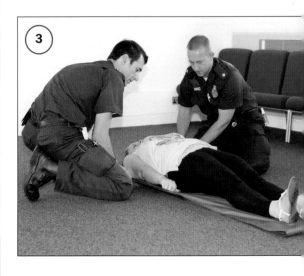

ACA

ECA

Q/SAP

TECH

PARA

SP CC

SP PC

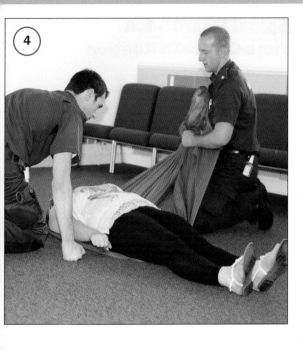

④

ACA

ECA

Q/SAP

TECH

PARA

SP CC

SP PC

Spinal Board – Extrication in a Time-Critical Situation

- Apply manual C-spine immobilisation to the patient throughout the procedure.
- Fit a correctly sized rigid cervical collar to the patient's neck.
- Assess the distal motor, sensory and circulation (MSC) function of each extremity.
- Place the foot end of the spinal board next to the patient's buttocks, perpendicular to the trunk.
- Ensure the trolley cot is under the long board.
- Turn the patient parallel to the long board and slowly lower them onto it – follow the commands of the person applying the manual C-spine immobilisation.
- Slide the patient up the long board until the patient is centrally positioned.
- Secure the patient to the long board by applying the body straps in the following order:
  1. Chest, pelvis, thighs, ankles, head blocks and straps.
  2. Reassess the patient's ABC's and MSC function in all the extremities and note the findings.
  3. Manage any injuries accordingly and transport the patient to the appropriate receiving care.

For non-time critical extrication, see KED.

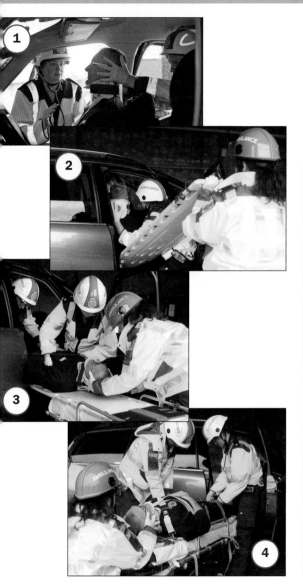

ECA

Q/SAP

TECH

PARA

SP CC

SP PC

323

Spinal Board – Immobilisation

- Explain and reassure the patient – gain their consent (if they are conscious).
- Apply an appropriate cervical collar or extrication device.
- Prepare the spinal board with the head pad in place.
- Use the appropriate techniques to place the patient on the board.
- Sliding techniques should be used rather than lifting ones.
- When an untrapped patient is moved from a supine position, the orthopaedic stretcher should be used.
- Use rolled up blankets to fill any voids between the sides of the patient and the sides of the board.
- Apply the body straps in the following order: chest, pelvis, thighs, ankles then the head blocks and straps.
- Lift the patient onto the trolley cot for transportation.
- Loosen the cervical collar to help prevent compromise of venous circulation and reduce the risk of increasing ICP.
- Document the time the patient was placed on the board.

Best practice if placing someone on a spinal board is to use the orthopaedic stretcher to do so.

ECA

Q/SAP

TECH

PARA

SP CC

SP PC

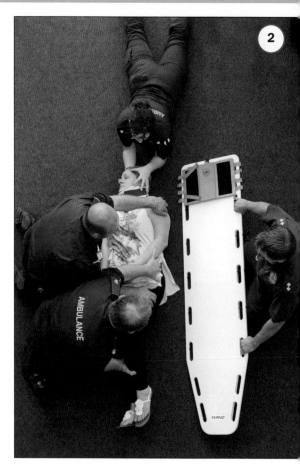

ECA

Q/SAP

TECH

PARA

SP CC

SP PC

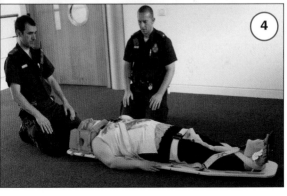

ECA

Q/SAP

TECH

PARA

SP CC

SP PC

Box Splint

- Gain the patient's informed consent.
- Provide analgesia if required prior to the procedure.
- Ensure the splint is clean and undamaged.
- Expose the injured limb and remove footwear where possible.
- Support the limb manually and raise it carefully while the splint is passed under it.
- Fold the two sides of the splint around the limb to form a box to support the limb.
- Ensure the foot piece is placed against the sole of the foot at 90 degrees (if the leg is the injured limb) or in a position comfortable for the patient.
- The Velcro straps should be carefully placed over the limb – avoid the area of injury.
- Recheck the distal neurovascular status of the limb after application of the box splint.

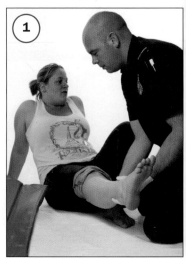

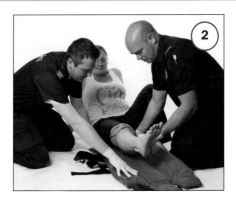

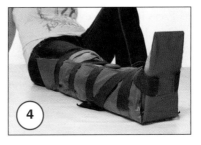

ECA

Q/SAP

TECH

PARA

SP CC

SP PC

329

Stoma Care

- Adopt standard precautions.

> **Refer to:** *Procedures: Standard Precautions and Hand-washing, pages 52–61.*

- Prepare the equipment prior to commencing changing the stoma bag: disposal bag, special wipes (if applicable), warm water and a towel, adhesive remover and scissors, the new appliance – the mat should already be pre-cut to the correct size; if it is not, trim it to fit correctly.
- Remove the old appliance carefully – use adhesive remover if needed, making sure not to cause any trauma or damage to the patient's skin.
- Check the patient's skin around the stoma site for signs of irritation or infection.
- Gently and carefully clean the stoma site with warm water – do not use soaps or baby wipes.
- Gently pat the skin dry prior to applying any protective film.
- Make sure the film has time to dry and then fit the new pouch.
- Press it on for several minutes and dispose of the old appliance and your gloves in clinical waste.
- Closed bags are usually changed twice daily; they have a filter, so if it becomes blocked fit a new bag.

- Drainage bags may be worn for 2–3 days and can be emptied when full.
- Two-piece appliances have a base plate that is accurately fitted round the stoma, and the stoma and the bag will stick or clip (or both) to it.

REMEMBER
- To avoid leakages, make sure the area is completely dry prior to fitting the new appliance.

SP PC

Subcutaneous Injection

- Adopt standard precautions.

> **Refer to:** *Procedures: Standard Precautions and Hand-washing, pages 52–61.*

- Explain the procedure to the patient, or parent/carer of the patient in cases of minors/vulnerable adults, to gain informed consent.
- Select the appropriate drug – with a colleague (if present), check the name of the drug, that it is in date and the clarity and container integrity.
- Select injection site: deltoid muscle or outer aspect of the thigh.
- Position the patient to expose the injection site and use ChloraPrep to clean the area.

Prepare drug accordingly

- Some drugs need to be mixed prior to injection. Draw up the required amount of water for the injection, inject into the powder container and mix the two constituents.
- Other drugs are 'ready to use' and require the clinician to snap the vial, draw up the fluid and replace the drawing up needle with an appropriately sized needle for injection (21 g or 23 g).
- Warn the patient, remove the needle guard and elevate the subcutaneous tissue (pinch the skin).
- With the needle bevel upwards, insert the needle at 45 degrees in one quick motion.
- Draw back the piston of the syringe – if there is no blood, smoothly administer the drug.

- Withdraw the needle at the same angle as it was inserted and gently massage the skin.
- Dispose of sharps appropriately.

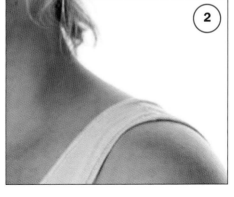

Suction – Laerdal™ Suction Unit

- Prior to using the unit, ensure there is no damage to it and no parts are missing.
- Sterile suction tubing and the appropriate suction instrument should be attached prior to use on a patient: Yanker catheter or soft catheter.
- The operating knob is the combined 'ON/OFF' switch and vacuum selector – each setting indicates the maximum achievable vacuum.
- The power ON indicator is a green LED light that is continuously lit while the LSU is switched ON; it flashes rapidly during the device test and flashes slowly while the automatic power save function is on.
- The external power indicator is a green LED light that is continuously lit while the external AC or DC power is connected.
- The red LED is lit when a possible malfunction has been detected.

Assembly

- Mount the disposable Abbott Liner in the Abbott Canister.
- Ensure that the yellow T-bar is securely tightened. Connect the yellow connector from the Abbott Liner to the yellow T-Bar on the Abbott Canister (yellow on yellow).
- Connect the blue vacuum connector on the tubing to the blue vacuum inlet (blue on blue).

- Place the canister in the canister holder and slide it into the suction unit.
- Connect the yellow connector on the vacuum tubing to the yellow T-Bar on the Abbott Canister (yellow on yellow).
- Connect the white angled connector to the patient tubing.
- Connect the white angled connector to the white patient inlet on the Abbott Liner (white on white).
- When the suction is complete, switch the operating knob to 'O'.
- After use, remove and dispose of (in clinical waste) the suction tubing, suction appliance and Abbott Liner.
- Clean the rest of the LSU as per the manufacturer's guidelines.
- When fully clean, prepare the LSU for the next patient.

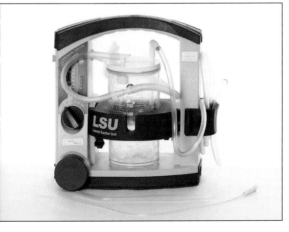

REMEMBER

– Not suitable for use in the presence of flammable liquids or gases.

– Place on continuous charge when not in use.

– Reusable LSUs must be used with a filter and disposable Abbott Liner.

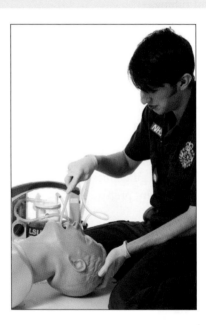

Suction – Res-Q-Vac™

- Test the vacuum handle prior to use to ensure that the unit produces a vacuum.
- Place your finger over the vacuum port and squeeze the handle – if no vacuum is felt do not use the unit.
- Attach the canister assembly to the pump by aligning the pump vacuum port with the adapter nozzle and push together.
- Based on the patient's size, determine an appropriately sized catheter and attach it to the canister cap by gently pushing it.
- Typically, 8Fr and 10Fr catheters are used for infants and small children, and 14Fr, 24Fr and 40Fr catheters for larger children and adults.
- Adopt standard precautions prior to use.
- Introduce the catheter into the patient's airway and suction by squeezing and releasing the handle.
- If the pump handle becomes difficult to operate, check for an obstruction.
- Do not carry on trying to suction until the obstruction has cleared.
- After use, remove the canister with the adapter and dispose in clinical waste.

CFR

ACA

ECA

Q/SAP

TECH

PARA

SP CC

SP PC

Surgical Airway

- Adopt standard precautions.

> **Refer to:** *Procedures: Standard Precautions and Hand-washing, pages 52–61.*

- Position the patient – head in mid line, and neck extended if the MOI allows.
- Palpate the cricothyroid membrane – between the thyroid and cricoid cartilages.
- Prepare the equipment required: scalpel blade, 10 ml syringe, Portex 6.0 tracheostomy tube or tracheal tube, tube tie, BVM, $EtCO_2$ monitoring, suction and ventilator.
- If the patient is conscious, surgically prepare and anaesthetise the area locally.
- Using a scalpel, perform a 2 cm *vertical* incision on the identified area. Pierce the skin and press the lateral edges outwards to reduce bleeding.
- Using Trousseau dilators, identify the cricothyroid membrane.
- Using a scalpel, perform a 1 cm horizontal incision on the lower aspect of the cricothyroid membrane.
- Rotate the scalpel blade to open up the hole in the membrane.
- Insert the tracheostomy tube.
- Inflate the cuff and ventilate, attaching the catheter mount and BVM.
- Attach the capnography sensor and confirm $EtCO_2$ detection.
- Observe lung inflations – auscultate the chest for adequate inflations.

SP CC

- Fix the tube with a tie.
- Suction the upper airway via the tube – remove any inhaled blood or vomit.

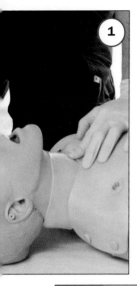

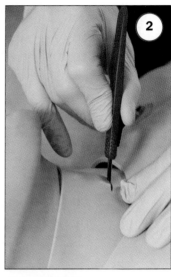

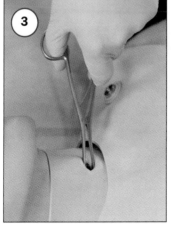

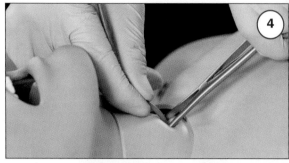

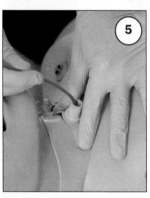

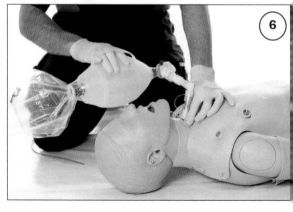

Vehicle Tail Lifts

- Where possible, ensure the ambulance is on level ground; the tail lift must only be used when the ambulance is stationary with the handbrake on.
- Open the rear-side door, turn the central isolator switch clockwise (the power should illuminate) and ensure the selector switch for the wander lead is turned to the right.
- Do not alter the tilt when the tail lift is loaded.
- Prior to deploying the tail lift, ensure the area to the rear of the ambulance is clear of people/obstructions for 2 metres; maintain good visibility of the area when operating the lift.
- Press the button on the top right-hand corner labelled 'OPEN/CLOSE' to lower the lift to the horizontal position.
- Press the 'UP/DOWN' button to lower the lift enough to allow the right-hand door to open, and ensure lower locking bar falls into position.
- Raise the hand rail by pressing the handle upwards until it releases, which allows the rails to be lifted into position.
- Lower the lift to the floor and close the right-hand door first, before raising and stowing the lift.
- Lower the hand rails until they lock into place.
- Ensure the 'SELECTOR' switch on the wander lead is turned to the left.
- On the wander lead, the 'BLACK' button is for lowering and the 'WHITE' button is for raising the lift.

ECA

Q/SAP

TECH

PARA

SP CC

SP PC

REMEMBER
- Maximum weight capacity is 500 kg or 78.5 stones in total.
- Ensure both rear doors are open when loading/unloading the stretcher onto the lift.

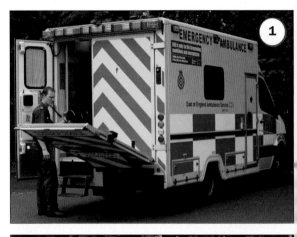

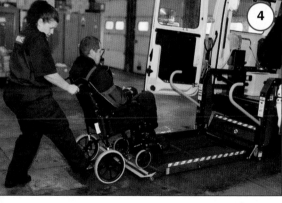

ECA

Q/SAP

TECH

PARA

SP CC

SP PC

Removal of Taser Barbs

- Use the appropriate PPE.
- Only approach the patient when instructed to do so by the Police Officer in charge.
- Cut the wires from the Taser barbs – these will be retained by the police as evidence.
- Obtain a full set of observations (including BM and 12-lead ECG).
- Clean the area and apply a non-adhesive dressing to the wound.
- Inspect the barbs to ensure they are intact; if any part remains in the patient, the patient must be transported to hospital.
- While keeping the skin taught, pull the barb sharply out.
- *Care must be taken to avoid a sharps injury.*
- Place the barbs in a suitable receptacle and pass them to the Police Officer present.
- Give the patient advice on wound care and signs of infection.

ECA

Q/SAP

TECH

PARA

SP CC

SP PC

REMEMBER

The Taser barbs should not be removed if:

- The patient refuses to have them removed in the pre-hospital setting.
- The individual is under 18 years of age.
- The person is pregnant.
- The barbs are in the face/eyes or the genital area.

Thermometers (Tempa-DOT™)

- Remove the Tempa-DOT from the packaging and place it on/in patient:
  - *Orally.* Place it as far back as possible under the patient's tongue (the dots can face up or down), ask them to press their tongue down on it and close their mouth. Wait 60 seconds for a recording.
  - *Axillary.* Place the thermometer on the skin, high in the armpit, with the dots facing the torso and the strip lengthways to the body. Lower the patient's arm to keep the Tempa-DOT in place and wait three minutes for a recording.
- Dispose of the used Tempa-DOT appropriately.
- The last little blue dot on the thermometer is the reading that you should record as a patient's temperature.
- If any dots are 'missed out', ignore them and record the last blue dot present.
- Temperature readings from the armpit are about 0.5°C lower than the readings taken from the mouth, and are therefore less reliable. However, at the pre-hospital stage it is an acceptable vital sign of the secondary survey.
- Record whether the temperature was taken orally or axillary.

ECA

Q/SAP

TECH

PARA

SP CC

SP PC

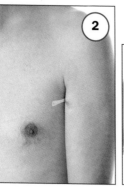

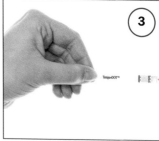

REMEMBER

- Very young or mentally impaired patients may swallow the thermometer: the axillary position may be more appropriate.
- *Do not expose* the dots to temperatures of more than 35°C, i.e., don't carry them on your person or leave them uncovered in a hot vehicle.

Needle Thoracocentesis

- Adopt standard precautions.
- Identify the need for the procedure – tension pneumothorax.
- Perform the primary survey and administer 100% oxygen. Confirm the diagnosis after auscultation of the chest using a stethoscope.
- Expose the chest and clean the skin over the 2nd intercostal space (just above the 3rd rib), through the mid-clavicular line on the side of the pneumothorax.
- Connect a 10 ml syringe to a 14 g cannula and insert the cannula fully at 90 degrees to the skin. Put 5 ml of water in the syringe to identify escaping air on correct insertion.
- Advance the cannula fully and remove the syringe and needle – listen for the escape of air.
- Secure the cannula in place.
- Reassess the patient and ensure continued monitoring.
- Ensure 100% oxygen is delivered before, during and after the procedure.

REMEMBER

- Leave the cannula in situ; if it becomes dislodged ensure A&E is informed.
- There is a 10–20% risk of causing a pneumothorax if it is not already present – be sure of your diagnosis.

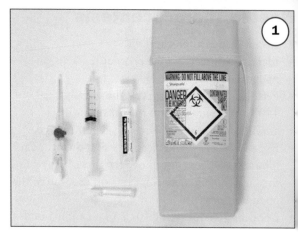

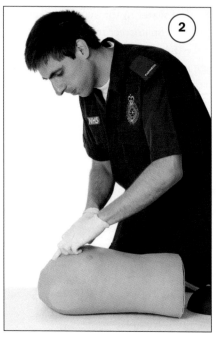

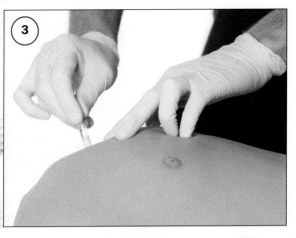

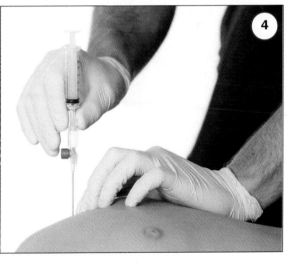

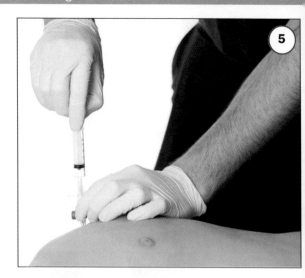

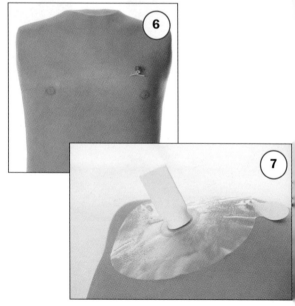

PARA

SP CC

SP PC

Tourniquet

- Identify the need for intravenous access.
- Explain the procedure to the patient and gain their consent.
- Ensure the tourniquet is clean, in its original packaging and single-use only.
- Ensure your hands are clean and that gloves are worn.
- Apply the tourniquet above the site chosen for IV access and allow the veins to fill – this creates additional vascular pressure to engorge the veins with blood below the tourniquet site.
- The tourniquet should be tight enough to significantly diminish venous flow, but should not hinder arterial flow.
- The tourniquet should only remain in position for long enough to complete the IV insertion.
- If blood is required, obtain this prior to removing the tourniquet.

- Once the tourniquet is removed, dispose of it in a clinical waste bin if soiled.

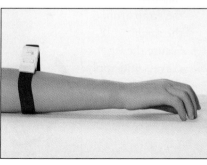

Traction Splint (Sager™)

- Remove the patient's shoes and clothing to expose the injured leg.
- Check MSCs (motor, sensation and circulation) distal to the injury site.
- Apply the cushioned end of the splint between the patient's legs and against the perineum.
- Apply the 'S' strap around the top of the thigh of the injured leg.
- Extend the splint so the ankle hitch lies between the patient's ankles.
- Apply the ankle harness beneath the heel and wrap it around just above the malleoli.
- Adjust the cushions to suit the size of the leg.
- Set the traction – 10% of the patient's body weight or until the patient is comfortable.

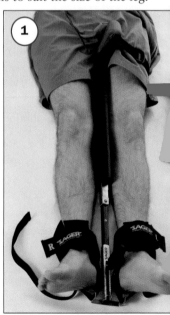

- Apply the leg cravats and, if required, tighten the strap around the thigh.
- Secure the leg cravats and apply the foot-binding strap in a figure-of-eight fashion.

ECA

Q/SAP

TECH

PARA

SP CC

SP PC

Manual Handling: Transfer Board

- Use the board when a patient cannot weight bear and needs to transfer laterally between two surfaces of a similar height.
- Highlight the need to use the board.
- Explain to the patient the aim and expectations of using the board.
- Operator 1 should support the patient and encourage them to lean to one side, raising the buttocks.
- Operator 2 should insert the curve board under the patient's buttocks, between the patient and the surface they are sat on.
- If possible, encourage the patient to self-transfer by sliding across the board.
- When assisting the patient to transfer, firmly apply a manual handling belt around the patient's waist.
- Using universal manual handling techniques to grip the manual handling belt, support and assist the patient (if required) to transfer from A to B.
- Ensure the board is clean prior to and after each use.

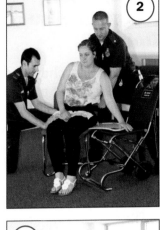

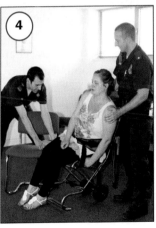

ACA

ECA

Q/SAP

TECH

PARA

SP CC

SP PC

Trolley Cots
(Ferno Pegasus/Pegasus MK2 Trolley™)

The following checks are recommended before the start of each shift's use of the Pegasus Trolley.

1. Does the trolley have a properly installed mattress and patient-restraining system? Check the mattress for damage; if any damage is found, it must be replaced.
2. Do the trolley cot sides raise, lower and lock in position properly?
3. Check that the wheels and brakes operate satisfactorily.
4. Does the trolley lower and raise satisfactorily?
5. Does the ambulance have a properly installed approved locking device?
6. Check the operation of the push/pull handles and ensure the head-end handle clips in the stowed position.
7. Does the headrest extension operate correctly and lock in position?

Once these checks have been completed, then the trolley is ready to be used in regular service.

Ensure that these procedures are complied with

1. Advise the patient before making adjustments, lifting or loading the trolley.

2. Stay with the patient and control the trolley at all times.
3. Keep the patient restrained and the cot side-rails up when using the trolley.
4. Use help when needed to ensure patient and operator safety.

Transferring a patient onto a trolley

1. Lower the cot side rails.
2. Place the trolley beside the patient and open the restraints.
3. Ensure that at least one wheel brake at each end of the trolley is applied.
4. Transfer the patient onto the trolley using recognised manual handling procedures.
5. Close the restraints around the patient
6. Raise the cot side-rails and lock in position.
7. Make adjustments as necessary.

> **Refer to:** *Procedures: Removal of a Patient from a Property, pages 238–240.*

Height adjustment – do not raise the trolley when located in the vehicle lock

1. The height adjustment of the Pegasus is achieved by a simple hydraulic pumping action.
2. The raising and lowering action is achieved by means of foot pedals, which are located on each side of the trolley. Note: ensure the pedals on both sides are clear before operating.

ACA

ECA

Q/SAP

TECH

PARA

SP CC

SP PC

3. The foot pedal is a rocker action about an off-centre pivot; the longer pedal is for raising the trolley top and the shorter one for lowering it.

4. To raise the trolley, operate the long side of the foot pedal through full strokes to achieve the desired height; this operation may be better achieved with two of the wheel brakes engaged.

5. To lower the trolley, depress the short pedal. A slight repositioning of the foot pedal will control the rate of lowering.

6. Two operators making use of both pump pedals can ease the raising of a heavily laden trolley. Practice is advised to achieve unison of action.

Cot sides

Cot sides should always be used when the patient has been placed on the trolley. These can be lowered by pulling out the lock pin; the cot sides lock automatically when raised to the vertical position.

Backrest

The backrest may be locked in any inclined position. Support the backrest with one hand (to avoid sudden movement), squeeze the control lever with the other hand, raise the backrest to the desired angle and release the lever to lock it in position. Support the backrest while making adjustments. The backrest also incorporates superior support for CPR. Do not under any circumstances use the backrest to manoeuvre the trolley. When using the trolley as a seat in a PTS vehicle, ensure the headrest is in its lowest position.

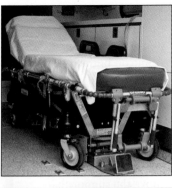

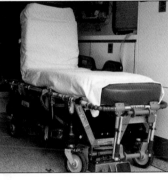

ACA

ECA

Q/SAP

TECH

PARA

SP CC

SP PC

Trendelenburg position

To raise the leg rest to the Trendelenburg position, grip and support the leg-rest frame at the foot end. Lift the leg rest until the support bar locks into position. Maintain a grip on the frame and gradually reduce your support of the leg rest until you are confident that the support bar has locked.

To lower the leg rest from the Trendelenburg position, hold the leg-rest frame on both sides at the foot end. Slide your hands forwards until the fingers contact the support bar on the underside of the leg-rest frame. At this point, simultaneously lift and move the support bar forwards, thus releasing it from its locked position, and slowly lower the leg-rest frame to its resting position.

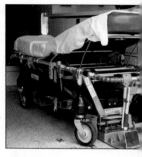

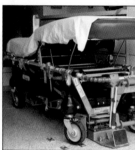

Knee-contour (Fowler) position

To raise the knee-contour position, hold both the lifting straps (yellow) and lift up. Gradually release the lifting straps, ensuring that the support bar has locked in position.

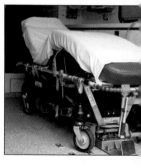

To lower the knee-contour position, hold both release straps (red), lift up and the pull straps in the direction of the foot end and slowly lower the frame to its resting position.

Head-end fold down

The benefit of a shorter trolley using the head-end fold section can only be achieved with the trolley in the elevated position and the backrest partially raised.

- Using the foot pedal, raise the trolley to its maximum height.
- Stand at the head end of the trolley and grasp the two knurled sleeves, located one each side of the trolley frame.
- Pull each knurled sleeve against the springs until the head-end section can be folded down.
- Adjust the backrest angle to achieve the shortest length possible while considering the comfort of the patient. Only leave the trolley in this condition until sufficient space allows its return to normal length. Always ensure that two operators are with a laden trolley at all times.
- To return the trolley to normal length, lift the folded head end and the spring-loaded knurled sleeves will return to their locked position. Adjust the backrest as necessary.
- Hold the foot pedal down and lower the trolley.

Foot-end fold down (PTS version only)

- Stand at the foot end of the trolley and grasp the two knurled sleeves, located one each side of the trolley frame.
- Depress the spring-loaded pins, which are positioned underneath each sleeve. This allows each sleeve to be pushed along the frame, thus releasing the foot end of the frame to drop down.
- The foot-end tray can now be shortened by simply pulling out the spring-loaded knob and folding the tray down.
- Stow the push/pull handle below the lock-bracket. Do not raise the trolley top when it is in this condition.
- The trolley is now ready for use as a seat base within the patient transport vehicle.
- To return the trolley to its normal length, the reverse procedure should be applied: raise the lowered foot end to its horizontal position and slide both sleeves back over the hinged positions until they lock in position. The trolley is now ready for normal use.

Cleaning

Regular cleaning helps reduce the risk of transmitting disease and enables equipment to function at its optimum.

Steam cleaning with a suitable cleaning additive is the most effective method. The same results may be achieved by using a sponge and mild detergent soap mixed in warm water. For particularly grimy cases, especially if the trolley has been in storage for a long period, it may be necessary to first wash the trolley with a cloth soaked in water-soluble solvent prior to using soap and water.

Once cleaned, dry the trolley with a soft towel, paying particular attention to swivel and sliding joints.

ACA

ECA

Q/SAP

TECH

PARA

SP CC

SP PC

Tympanic Thermometer

- Adopt standard precautions.

> **Refer to:** *Procedures: Standard Precautions and Hand-washing, pages 52–61.*

- Explain the procedure to the patient or the parent/carer of the child/vulnerable adult.
- Remove the thermometer from the base, ensure it is clean and the probe end is clear.
- Place a disposable plastic probe cover on the probe end as per the manufacturer's guidelines.
- Carefully place the probe end in the patient's ear canal, ensuring a snug fit.
- Press the 'SCAN' button as per the manufacturer's guidelines.
- Allow the thermometer to take the reading by listening for a beep.
- Remove the probe as soon as the measurement is complete.
- Read the recording and document it, including which ear was measured.
- Remove and dispose of the probe cover.

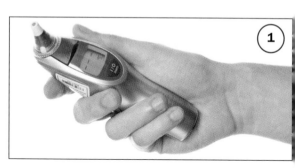

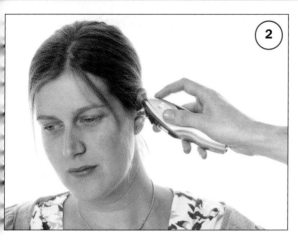

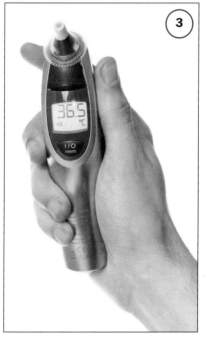

ECA

Q/SAP

TECH

PARA

SP CC

SP PC

365

Urinalysis (Urine Dip)

- Adopt standard precautions.

  > **Refer to:** *Procedures: Standard Precautions and Hand-washing, pages 52–61.*

- When the sample is obtained, using macroscopic methods look at the:
  - colour (is it dark?)
  - clarity (is it cloudy?)
  - presence of blood
- Make sure the dip-stick packaging is intact and in date.
- Take one stick from the container, and holding just the one end – where there are no squares – dip it into the patient's urine.
- After a few seconds, and when each small square has been submerged in urine, remove the stick.
- Compare the colour changes on the stick with the container guideline chart.
- Dispose of the used stick and your gloves in a clinical waste bin.

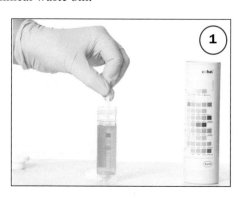

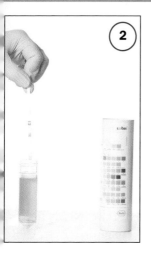

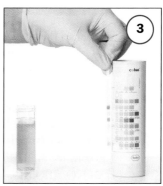

REMEMBER
- Foods, medications and metabolic products can all cause abnormal urine colours and odours.

SP PC

Ventilator
(Pneupac Parapac Medic Model 200D Ventilator™)

- Connect to the gas supply and switch the ventilator to (CMV/DEMAND).
- Allow the ventilator to complete a self-check for approximately 60 seconds.
- Ensure the pressure indicator shows O_2 (red – no supply, white – supply).
- Set frequency (supply) and tidal volume (VTDEL) for ADULT, CHILD or INFANT.
- Set to NO AIR MIX for respiratory arrest, CPR or in a contaminated atmosphere.
- Set RELIEF/ALARM PRESSURE to 40 cmH_2O and set the ventilation parameters to suit the patient.
- Temporarily occlude the patient connection to confirm the relief pressure and alarm function, and adjust if required.
- Connect the mask/ET tube in the correct manner.
- Check for air tightness and adequate chest movement, and adjust the tidal volume as appropriate.
- Check the correctness of the indicated air pressure.
- A high-pressure alarm may indicate an excessive tidal volume, incorrect airway position or kinked ET tube.
- A low pressure alarm may indicate a leakage or insufficient tidal volume.

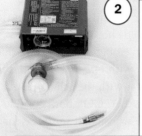

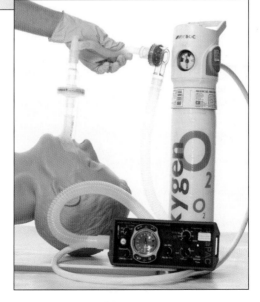

Q/SAP

TECH

PARA

SP CC

SP PC

369

Manual Handling: Wheelchair onto a Ramp/ Tail Lift

- Position the wheelchair at the bottom of the ramp.
- Ensure the vehicle doors are opened as wide as possible.
- One crew member remains at the rear of the wheelchair and holds both handles.
- The second crew member stands to one side and holds the arm rest with one hand and pushes against the backrest with the other.
- On 'READY, STEADY, GO', both crew members push the wheelchair until it is inside the vehicle.
- One crew member stays behind the wheelchair and the other enters the vehicle through the side door.
- The patient can then be transferred into a seat or the wheelchair can be secured with clamps.

Standing by the wheelchair

At the top of the ramp

ACA

ECA

Q/SAP

TECH

PARA

SP CC

SP PC

Manual Handling: Wheelchair – Getting Up and Down Kerb/Step

Getting up a kerb/step

Look for a dropped kerb or ramp to use. If none:

1. Position the chair so the front and rear wheels are in alignment. Tell the occupant you will be tipping the chair.
2. Grip the handles firmly and place one foot on the tipping lever.
3. Push down on the tipping leaver – pull the handles towards you and, while balancing the chair on rear wheels, place the front wheels on the kerb.
4. Push the chair forwards until the front wheels are on the pavement. The rear wheels will climb the kerb by momentum – *do not lift them.*

Getting up the kerb

Getting down a kerb/step

Look for dropped kerb/step. If none:

1. Check the road is clear, or get help to stop traffic.
2. Position the chair with the back to the kerb and the front and rear wheels aligned. Tell the occupant you will be tipping the chair.
3. Lower the chair to the road by wheeling backwards with the rear wheels against the kerb. *Make sure both rear wheels touch the floor at the same time.*
4. Support the patients' weight by pushing down on the tipping lever as you take the front wheels off the pavement and gently down onto the road.

The patient can then be transferred into a seat or the wheelchair can be secured with clamps.

Getting down the kerb

3

Clinical Management Plans

Abdominal Pain

Abdominal pain can have a wide variety of causes, and therefore it is vital to undertake a thorough examination and history prior to making any treatment decisions. The difficulty of determining the cause of abdominal pain in the pre-hospital setting means that many patients will require hospitalisation.

> **Refer to:** *Aide-memoire: Patient Assessment: Gastrointestinal Assessment, pages 31–32.*

In this table, red text = red flags.

Possible causes of abdominal pain

Common	Occasional	Rare
Peptic ulcer	Cholecystitis	**Perforation leading to peritonitis**
Biliary colic	Diverticulitis	Hepatitis
Appendicitis	**Acute or sub-acute bowel obstruction:** *Small bowel* (usually adhesions, check for post-operative scars, minimal distension) *Large bowel* (distension, colicky pain, tympanic to percussion)	Crohn's and ulcerative colitis (IBD)
Gastroenteritis		Ischaemic bowel
Renal colic	**Pancreatitis**	**Dissecting/leaking AAA**
Pelvic inflammatory disease (PID)	**Ectopic pregnancy**	Diabetic ketoacidosis
Pregnancy complications	Ruptured ovarian cyst	
	Pyelonephritis Muscular wall pain	**Myocardial infarction** Pneumonia Sickle cell crisis Twisted fibroid

Q/SAP

TECH

PARA

SP CC

SP PC

Possible causes of abdominal pain by location

Location	Possible conditions
Upper right quadrant	Pancreatitis, pneumonia with pleurisy, cholecystitis, duodenal ulcer, pyelonephritis
Upper left quadrant	Pancreatitis, pneumonia, duodenal ulcer, pyelonephritis
Lower right quadrant	Appendicitis, ectopic pregnancy, diverticulitis, renal colic, ruptured ovarian cyst, PID, AAA
Lower left quadrant	Ectopic pregnancy, diverticulitis, renal colic, ruptured ovarian cyst, PID, AAA
Unlocalised	Bowel obstruction, food poisoning, neurological lesion, metabolic problem

Q/SAP

TECH

PARA

SP CC

SP PC

Management pathway

Consider the following factors
- Haemodynamically stable
- GCS 15/15
- No pertinent SH/PMH
- Patient not left alone
- Red flags excluded

YES

NO

Refer to GP

Refer to any hospital for access (Specialist Paramedic only if available).

Safety net – advice on requirement to call back if condition worsens.

Transport to hospital (rapid with pre-alert if necessary).

Admit to acute speciality (Specialist Paramedic only if available).

Refer to: *Aide-memoire: Patient Assessment: ATMISTER, page 4.*

379

Depression

Although mental health problems are very common – affecting around one in four people in Britain – stigma and discrimination towards people with mental health problems remains prevalent and there are many myths about what different diagnoses mean.

Depression can be managed to allow a person to live a 'normal' life; however, it can 'flare up' in times of crisis or can present initially in a dramatic way that often leads to an ambulance being summoned. It can also be picked up in patient assessment for another condition. Left untreated, depression can lead to suicide or progress to a psychotic illness.

Management plan

Key features

During the past month, has the patient often been bothered by:

– feeling down, depressed or hopeless?

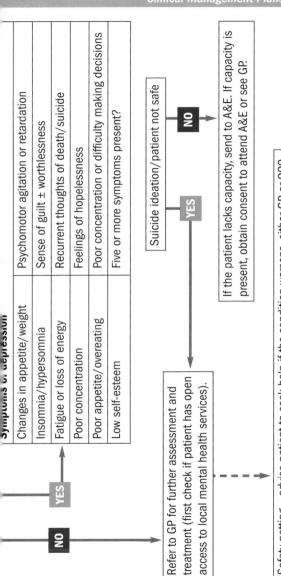

Symptoms of depression

Changes in appetite/weight	Psychomotor agitation or retardation
Insomnia/hypersomnia	Sense of guilt ± worthlessness
Fatigue or loss of energy	Recurrent thoughts of death/suicide
Poor concentration	Feelings of hopelessness
Poor appetite/overeating	Poor concentration or difficulty making decisions
Low self-esteem	Five or more symptoms present?

YES

NO

Refer to GP for further assessment and treatment (first check if patient has open access to local mental health services).

Suicide ideation/patient not safe

YES

NO

If the patient lacks capacity, send to A&E. If capacity is present, obtain consent to attend A&E or see GP:

Safety netting – advise patient to seek help if the condition worsens, either GP or 999.

CFR

ACA

ECA

Q/SAP

TECH

PARA

SP CC

SP PC

Feverish Illness in Children under Five Years Old

Feverish illness in young children usually indicates an underlying infection of some kind and, as such, the condition may be a cause of concern for parents and carers. The condition may also be a diagnostic challenge for healthcare professionals, and infectious diseases remain a major cause of childhood mortality and morbidity in the UK. As a result, there is a perceived need to improve the recognition, evaluation and immediate treatment of feverish illnesses in children.

> **Refer to:** *Aide-memoire: Paediatric Emergency Treatment, pages 19–23.*

If leaving at home, please give parents the leave-at-home advice sheet.

Safety net – advise parents/carers to seek help if the condition worsens, either GP or 999

National Institute for Health and Clinical Excellence (2007). *Feverish illness: assessment and initial management in children younger than 5 years.* London: NICE. Available at www.nice.org.uk/CG047.

Management plan

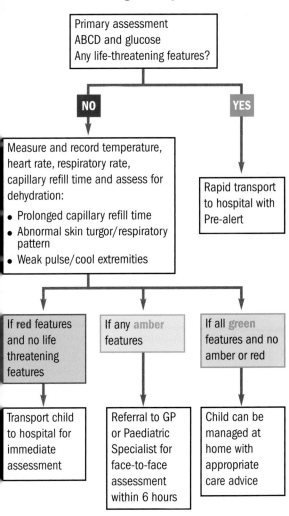

Primary assessment
ABCD and glucose
Any life-threatening features?

NO

YES

Measure and record temperature,
heart rate, respiratory rate,
capillary refill time and assess for
dehydration:

- Prolonged capillary refill time
- Abnormal skin turgor/respiratory
  pattern
- Weak pulse/cool extremities

Rapid transport
to hospital with
Pre-alert

If **red** features
and no life
threatening
features

If any amber
features

If all green
features and no
amber or red

Transport child
to hospital for
immediate
assessment

Referral to GP
or Paediatric
Specialist for
face-to-face
assessment
within 6 hours

Child can be
managed at
home with
appropriate
care advice

Q/SAP

TECH

PARA

SP CC

SP PC

Headache

Headache is a very common call for the ambulance service. In most cases it has a simple cause that can be dealt with easily. However, in a small number of cases it can be a symptom of a life-threatening condition; therefore, it requires a thorough and skilled assessment to determine which category it falls into.

> **Refer to:** *Aide-memoire: Patient Assessment, Neurological System, pages 34–35.*

Specific questions

Time:
- When/onset
- New/changes in pattern
- Frequency
- Pattern
- Duration
- Why seeking help now?

Character:
- Nature and quality
- Site and spread
- Nausea/vomiting, visual disturbance, photophobia, neurological signs and symptoms

Cause:
- Predisposing factors and/or triggers
- Aggravating or alleviating factors
- FH

Response:
- Medicines used (type, dose, frequency, timing)
- Effect on patient (go to bed, continue with day)?

Health between attacks:
- Complete recovery or lingering symptoms
- Any anxieties and concerns?

Headache *continued*

	Cause	Features	Management
Acute new headache	Suspected meningitis	Fever, photophobia, rash	**IV/IM Benzyl penicillin** Rapid transport to hospital
	Encephalitis	Fever, confusion, ↓ LOC	Rapid transport to hospital
	Sub-arachnoid haemorrhage (SAH)	'Thunder-clap' onset, stiff neck, vomiting	Rapid transport to hospital
	Head injury	Bruising/injury, ↓ LOC, intermittent lucid periods, amnesia	**Consider transport to NRSH depending on severity/review**
	Sinusitis	Tender over sinuses ± Hx upper respiratory tract infection	Refer to GP
	Dental caries	Facial pain ± tenderness	Refer to dentist
	Tropical illness	Hx recent foreign travel, fever	Transport to hospital
Acute recurrent headache	Migraine	Aura, visual disturbance, nausea/vomiting, triggers	Refer to GP

			NSAID (Specialist Paramedic (SP) and above)
	headache		
	Trigeminal neuralgia	Intense stabbing pain lasting seconds in trigeminal nerve path	**Refer to GP**
	Glaucoma	Red eyes, haloes, ↓ visual acuity, abnormal pupils	**Refer to GP or ophthalmology (depending on grade)**
Sub-acute headache	Temporal (giant cell) arteritis	>50 years, scalp tenderness, rarely ↓ visual acuity	**Refer to GP**
Chronic headache	Tension-type headache	Band around head, stress, low mood	**Avoid codeine Liaise with GP**
	Cervicogenic headache	Bi/unilateral, band from neck to forehead, scalp tenderness	**Refer to GP**
	Medication overuse	Rebound headache on stopping medication. Take detailed OTC DH	**Refer to GP**
	Raised ICP (e.g., chronic subdural bleed)	Worse on waking/sneezing, neurological signs, ↑ BP, vomiting, Hx of minor head	**Rapid transport to hospital**

RED FLAG SIGNS – *Crescendo headache. Unfamiliar headaches. Migraineurs are at risk from serious intracranial events – blood pressure must be checked. Any headache that is persistent or associated with LOC or altered behaviour is significant*

SP PC | SP CC | PARA | TECH | Q/SAP

Hip Pain (Mobilising after Fall)

Falls are a major cause of disability and the leading cause of mortality resulting from injury in people over 75 years of age in the UK (Scuffham and Chaplin, 2002). Furthermore, more than 400,000 older people in England attend A&E departments following an accident, while up to 14,000 people die annually in the UK as a result of an osteoporotic hip fracture (National Service Framework for Older People, 2001). It is clear that falling has an impact on quality of life, health and healthcare costs (NICE, 2005).

> **Refer to:** *Aide-memoire: Cardiac Synocope and Falls, page 8. and Abbey Pain Score pages 2–3.*

Management plan

Consider the following
- Hx of degenerative bone disease
- Multiple falls/Hx of trauma
- Taking bisphosphonates ± warfarin
- Acute onset of pain
- Living alone
- Hx of cancer

YES → Analgesia

↓

Falls referral

↓

Transfer to A&E (Great Yarmouth Area refer to NOF referral pathway)

↓

Assessment
- No deformity
- Normal level of activity
- Normal ROM
- Haemodynamically stable
- No distracting injuries
- Able to weight bear
- Rule out pelvic injury
- *SPECIALIST PARAMEDIC (SP) and above:* urinalysis normal

NO → Falls referral

YES

↓

Refer to DOS section for any falls schemes in your local area

←

- Falls referral completed ± referral to falls team (or GP if such services do not exist) for follow-up on the same day
- Bed rest
- Analgesia advice
- *SPECIALIST PARAMEDIC (SP) and above:* Issue analgesia as appropriate under relevant PGD

Safety net – advise patient to seek help if condition worsens, either GP or 999.

Q/SAP

TECH

PARA

SP CC

SP PC

389

Syringe Drivers

A syringe driver is a small, lightweight machine approximately 6 × 3 inches (21 × 10 cm) in size, which is battery operated.

It is designed to give medication, in liquid form, over a 24-hour period through a small needle, which is inserted just under the skin.

The syringe, which contains the medicines, is secured in place by a small strap on the syringe driver. There is a thin piece of tubing about 1 m long, which has a small needle on the end of it. This needle is secured into the skin with a clear dressing.

The syringe driver is portable and can be concealed in clothing or a holster, which is usually provided. Alternatively, it can be placed discreetly under a patient's pillow if they are spending more time in bed.

The use of a syringe driver allows a continuous subcutaneous infusion of medication to be delivered to the patient for symptom control.

Indications for use

- persistent nausea and vomiting
- dysphasia
- patient too weak to take oral medication
- oral, throat or oesophageal lesions/severe infection
- reduced level of consciousness or severely restless patient
- impaired absorption of oral medication

- intestinal obstruction
- poor symptom control, e.g., pain/nausea
- rectal route inappropriate

Advantages
- avoids the need for injections every four hours
- provides stable plasma levels of analgesics/medication that may be required for current symptom management
- patients can retain mobility and independence

Commonly used syringe drivers in palliative care
The McKinley T34 model is calibrated in millilitres/hour, rather than millimetres. This is a digital driver that allows a designated amount of fluid to be delivered over a 24-hour period (one day).

How to temporarily stop the infusion
The infusion should not be stopped temporarily – it is not normal practice and should only be done in exceptional circumstances. The procedure should not be used for priming a second line.

Press 'STOP', disable the keypad lock and press and hold the 'ON/OFF' button. Do not remove the syringe from the pump.

Resuming the infusion
- Check that the prescription, syringe label and patient details match, to ensure that this is the correct syringe for this patient.
- Reconnect the line to the syringe on the pump if it has been disconnected.

- Press and hold the 'ON' button until a beep is heard. The screen will request confirmation of the syringe size and syringe brand – press 'YES' to confirm.

Table 2 Reasons for the alarms to sound.

LCD display	Alarm type	Possible cause	Action
Occlusion or syringe empty: • check line and syringe • press 'YES' to confirm	Audible and visual alarm	Patient cannula/line blocked, kinked Infusion has finished	Remove occlusion and restart Flush/change cannula as per local policy End of program, switch pump off
Syringe displaced: • check line and syringe • press 'YES' to confirm	Audible and visual alarm Intermittent beep	Syringe has been removed or displaced	Check and confirm syringe is seated correctly and resume infusion Syringe flanges need to be in the vertical position at all times
Pump paused too long Press 'YES' to confirm	Audible and visual alarm Intermittent beep	Prepare to change battery and resume infusion	Start infusion, continue programming or switch off

Problem with the infusion

When the McKinley T34 pump detects a problem (Table 2) four things occur:

- the infusion stops
- an audible alarm is activated

Near end	Audible and visual alarm Intermittent beep	15 minutes from end of infusion	Prepare to change syringe or switch off
End program	Audible and visual alarm Intermittent beep	Infusion complete	Pump will alarm. Press 'YES' to confirm end of program and 'OFF' to switch pump off
Low battery	Visual alarm	Battery is almost depleted (30 minutes left)	Prepare to change battery and resume infusion
End battery	Visual alarm	Battery is depleted	Change battery and resume infusion

- a message appears on the display screen indicating the cause of the alarm
- turns RED

Other syringes used

The Graseby MS16 (blue) syringe driver allows a designated amount of fluid to be delivered in millimetres over a 60-minute period.

The Graseby MS26 (green) syringe driver allows a designated amount of fluid to be delivered in millimetres over a 24-hour period.

Changing the battery

- Remove the battery cover and take out the old battery.
- Insert the new battery. A low-pitched alarm will sound if the battery is inserted correctly. This will fade after 10 seconds. Replace the battery cover.
- Start the driver again by pressing the white 'START/TEST' button. The yellow light will start flashing.

Alarms

The driver will give an audible alarm lasting about 15 seconds when:

- A battery is put in.
- When the 'START/TEST' button is held down for longer than five seconds.
- When the syringe is empty.
- When the driver has stopped. This may be because the infusion line is blocked or trapped,

or the site of the needle is swollen, inflamed or hardened, or the needle/cannula has become dislodged.

The indicator lamp will stop flashing when:
* The driver has stopped and is switched off.
* When the battery needs replacing.

When encountering a patient who has both a syringe driver and a medical emergency, consider that it may not always be the syringe driver that is the problem.

Starting the infusion

Press the 'START' button. You will hear a whirring noise from the pump. This is the motor turning and it will continue to happen every few minutes. The yellow light on the front of the driver will be flashing.

Stopping the infusion

There is no 'ON/OFF' switch on the driver. To stop the infusion the battery can be removed. To restart the driver you will need to reinsert the battery and push the 'START' button again.

ECA

Q/SAP

TECH

PARA

SP CC

SP PC

4

Equipment

Digital Radio: Sepura Airwave Terminal with GPS

Removable antenna

Emergency button

Navi-knob

LED

Telephone earpiece

On/off mode button

Radio microphone

PTT (Press to talk)

Ear piece port

LCD screen

Navigation keys

Green call and confirm key

Red end call and cancel key

12-key alpha numeric keypad and softkeys

AIRWAVE

Telephone microphone

Functions:

Switch On & Off:

On – Press & release mode button

– Enter PIN

– Press Green Button

Off – Press and hold Mode Button until terminal displays 'Switching Off'

Caution – Handset locks after three incorrect PIN entries

Changing Talk Group:

– Press Mode Button

– Type new Talkgroup number, or rotate Navi-knob until T/G is found

– Press PTT or just leave until green tick is shown as accepted T/G

Change Talk Group only if advised to by HEOC or during a Major Incident and instructed to by Silver or HEOC

GATEWAY MODE AND SETTINGS

Vehicle radio:

Should automatically set when ignition off

When in run lock manually turn on, by press and hold 5

To revert to TMO normal mode, press and hold 4

ACA

ECA

Q/SAP

TECH

PARA

SP CC

SP PC

Handsets:
When the need arises, handsets must be manually placed in and out of Gateway mode

On handheld, press soft key No 6

Return to normal TMO radio mode simply press soft key No 4
(You must always ensure that during normal business and good covereage, the handset is always in normal TMO mode)

Receiving Calls:
Most calls are point-to-point (i.e. one-to-one).

Radio vibrates, bleeps & displays 'Individual Call'

– Press PTT, pause momentarily then speak to accept call
– Identify yourself using call sign, then release PTT

Contacting HEOC routinely via RQS (Request to Speak):
– Press and hold soft key 1
– Check "Delivered RQ Speech" is displayed

If not, press the 1 key again until it is displayed.
– Wait for HEOC to call you back by individual Call
(Your request is queued, so HEOC may not respond immediately)

– Receive call a described above

Contacting HEOC with Priority Message, (NOT CREW IN DANGER):

– Press and hold the # Key
– Check 'Delivered Priority RQS' is displayed

Your request is queued but at a higher priority so HEOC should respond immediately

– Receive call as described above

Batteries:

– **Fully charged** batteries should last 12 hours
– Change your battery at start of shift and ensure you have spares on the vehicle charge units
– Put spare battery in charger (metal contacts to rear)
– Check that charger indicator light comes on

Radio Signal Low/no signal indication

– LES flashes quickly 4 × red continuously
– Audible tone repeated every 60 seconds
– Check signal-strength scale (right of screen)

Radio operates best at shoulder height – carry on clip if possible. If no handset signal but vehicle set working, switch handset to Gateway mode.

CAUTION: Emergency button not functional if no signal

ACA

ECA

Q/SAP

TECH

PARA

SP CC

SP PC

EMERGENCY Button for when staff in danger only

– Press and hold Emergency button for 2 seconds
– State your location and circumstances if possible
– Clear by pressing RED button

Hot Keys:

1. RQS (Request to speak)
2. TX Inhibit on. (Press again TX Inhibit off)
3. Crew acknowledge SDA message
4. TMO Normal use mode
5. Vehicle set only to Gateway mode (if not automatic)
6. Handset to Gateway / DMO Mode
7. Omniguard Activate / Deactivate
8. Invert Display
9. Display Size
*. Keylock
#. Priority RTS
0. This Help Text

Point-to-point calling:

From the home screen dial the ISSI number 825XXXX

Ensure the radio symbol is displayed, if not scroll up/down once

Press PTT to dial and use the handset like a radio, releasing the PTT between messages

NB 10 seconds of inactivity will end the point-to-point call and return the handset back to trunked (normal) mode (Group Call)

To dial a pre-programmed phone number:
From the home screen press the right or left arrow key to access the terminal's phone book

Scroll left/right to desired group e.g. "Alert" ".PPCI"

Scroll down to enter the group and select desired contact e.g. "Norfolk & Norwich"

Press green key twice to dial and start the call

Handset works like a conventional phone

Red key ends the call but also takes you to main screen if stuck at any time.

Fault Reporting
All Digital faults should be reported to HEOC DM only, (see Contact Us on rear of Z-Card).

Aerials, broken batteries, radio clips and Navi-knobs can be replaced at the HEOCs where logistically possible.

Your radio handsets must be worn at all times whilst on duty, and secured away on vehicle when not being used.

Contact us

All radio faults major or minor must be reported verbally to HEOC Duty manager only. (Ensure basic radio checklist is followed prior to reporting any faults).

Further assistance can sought by EEAST Regional Airwave manager on 01603 422708 / 07834 249872

Refer to: *Operational Instructions: Operational Instructions: 126 & 127 on EAST 24 for further information*

Refer to: *Aide-memoire: Call Catergories: for the description of the radio display for each call category, pages 5-6.*

Creation and Completion of an ePCR using the Panasonic Toughbook

Logging on to the ePCR system

1. Select the **ePCR** button on the Windows screen.
2. Enter the password.
3. 'Run daily maintenance tasks', click 'Yes'.
4. Always click 'OK' to 'Number of files cleaned'. This will help Siren to run more efficiently.
5. Select the Siren field 'User Application' icon.
6. Enter your call sign (see also below), vehicle base station and vehicle type.
7. Add 'System Users'.
8. Enter the 'User Name' and 'Password'.
9. Click 'OK'.

Correct call sign

The correct format for signing in is as follows:
N = Area (N = Norwich, E = Essex, B = Beds & Herts)
A = DSA
R = RRV
O = Officer Car
U = Urgent
DSA = NA, ..., so for 853, NA853 is used
RRV = NR, ..., so for 680, NR680 is used

In Peterborough, vehicles 949, 952, 954, 978 and 981 will always use the NU prefix.

In Essex, vehicles 330, 356, 364, 370, 373 and 384 will always use the EU prefix.

ECA

Q/SAP

TECH

PARA

SP CC

SP PC

CAD pull

1. Click 'New' to begin a new ePCR.
2. Select the 'Incident Number' field.
3. Enter the four-digit 'Incident Number' to the job reference to pull the CAD information.

Unable to pull down CAD details?

1. Is your call sign entered correctly (see above)?
2. The incident number entered by the crew must be a four-digit number – use preceding zeros if necessary.
3. Check the date is correct for the incident. If you start a new ePCR after 00:00 hours and the job started before this then the CAD reference will have yesterday's date. You will therefore need to input the CAD Incident Number in full.
4. Have you got a mobile network signal?
   If the right 'ball' is constantly red then you are not connected. Try: Window → Minimise and double click on 'EASTAMB'. This should reconnect you. If this does not work, you are out of range and will have to wait until a signal is found – however, you can still complete the rest of the ePCR, and it will go up to the data centre when the connection is re-established.

Entering data into the ePCR

Use the **Incident** button to enter the incident date/time, details, outcomes, vehicle/crew and call type.
This should be populated from the CAD pull/push function, but if this is

not available (e.g., connectivity problems), you will need to manually enter them into the ePCR.

Give response outcomes and destination if 'Transported' is selected as an outcome. *Change destination if you are re-routed to a different hospital.*

 Use the **ID** button to enter the patient's name, DOB, address and GP practice. Add next of kin if the information is available. Access 'Chief' and 'Secondary' complaints from this tab.

 Use the **ABCD** button to record the primary survey information:
- General:
  - primary survey summary
  - AVPU patient position found
  - alcohol/drugs, use Indicators
- (A) airway/C-spine
- (B) breathing
- (C) circulation
- (D) disability
- FAST test.

ECA

Q/SAP

TECH

PARA

SP CC

SP PC

Use the **History** button to enter:

- symptoms
- PMH
- drug history
- allergies.

Use the **Vitals** button to enter a minimum of two sets of observations (if applicable). Enter values as pertinent to the patient condition and incident for:

- pulse
- blood pressure
- pain score
- BM.

Use the **Physical Exam** button to record the general examination results that specifically relate to the presenting complaint. Use the 'Area Specific' tab to enter, e.g., rash, pallor, pain, bruising, etc. Use the 'Extended System' tab for a more in-depth examination.

The **Treatment** button provides access to:

- 'Treatment' – choose treatments and/or drugs.
- 'Reassess' – secondary assessment of the patient.
- 'Summary' – check to make sure your interventions are in the correct order and time stamped.

The **Care Plan** button provides access to:

- 'Record Clinical Impression' – mandatory.
- 'Free Text Area' – to complete care-plan notes.

In the 'CAD Reconciliation' box (top right, next to the connection lights), a red number or question mark indicates any differences between CAD and the data entered manually. Click into the box and reconcile differences as necessary. A green tick signifies complete reconciliation.

Review your ePCR Report

Click on the **Review** button. Select 'Review Report' and the completed ePCR will be displayed.

Finalising the ePCR

Click 'Finalise' at the top of the screen to finalise the record. Once finalised you will be unable to make any further changes to the ePCR.

Records can be viewed via a laptop or PC using Webviewer. For this you will need a Smartcard.

Finalising locks the record down and you will not be able to make changes to it. You cannot finalise the record if the following mandatory fields are not completed:

- Incident Date/Time (**Incident** button).
- Incident Number (**Incident** button).
- Incident Location (**Incident** button).
- Incident Destination (**Incident** button →
  'Outcomes' tab).
- Outcomes (**Incident** button → 'Outcomes' tab).
- Crew Signature (**File** → 'Sign' tab → 'Crew' tab).
- Check you have completed all the mandatory
  fields by clicking on the **File** button at the top
  left corner of the screen.
- Click on **Required fields**. Any outstanding
  fields will be shown. Return to record and
  complete as appropriate (you can
  Minimise/Restore the mandatory field
  checking results and then **Refresh** .
- Click the **File** button at the top left corner of
  the screen.

How to start a T2T

1. Ensure the 'Incident Date/Time', 'Incident
   Number' and 'Crew Signature' sections are
   completed.
2. The only mandatory field is your signature
   (**File** → 'Sign').
3. Go to Patient List screen (**File** → 'Patient List'.
4. Highlight your patient and click 'Transfer
   Control'.
5. Ensure the selected TB is within range (within 10
   metres).
6. Enter the four-digit numeric PIN, and enter your
   name in the "sent by" field.

How to receive a T2T

1. The 'Transfer Package' box appears. Enter the four-digit numeric PIN.
2. Select 'View Details', 'Accept', 'OK'.
3. The record will now be in your 'Patient List'; highlight the record and click 'Open'.

End of shift – delete all ePCRs

You must delete all completed ePCRs from the Toughbook at the end of a shift.

Records can only be deleted by the crew who created the record. You can check the number under the connectivity balls to see if there are any data left to synchronise.

Deleting an ePCR or all ePCRs

1. From the **File** menu on the top left-hand corner of the screen, select 'Patient List'.
2. Click 'Delete all'.
3. Select your login from the screen display and click 'OK'.
4. Enter your 'Password' and click 'OK'.
5. Select 'Reason for Deletion', click 'Delete All'.
6. Click 'Yes' to continue.
7. To delete *individual* records, select 'Delete Selected'.
8. Select record, and then select 'Delete Selected' and follow steps 2, 3 and 4 again.
9. Your selected records will now be deleted from the Toughbook.

Closedown ePCR and Toughbook

1. Once you have deleted the ePCRs on the Toughbook, select 'Exit Siren' to close the application and ensure you and your crew are not assigned to the next patient record.
2. Then close down the Toughbook completely by selecting:
   'Start – Turn Off, Computer – Turn Off'.
3. Your patient-care records will not be lost, even though you might be deleting them before you have received a signal, because when the Toughbook next connects, the records will be updated to the data centre.

What do I do if there is a problem with the Toughbook or an ePCR?

If you have a problem with a Toughbook or ePCR then contact your DOM. If they cannot fix the problem, they should e-mail or call the IT Service Desk and log the problem (itservicedesk@eastamb.nhs.uk or call 08456 012509), providing contact details, base station and brief information on the problem, etc. The IT Service Desk acts as the Trust's 'SPOC' for all Toughbook- and ePCR-related issues.

NMI Rotating King RIPS Mk2

Ensure that you have received the appropriate training.

Detailed Instructions for the operation of this equipment can be found in the vehicle.

King RIPS Mk2 in the wheelchair-user mode. *(Note: this is shown here in a semi-rotated position, which is not suitable for wheelchair attachment.)*

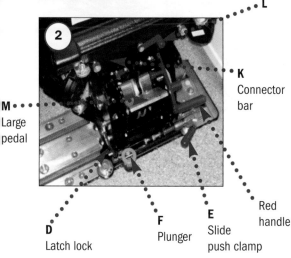

L

K
Connector bar

M
Large pedal

D
Latch lock

F
Plunger

E
Slide push clamp

Red handle

ACA

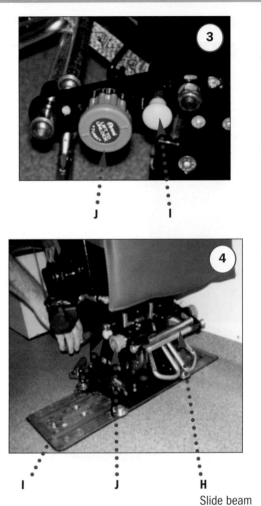

J   I

I   J   H

Slide beam

Figures 2–4

For descriptions of D, E, F, H, I, J K, L and M, see the following text.

When not in use, the Rotating King RIPS Mk2 should be stored on the vehicle in a front-facing locked position, in either the wheelchair-ready mode or the standard seat mode.

Note: King RIPS Mk2 cannot be locked securely in the sideways position, which should be adopted only when allowing a wheelchair-user room to pass.

Operation 1: Moving the King RIPS Mk2 aside to let a wheelchair user pass

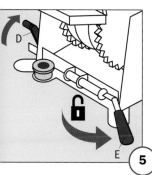

To unlock, lift up latch lock **D** and hold it up while unclamping **E** by pulling it away from the base to its furthest point.

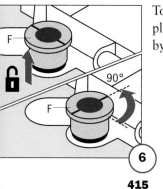

To rotate the seat, lift plunger **F** and rotate by 90 degrees.

ACA

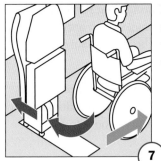

Rotate and slide the seat base to the side, so the wheelchair user can now pass the seat.

(7)

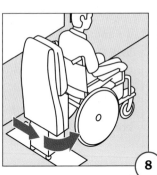

Slide and rotate the seat to align with the back of the wheelchair.

(8)

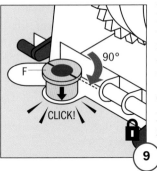

Now relock the seat. First, make sure it is facing forwards, and then rotate plunger **F** by 90 degrees until it drops down. This prevents the seat from rotating.

(9)

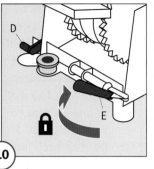

To lock the seat and prevent it from sliding, push clamp **E** towards the base to lock it. **D** will automatically drop down into position. The seat should not be moveable.

Operation 2: Preparing the flexi beam to meet the wheelchair

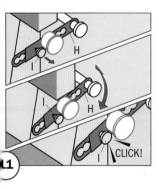

To adjust flexi beam **H** in order to angle it up or down to receive the wheelchair, pull plunger **I**. While holding plunger **I**, raise and lower **H** to the preferred angle, and then let go of **I**. **I** should snap in to lock the angle. (You may have to alter the angle of the beam to the closest point. **I** will snap in.) Repeat the procedure on the other side of the seat base.

ACA

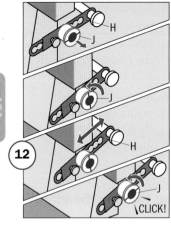

12

To alter the length of flexi beam **H**, pull out plunger **J** and rotate 90 degrees. Slide beam **H** to the required length, and then turn **J** so the marks line up with the length of the beam. **J** should click back into place to lock; if it does not, then adjust the length of **H** slightly until it does.

Repeat the procedure on the other side of the seat base (see *Figures 3* and *13*).

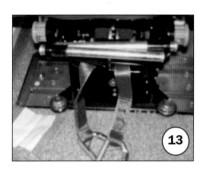

13

The flexi beam bars will slide to the appropriate position to meet the wheelchair frame. Repeat the procedure on the other side of the seat (*see Figure 15*).

(14)

ACA

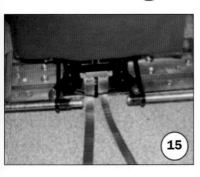

(15)

Operation 3: Securing the wheelchair and user

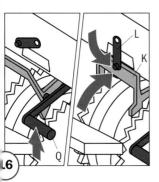

To release the webbing, lift up the red handle **Q**, which will lift up connector bar **K**. Push **K** forwards as far as possible and hold it while rotating **L** down to keep **K** off the ratchet drums.

419

ACA

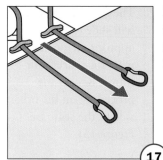

Pull the webbings to their full extent from the front of the seat base.

(17)

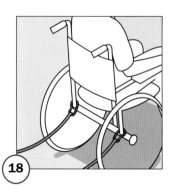

(18)

Attach the karabiners to the rear of the wheelchair frame as low as possible on the manufacturer's recommended points.

Caution: under no circumstances attach the karabiners to the front of the wheelchair!

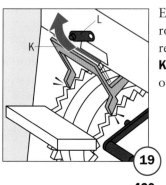

L

K

(19)

Engage the webbing by rotating **L** upwards to release **K**. Make sure **K**'s dogs are engaged on the drum teeth.

420

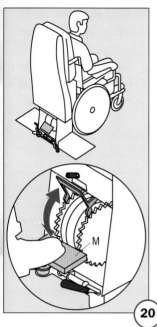

Operate the large pedal **M** in an up-and-down motion to ratchet in the wheelchair until it fits snugly against the seat back and the flexi beams.

It is advisable to use the wheelchair handles during this process to guide it as it reverses.

ACA

(20)

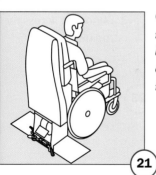

Caution: there must be no forwards or backwards movement of the wheelchair once it has been secured.

(21)

421

Secure the passenger using the two all-age inertia belts. Take one belt and insert it into the buckle. Repeat this procedure using the other all-age inertia belt, fix it into the buckle on the other side of the seat.
Note: it is acceptable practice to use one all-age inertia belt if thought appropriate.

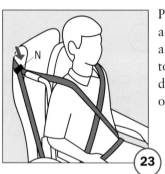

Position the age adjuster **N** (on both all-age adjuster belts) to ensure the webbing does not cut across the occupant's neck.

Operation 4: Releasing the wheelchair and user.

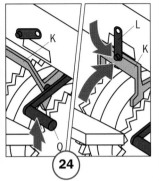

Detach the user from the all-age belts. To release the webbing from tension, lift up the red handle **Q**, which will lift up the connecter bar **K**. Now, using your hand, push connecter bar **K** as far as it will go and rotate the red arm **L** down to hold it in place.

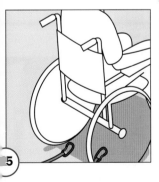

Extend the webbing out to their full extent from the front of the wheelchair base. Detach the karabiners from the rear of the wheelchair frame.

ACA

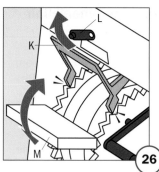

Engage the webbing by rotating **L** upwards to release **K**. Then retract the webbing by pumping the foot pedal **M**.

(26)

Procedures to convert the King RIPS Mk2 from the standard seat mode to the wheelchair mode and reverse the process

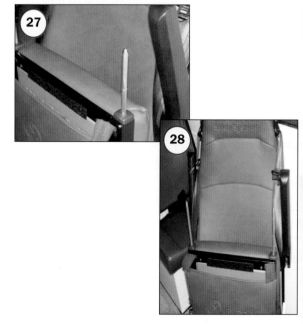

Procedure 1: Converting the King RIPS Mk2 from the standard seat mode into the wheelchair-user mode by setting up the seat back

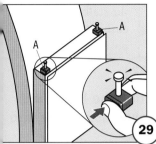

Squeeze **A** to get the extension stalks to pop up.

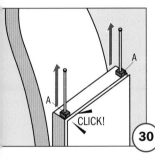

Keep squeezing **A** and slowly pull the stalks up until they click into the second groove and stay in position.

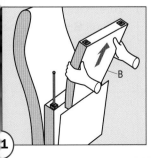

Remove the extension cushion **B** from the elastic pouch.

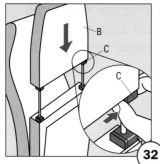

Align the holes in the bottom of cushion **B** with the stalks, squeeze **B** (located on one side) to pop onto the stalks and push cushion **B** down into position.

32

Procedure 2: Converting the King RIPS Mk2 from the wheelchair-user mode into the standard seat mode

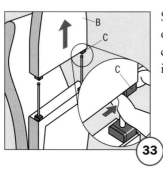

Squeeze **C** at one side of the extension cushion **B** and hold it in while lifting **B** off.

33

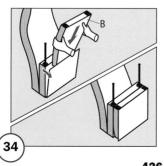

Store extension cushion **B** in the elastic pouch at the front of the seat squab.

34

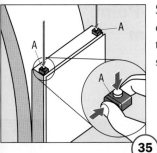

Squeeze **A** and push down the stalks until they are flush with the seat squab.

ACA

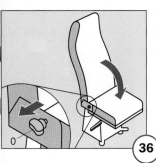

To turn it into a seat, pull out plunger **O** and lower seat squab at the same time.

Armstrong, M. (2011). NMI Rotating King RIPS Mk2. Standard Operating Procedure. x(x), 1–12.

The Unwin Four-Point Tie-Down System

'Three-finger space' for patient comfort

Buckle for black belt

Black 'belly' patient safety belt

Red 'shoulder' patient safety belt

Locking clip

Double-inertia reel housing

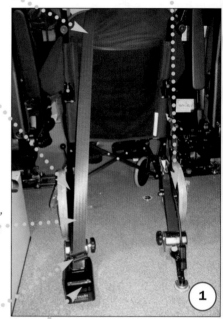

Slot

Floor stud (one of eight)

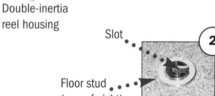

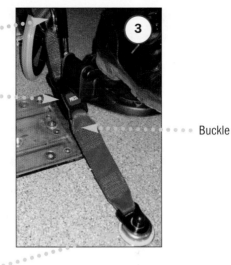

D-ring

Tongue

Buckle

Slide over
stud and
rotate

ACA

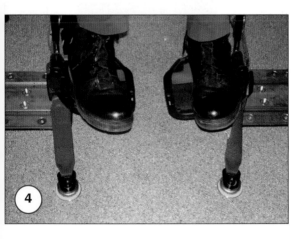

429

ACA

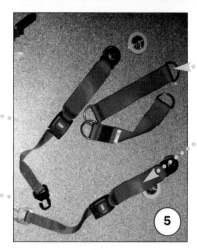

Buckle

Tongue

D-ring

Front tie

5

6

'BLACK' adjusting knob

Locking clip

A: Double-inertia reel-belt housing (to be positioned on the left-hand side to the rear of the wheelchair)

'BLACK' adjusting knob

'YELLOW' button

B: Inertia belt receiving module (to be positioned on the right-hand side to the rear of the wheelchair)

Karabiner

Buckle for insertion of the black belt tongue

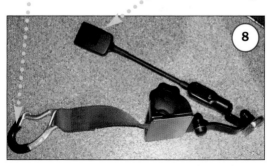

431

Please see the *Figures 1–8* on the previous pages to identify the components of the system referred to in the text below. The wheelchair ties operate to secure the wheelchair, whereas the black and red inertia belts are designed to restrain the patient.

Important information

The four-point tie-down system should only be used to secure specialist wheelchairs for which the King RIPS Mk2 system is unsuitable or inappropriate (e.g., where the fore and aft dimensions of the wheelchair are too large for the King RIPS Mk2 deployment area).

The four-point system must never be considered as the 'quick option' alternative.

In terms of safety grading, the rear folding seats on the ambulance are classified as Grade A, whereas the King RIPS is Grade B and the four-point system is Grade C.

Positioning the wheelchair
- Position the wheelchair so that the front of the chair is approximately 10–20 cm behind the front floor-attachment studs (see *Figures 1* and *5*). The choice of studs to be used is discussed later.
- Locate the front ties to the appropriate floor-attachment stud. Slide the receptor end of the front tie over the slotted floor stud and rotate to secure it (*see Figure 3*).

Securing the wheelchair to the ambulance

- Place the front ties around suitable (possibly labelled) rigid attachment points on the wheelchair, using the tongue and buckle (see *Figures 3* and *4*).
- If a greater length of front tie is required, then the D-rings should be employed (see *Figure 5*).
- Pull the wheelchair backwards to take up the slack in the front ties (see *Figure 4*).
- Apply the wheelchair breaks.
- Attach the rear tie and restraining belt modules to the appropriate floor-attachment studs. The steeper the angle of the restraining belts, the better the chair will be secured (see *Figures 6* and *7*).
- The rear module that houses the red and black inertia belts with tongue ends labelled **A** in *Figure 6* should be positioned to the left-hand side behind the wheelchair as you look at it. The rear module that houses the inertia belt buckle labelled **B** in *Figure 7* should be positioned on the right-hand side behind the wheelchair as you look at it. This means that the adjusting knobs on each rear tie module face inwards towards each other – the preferred placement position (see *Figures 6* and *7*).
- In turn, press the 'YELLOW' button on each rear tie-down module and fully pull out the webbing straps with the attached karabiners.
- Attach each karabiner to an appropriate rigid attachment point (possibly labelled) on the rear of the wheelchair. The higher this attachment

point is located, the more secure the wheelchair will be.

- In turn, press the 'YELLOW' buttons to tighten the webbing belts automatically. Wind the 'BLACK' adjusting knobs on the side of the rear tie module to apply maximum tension to the webbing belts. *The steeper the angle of the belts to the floor, the greater the securing efficiency.*

Restraining the patient to the wheelchair

- The Unwin four-point wheelchair tie-down system employs two patient-restraining belts coloured black and red and located within the double inertia reel housing (see *Figures 6* and *7*).
- Fully extend the black restraining belt and place it around the patient's waist so that its tongue may engage into the buckle of the opposite rear restraining floor unit (see *Figure 8*). This belt should be positioned across the patient's iliac crest (bony part of pelvis) to offer maximum restraint (see *Figures 1* and *8*).
- Fully extend the red restraining belt and place it over the patient's left shoulder while locating the tongue of the red belt in a buckle holder attached near the end of the deployed black belt. *The tongue of the red belt will not locate in the buckle found on the rear restraining floor unit, which is designed to receive the tongue of the black belt.*
- To ensure patient comfort, place three of your fingers under the red belt where it passes over the patient's left shoulder. With your fingers still

relieving some belt pressure off the patient's shoulder, secure the locking clip at the bottom of the red belt (near the reel housing – see *Figures 1* and *6*) to maintain the reduced pressure tightness in the belt. Now remove your fingers. *When applying both the black and red restraining belts, ensure patient comfort and dignity during the placement process.*

- Recheck that the wheelchair is safely secured and that the restraining straps are comfortable for the patient.
- Reverse the above procedures to release the patient and wheelchair.

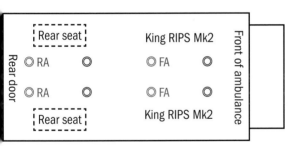

RA = preferred rear attachment stud position;
FA = preferred front attachment stud position.

(**9**) Choice of floor attachment studs.

IMPORTANT NOTICE

Please ensure that when carrying out the above procedures you 'risk assess' each manoeuvre to ensure the safety of yourself and your patient.

5

Pathways

Acute Inter-hospital Transfers

Step one

Hospitals

When the attending medical staff consider that a particular patient may need to be transferred, however tentative that thought is, the hospital staff *must* convey this possibility to the Ambulance Health and Emergency Operations Centre (HEOC).

This telephone will be answered as soon as possible, but if there is a delay please appreciate that HEOC staff may be busy on the radio system. The hospital will inform HEOC that there is a patient in 'hospital X' who may require a 'Critical Patient Transfer'. At this stage it is not essential to give a pick-up time, but a rough idea is helpful to the ambulance Dispatcher. Whether a clinical escort will be travelling and what skill level of the ambulance crew is required needs to be established as early as possible. Additionally, the HEOC needs to know if a transfer trolley or other specialist equipment is to be used, which might have a direct bearing on the type of ambulance that is dispatched to the call.

Ambulance

1. Populate the urgent-call screen in the normal manner, marking the problem/nature field with 'U Transfer'.

2. The destination field will be marked 'TBC'.
3. The request pick-up time will be four hours from the time of booking to the next quarter hour.

Rationale

If Step One is followed the ambulance Dispatcher will have forewarning and be able to make plans to ensure that ambulance cover can be maintained and the ambulance resources deployed appropriately.

Hospital staff need to understand the skill levels and abilities of ambulance staff and not just assume the need for a paramedic, particularly as ambulance provision is changing.

Step two

Hospitals

Once a bed is available in the receiving hospital and the patient is being prepared for transfer, the hospital staff should telephone the Ambulance HEOC. They should inform the Dispatcher that the 'Critical Patient Transfer' is ready. They should tell HEOC the pick-up point and the destination hospital. The hospital should let HEOC know when the patient will be ready. At particularly busy times it might take 20–30 minutes for a particular type of ambulance to be available, but in most situations a nearby ambulance will be dispatched immediately.

Whenever possible, give HEOC up to 30 minutes. In life-threatening emergencies an ambulance will be dispatched immediately.

In more urgent or emergency situations, then shorter times may be appropriate and the ambulance Dispatcher will try and oblige. The travel to the hospital will be undertaken at normal road speed and not under emergency driving conditions.

Although the ambulance is dispatched directly to the hospital, if on the way to the hospital a community-based life-threatening emergency (Red 1 or Red 2) requesting ambulance assistance arises and this vehicle is close by, then it will be diverted to the emergency call and a second ambulance will be dispatched to the hospital. Other 999 calls (Green 1, 2, 3 and 4) will not cause the vehicle to be diverted.

Ambulance

1. The problem/nature field is upgraded to 'U Blue light transfer'.
2. The destination field is completed.
3. The request pick-up time is given a realistic journey time plus one hour.

Rationale

By alerting HEOC to the possible need to move a patient, the ambulance Dispatcher can begin to plan that movement from the point of views of both staff and vehicle. All variations will be considered by the Dispatcher.

The second call requesting the transfer should be made as the final patient preparations are being made, recognising that the ambulance service may be stretched and so, whenever possible, giving the Dispatcher about 20–30 minutes warning of the readiness to move is appreciated.

Although the Dispatcher will try not to divert the ambulance, if there is a life-threatening call in the community it will take precedence over the call to the patient in the hospital. In these situations the patient in the community presents a greater risk than the patient in the hospital. For other 999 calls the risks are reversed and the ambulance will proceed to the hospital.

Ambulances responding to hospital requests will travel under normal road driving conditions to the discharging hospital to reduce any potential risks to both the public and the staff. If the transfer has been deemed to be life-threatening, emergency driving will be utilised.

It is essential that hospital staff recognise the skills of ambulance technicians and paramedics and request the appropriate staffing level. Patients who require clinical support during the journey will require a hospital clinical escort. Other patients may be transferred supported by ambulance staff only.

ACA

ECA

Q/SAP

TECH

PARA

SP CC

SP PC

Recognising the needs of the patient early on can be very helpful to planning the vehicle which is to be assigned to the transfer. As a result of the changes in ambulance staffing, paramedics are often in the community acting as single responders and ambulances are staffed by ambulance technicians. The future developments in staffing levels on front-line ambulances may further change the situation as Emergency Care Assistant roles become clearer.

Step three

Transferring hospital

The ambulance will be dispatched to the transferring hospital to arrive at or near to the agreed time. It is recognised that for both ambulance and hospital it can be problematic to be absolute or certain of time; problems can arise with, for example, other emergencies occurring in the community or in the preparation of the patient. A degree of flexibility and tolerance is required.

However, if after arrival at the hospital there is a delay in preparation of the patient of 30 minutes, then the ambulance may be redirected if there is other outstanding work in the community.

If the ambulance had to be diverted and another ambulance is not available, then after 30 minutes HEOC will upgrade the call within the ambulance vehicle deployment.

Critical care inter-hospital transfers

Patient admitted who may need to be transferred to
another hospital for critical care purposes

Recognition of possible transfer

Hospital to telephone the HEOC to alert them of the
possible transfer

Receiving hospital agree to transfer and the patient
is prepared for transport

Second confirmatory telephone call to HEOC to
set-up transfer process and to agree a pick up time

Arrival of ambulance at the hospital and transfer of
the patient into the ambulance

ACA

ECA

Q/SAP

TECH

PARA

SP CC

SP PC

If the transferring hospital has recognised a life-threatening emergency, the responding ambulance will not be diverted.

Between hospitals

Once the patient is safely transferred into the ambulance, together with all the necessary paperwork, the transfer between hospitals is undertaken. The speed of the transfer is agreed between the ambulance staff and the medical staff responsible for the patient. The ambulance will, where appropriate, travel under 'Blue Light' emergency conditions in line with the current Operational Policy.

If a clinical escort is not to accompany the patient, then it is essential that the ambulance staff are briefed on how to deal with any emergency problem that might arise during the journey, including resuscitation.

The receiving hospital

The patient is transferred into the care of the medical staff at the receiving hospital and a handover is undertaken.

Staff who have acted as an escort and equipment from the transferring hospital are required to be returned to their own hospital. The Ambulance trust will endeavour to undertake this, but because of vehicle movement and deployment, the parent trust may be required to provide alternative transport.

Stand down

If, after alerting HEOC, the discharging hospital decides not to transfer the patient, they should contact HEOC and inform them so that the Dispatcher is fully aware and knows that the transfer is no longer taking place and the vehicle planning and movement of vehicles can follow the ambulance deployment plans.

ACA

ECA

Q/SAP

TECH

PARA

SP CC

SP PC

Interim Bariatric Pathway for Front-line Staff

Inclusion criteria

Any patient that because of their size exceeds the capability of front-line resources on scene to move them safely.

CFR
ACA
ECA
Q/SAP
TECH
PARA
SP CC
SP PC

Is the patient time critical?	• Advise Clinical Co-ordinator. Begin a Dynamic Risk Assessment (DRA) of risks facing the patient and staff. Highlight findings to the co-ordinator. • Request DOM to the scene. • Consider support from Critical Care Desk, and Fire & Rescue Service to assist with extrication. (The patient will likely exceed the capability of the air ambulance to transport.) • If the patient cannot be transported safely on a Trust ambulance, request a Bariatric PAS/VAS ambulance; request ETA.
Does the patient have any clinical features that could deteriorate or are they in pain (post-analgesia?)	• Request DOM to the scene, advise clinical co-ordinator. • Request bariatric PAS/VAS; confirm the ETA. • If extrication required, request a fire officer to assist in scene assessment.
Can the patient be rebooked as an urgent admission? (Paramedic crew only.)	• Complete patient report form. • Advise the clinical co-ordinator and request a PAS/VAS bariatric crew; advise patient of ETA. • Leave the patient with advice to re-call 999 if anything gets worse.

For support from Critical Care, BASICS and HART contact the Critical Care Desk. Channel 202 or 01245 444496

Interim Bariatric Pathway for Clinical Co-ordinators

Inclusion criteria

A request for support from a Trust resource for any patient that because of their size exceeds the capability of front-line resources to move them safely.

Is the patient time critical?

- Dispatch DOM to the scene.
- Consider support from Critical Care Desk and from Fire Service to assist (i.e., with additional staffing).
- Locate and dispatch the nearest appropriate bariatric support ambulance; relay ETA to crew.
- Monitor on-scene times and ensure liaison and support with DOM regarding additional/specialist resources.
- Notify the receiving hospital at the earliest opportunity to allow them to assemble resources and staff.

Does the patient have any clinical features that could deteriorate or are they in pain (post-analgesia?)

- Dispatch DOM to the scene, and request bariatric PAS/VAS; relay ETA to crew.
- If extrication is likely to be difficult, request attendance of fire officer.
- Monitor on-scene times and ensure liaison and support with DOM regarding additional/specialist resources.

Can the patient be rebooked as an urgent admission?

- Advise the locality DOM and request a PAS/VAS bariatric crew (see approved list) and relay ETA.
- Pass to bariatric crew any pertinent information from the crew regarding extrication.

For support from Critical Care, BASICS and HART contact the Critical Care Desk. Channel 202 or 01245 444496

CFR

ACA

ECA

Q/S/P

TECH

PARA

SP CC

SP PC

Interim Bariatric Pathway
for Duty Operational Managers

Inclusion criteria

A request for support from a Trust resource for any patient that because of their size exceeds the capability of front-line resources to move them safely.

Is the patient time critical?

- Consider support from the Critical Care Desk.
- Consider the attendance of Fire Service to assist with extrication. Consider HART if believed they will be able to assist.
- Ensure that a bariatric ambulance is en route and establish ETA.
- Ensure dynamic risk assessment is completed. If significant risks are present, ensure a log is completed to include a written risk assessment.
- Ensure the receiving hospital is alerted by the clinical co-ordinator at the earliest opportunity to allow the hospital to assemble equipment and staff.

- Consider additional support from the Critical Care Desk or HART.
- If extrication is likely to be challenging request a Fire Officer to the scene.
- Complete dynamic risk assessment; if any delays or risks are deemed significant ensure that a log is completed.
- Ensure a bariatric ambulance is en route and establish ETA.
- Attempt to minimise delays to Trust resources on scene; consider releasing front-line resources.
- Contact the receiving hospital at the earliest opportunity to allow them to assemble equipment and staff.

Does the patient have any clinical features that could deteriorate or are they in pain (post-analgesia?)

- Consider the need to attend the scene to ensure the safe transfer of the patient to hospital.
- Contact the receiving hospital at the earliest opportunity to ensure staff and equipment can be assembled.
- Provide support in the event of a challenging extrication.
- Ensure liaison between the private provider and Clinical Co-ordinator, and the receiving hospital.

Can the patient be rebooked as an urgent admission?

449

Interim Bariatric Pathway for Dispatch Managers

CFR

ACA

ECA

Q/SAP

TECH

PARA

SP CC

SP PC

Inclusion criteria

A request for support from a Trust resource for any patient that because of their size exceeds the capability of front-line resources to safely move them.

Is the patient time critical?

- Dispatch the nearest available DOM.
- Flag incident to Clinical Co-ordinator.
- Locate the nearest appropriate bariatric ambulance.
- Request additional support from the Fire Service and Critical Care Desk.
- Consider requesting HART to support front-line operations (i.e., additional staffing).
- Obtain scene information from crew and add to CAD notes.
- Pass ETA of bariatric ambulance to DOM/crew.

Does the patient have any clinical features that could deteriorate or are they in pain (post-analgesia?)

- Dispatch the nearest available DOM.
- Flag incident to Clinical Co-ordinator.
- Locate the nearest appropriate bariatric ambulance.
- Prompt the crew to consider support from the Fire Officer and Critical Care Desk.
- Consider requesting HART to support front-line operations.
- Obtain scene information from crew and add to CAD notes.
- Pass ETA of bariatric ambulance to DOM.

Can the patient be rebooked as an urgent admission?

- Contact locality DOM and make them aware of the incident.
- Locate the nearest appropriate bariatric ambulance and flag this to the Clinical Co-ordination Desk.
- Obtain scene information from crew and add this to the CAD notes.

450

Location of approved front-line bariatric providers

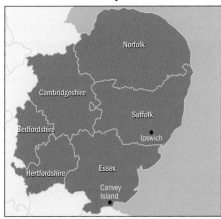

Additional considerations for staff

- Ensure at all times that the risks staff take are proportionate to the possible benefits to the patient.
- Be mindful of the load limits of the floors and stairs in houses; if any doubt exists as to the structural integrity, request a fire officer to attend and assist.
- Consider requesting (via the fire service) the use of a USAR team, rope rescue team or aerial platform. Advice as to the suitability of these resources can be obtained from the HART supervisor in the absence of a fire officer.
- If the need arises to move the patient using a rope or ladder system inform, the HART supervisor and have SWAH trained staff dispatched at the earliest opportunity to minimise risk exposure for untrained staff.

- Consider the value of a hot debrief to highlight opportunities for learning, and ensure that any risks are raised through the Datix process.
- The responsibility for declaring the condition of the patient rests solely with the lead clinician. Any dispute with any other agency in this regard must be referred back to the Clinical Co-ordinator.

Prior to requesting a bariatric ambulance please identify the following:

- Are any medical interventions likely during transport?
- Does the patient know their weight? If so, when and how was this measured?
- A brief description of the location of the patient (e.g., in a house, adapted property, care/nursing home, public place).
- Is the patient on the ground floor? If not, is there a lift or staircase?
- The current mobility of the patient (are they able to transfer to a wheelchair or stretcher?)
- Are doorways of conventional size or width? (The width of a standard door is 32 inches, which is the approximate width of a trust stretcher.)
- Are there any steps or door thresholds to pass over?
- Is there a slope or restricted egress outside the property?
- Is equipment and/or a suitably trained individual on the scene to assist in moving the patient (e.g., a carer with a hoist)?

Chronic Obstructive Pulmonary Disease Admission Avoidance (Suffolk, Norfolk, Central, North East Essex only)

Introduction

An exacerbation of COPD is defined as a sustained worsening of symptoms, which is acute in onset and worse than the normal day-to-day variations, and a hospital admission would be considered if the admission-avoidance service was not available.

This section provides approved and safe clinical guidance to allow ambulance personnel to refer patients with an acute exacerbation of COPD to this service after an emergency response. This will prevent an unnecessary hospital admission for the patient, and hospital delays for the ambulance service.

A full copy of this guidance is available from your local DOM or COM.

Background

Three service providers offer cover across Suffolk, Norfolk and parts of Essex (*Table 1*).

These services are provided within the NICE Guidelines *Chronic Obstructive Pulmonary Disease: Management of chronic obstructive pulmonary disease in adults in primary and secondary care* (CG012) and a locally produced guidance document for GPs (soon to be updated).

The responsibility of any patient referred to the COPD Services remains with their GP.

Table 1   Service providers

Name	Hours of operation	Contact number	Area covered
Suffolk COPD Services	08.00–18.30 Mon to Fri 08.00–16.00 weekends/ Christmas, 365 days a year	West Suffolk Hospital switchboard (01284) 713000, then request COPD services, extension 2705	Person registered with GP in East and West Suffolk area (including Thetford, call if unsure)
Central Essex Community Services (CECS)	09.00–17.00 Mon to Fri and Bank Holidays 09.00–15.00 weekends (t.b.c.)	Dedicated mobile number, 07867797821	Person registered with GP in Mid Essex (please call if unsure)
ACE COPD	09.00–17.00 Mon to Fri	Dedicated mobile number, 07932087741	Person registered with a GP in North East Essex (please call if unsure)

Referral to COPD Services

Ambulance crews will be issued with a clear protocol that details the assessment and referral criteria (see Appendices 1–3). These are based on a locally produced guidance document for GPs (soon to be reviewed) and JRCALC guidelines (2006).

The ambulance crew will differentiate an exacerbation of asthma from COPD. Those with an exacerbation of asthma will be excluded from this pathway. Temporary residents are also excluded from this pathway.

Assessment
- On attending the call, the ambulance crew will assess the patient. If any life-threatening signs are present (in accordance with guidelines set by JRCALC) or the patient does not improve with treatment, then the patient will be transported immediately to the nearest suitable receiving hospital.
- If, on taking the patient's past medical history, it is apparent they have had previous admissions to an Intensive Care Unit, are currently using non-invasive ventilation systems at home, or have Type II respiratory failure (see Appendix 5), they are not suitable for the Admission Avoidance Service and should be transported to hospital for assessment.
- The service is starting to provide oxygen-alert cards to patients with known CO_2 retention (see Appendix 6). These provide recommendations for the use of controlled oxygen.

ECA

Q/SAP

TECH

PARA

SP CC

SP PC

- Patients known to all of the service providers will have a self-management system, which for all areas is the British Lung Foundation Airway Code, and will have been given advice on how to manage an exacerbation. Under this programme, they can self-initiate a course of steroids and antibiotics (either kept at home or automatically prescribed by a GP or Nurse Practitioner).

> Patients already under the COPD teams may also be part of the 'Red Card Scheme'. They will have their notes at home with them for as long as they are under the care of the COPD, which clearly state they are part of the scheme. The red card advises the patient to contact the team during the day, and to dial 999 if they become unwell overnight. If these patients do dial 999 they must automatically be transported to Accident and Emergency along with their notes.

- For those patients who call and are not under the care of any of the COPD services, a referral can still be made (*Table 2*).

Table 2 Referral to COPD services

Name	Process of referral
Suffolk COPD Services	Contact service on an individual basis
CECS and ACE COPD Services	Patients who are not known to the COPD service and who meet the following criteria: • over 35 years • diagnosed COPD by spirometry (may need confirmation from GP) • smoking history • chronic cough • regular sputum production • frequent winter chest infections • wheeze Patients who meet these criteria can be referred to the COPD service and a decision will be made to accept the referral or to follow the patient up if admitted to hospital

- Patients who do not fulfil the Admission Avoidance Service criteria will be discharged from the ambulance service as per the normal procedure.
- The crew should complete a full assessment of the patient including a full set of observations (*a 12-lead ECG must be performed*). If treatment is required this should be initiated in line with JRCALC guidelines. Post-treatment, at least two sets of observations should be taken 15 minutes apart to assess its effectiveness.

- The NICE Guidelines *Chronic Obstructive Pulmonary Disease: Management of chronic obstructive pulmonary disease in adults in primary and secondary care* (CG012) do not include peak flow readings as an assessment tool of acute COPD exacerbation (NICE, 2004). Although the peak-flow assessment is not used for the assessment of the suitability for referral to the admission avoidance service or hospital, it should still be performed by ambulance crews to gauge the effectiveness of any nebulised treatment given.

- If, after treatment, the patient is stable with SpO_2 >92%, the flowchart can be used to assess their suitability for referral to the Admission Avoidance Service. If the SpO_2 <92% and the patient appears clinically stable, the attending crew can contact the service for advice to see if the patient is still suitable for referral.

- Prior to calling, the service crews are to complete their Patient Care Record (PCR) and the Referral Form (see Appendix 5). The Referral Form has been designed so that the information requested matches the questions asked by the Admission Avoidance Service when the referral is made. Phones should be manned at all times, but if for any reason the call cannot be taken, the referring crew will leave an answer phone message on the office answer phone on weekdays (or call the dedicated mobile numbers for the Essex services) and the mobile phone at weekends leaving their name and contact details, and their call will be returned within 30 minutes.

- Once the patient has been accepted by a particular service, the crew will record this on the notes section of the PCR along with an ETA for a team member's arrival (within a four-hour limit). The patient should be advised that if their condition deteriorates prior to the arrival of the Admission Avoidance Service, they should redial 999.

- As part of the referral process, the crew should complete the Crew Referral/Feedback Form (Appendix 6).

- It has been agreed with the service that if a patient feels that their condition has deteriorated prior to the arrival of the team member, they are to dial 999 again. If the crew is again able to stabilise the patient on the scene, they are to contact the service for advice to ensure that the patient is still able to remain at home and await the arrival of the team member.

- If the patient is unable to remain at home (owing to either their deterioration or if, after the above process, the admission avoidance team advise to transport the patient to hospital), then the transporting crew will be responsible for completing and faxing the feedback form.

Appendix 1   Referral Chart for Suffolk COPD Service

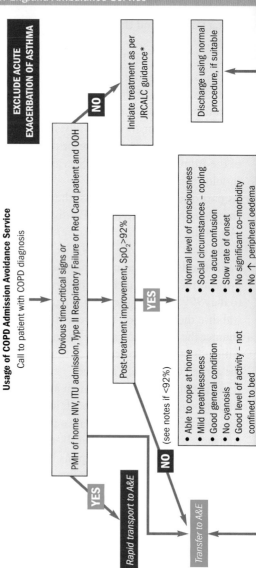

Usage of COPD Admission Avoidance Service

Call to patient with COPD diagnosis

Obvious time-critical signs or
PMH of home NIV, ITU admission, Type II Respiratory Failure or Red Card patient and OOH

YES → *Rapid transport to A&E*

**EXCLUDE ACUTE
EXACERBATION OF ASTHMA**

NO → Initiate treatment as per JRCALC guidance*

Post-treatment improvement, SpO₂ >92%

NO
(see notes if <92%)

Transfer to A&E

YES

- Able to cope at home
- Mild breathlessness
- Good general condition
- No cyanosis
- Good level of activity – not confined to bed

- Normal level of consciousness
- Social circumstances – coping
- No acute confusion
- Slow rate of onset
- No significant co-morbidity
- No ↑ peripheral oedema

Discharge using normal procedure, if suitable

ECA   Q/SAP   TECH   PARA   SP CC   SP PC

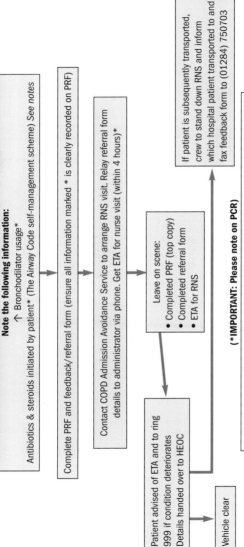

Note the following information:

↑ Bronchodilator usage*

Antibiotics & steroids initiated by patient* (The Airway Code self-management scheme) *See notes*

↓

Complete PRF and feedback/referral form (ensure all information marked * is clearly recorded on PRF)

↓

Contact COPD Admission Avoidance Service to arrange RNS visit. Relay referral form details to administrator via phone. Get ETA for nurse visit (within 4 hours)*

↓

Leave on scene:
- Completed PRF (top copy)
- Completed referral form
- ETA for RNS

(*IMPORTANT: Please note on PCR)

Patient advised of ETA and to ring 999 if condition deteriorates
Details handed over to HEOC

↓

Vehicle clear

If patient is subsequently transported, crew to stand down RNS and inform which hospital patient transported to and fax feedback form to (01284) 750703

COPD Services RNS to inform GP that patient referred to service and relay the outcome

Abbreviations: Non-Invasive Ventilation (NIV), Respiratory Nurse Specialist (RNS), Expected Time of Arrival (ETA).

ECA

Q/SAP

TECH

PARA

SP CC

SP PC

461

Appendix 2 Referral Chart for CECS Service – COPD Admission Avoidance Flowchart

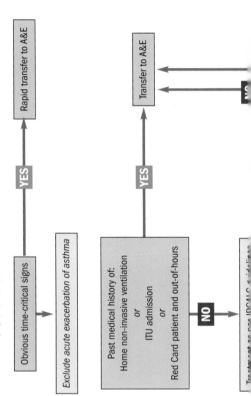

Obvious time-critical signs

YES → Rapid transfer to A&E

Exclude acute exacerbation of asthma

Past medical history of:
Home non-invasive ventilation
or
ITU admission
or
Red Card patient and out-of-hours

YES → Transfer to A&E

NO →

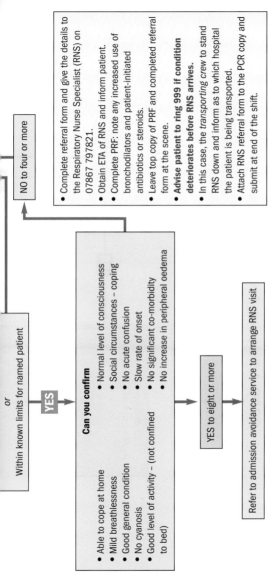

NO to four or more

- Complete referral form and give the details to the Respiratory Nurse Specialist (RNS) on 07867 797821.
- Obtain ETA of RNS and inform patient.
- Complete PRF: note any increased use of bronchodilators and patient-initiated antibiotics or steroids.
- Leave top copy of PRF and completed referral form at the scene.
- **Advise patient to ring 999 if condition deteriorates before RNS arrives.**
- In this case, the *transporting crew* to stand RNS down and inform as to which hospital the patient is being transported.
- Attach RNS referral form to the PCR copy and submit at end of the shift.

or

Within known limits for named patient

YES

Can you confirm

- Able to cope at home
- Mild breathlessness
- Good general condition
- No cyanosis
- Good level of activity – (not confined to bed)
- Normal level of consciousness
- Social circumstances – coping
- No acute confusion
- Slow rate of onset
- No significant co-morbidity
- No increase in peripheral oedema

YES to eight or more

Refer to admission avoidance service to arrange RNS visit

ECA

Q/SAP

TECH

PARA

SP CC

SP PC

463

Appendix 3   Referral Chart for ACE COPD Service only –
COPD Admission Avoidance Flowchart

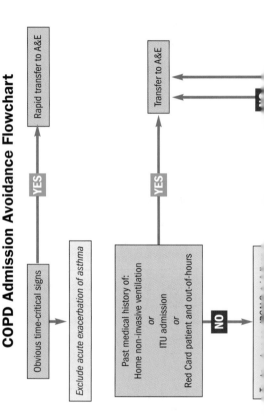

Obvious time-critical signs → **YES** → Rapid transfer to A&E

Exclude acute exacerbation of asthma

Past medical history of:
Home non-invasive ventilation
or
ITU admission
or
Red Card patient and out-of-hours

YES → Transfer to A&E

NO

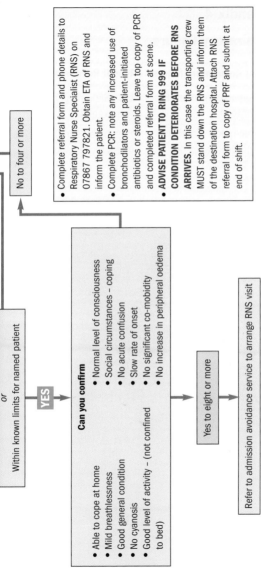

No to four or more

- Complete referral form and phone details to Respiratory Nurse Specialist (RNS) on 07867 797821. Obtain ETA of RNS and inform the patient.
- Complete PCR: note any increased use of bronchodilators and patient-initiated antibiotics or steroids. Leave top copy of PCR and completed referral form at scene.
- **ADVISE PATIENT TO RING 999 IF CONDITION DETERIORATES BEFORE RNS ARRIVES.** In this case the transporting crew MUST stand down the RNS and inform them of the destination hospital. Attach RNS referral form to copy of PRF and submit at end of shift.

or

Within known limits for named patient

YES

Can you confirm

- Able to cope at home
- Mild breathlessness
- Good general condition
- No cyanosis
- Good level of activity – (not confined to bed)
- Normal level of consciousness
- Social circumstances – coping
- No acute confusion
- Slow rate of onset
- No significant co-mobility
- No increase in peripheral oedema

Yes to eight or more

Refer to admission avoidance service to arrange RNS visit

ECA

Q/SAP

TECH

PARA

SP CC

SP PC

465

Appendix 4

Respiratory Failure

Type I Respiratory failure	Type II Respiratory failure
Low blood oxygen levels (hypoxaemia)	Low blood oxygen levels (hypoxaemia)
Normal or low blood carbon dioxide levels	High blood carbon dioxide levels (hypercapnia)

Appendix 5

Oxygen Alert Cards

Mid Essex CECS Services

OXYGEN ALERT CARD

Information for Emergency Medical Teams

I have COPD and have previously had type II Respiratory Failure with a raised CO_2 level on blood gas testing

DO **_NOT_** EXCEED OXYGEN SATURATION............%

This has been achieved by the use of .... % oxygen, ideally by Venturi Mask

>Use air compressor supplemented by nasal oxygen at a flow rate of 1-2 litres/min

Mid Essex

Central Essex Community Services

OXYGEN ALERT CARD

Notes for patient

Please carry this card with you at all times and show it to Ambulance Staff or A&E Department doctors

When you have an acute deterioration in your COPD (usually due to a chest infection), it is essential that you do not receive too much or too little oxygen. Too much oxygen can cause a rise in the level of Carbon Dioxide in your blood and this can make you drowsy and slow your breathing. Too little oxygen can also be dangerous for you.

The purpose of this card is to make sure that doctors and ambulance staff are aware of your special needs regarding oxygen therapy. Further details can be obtained from your medical records at:

Name: ....

Chest Consultant Dr: ....

Hospital Number: ....

Suffolk COPD Services

Oxygen Alert Card

Information for Emergency Medical Teams

I have got COPD and I have previously had type ii Respiratory Failure with a raised CO_2 level on blood gas testing. The results of blood gas tests done during previous exacerbations have indicated that the safest oxygen therapy in any case (pending blood gas results) is as follows:

Do not exceed Oxygen Saturation ....%
This has been achieved by the use of ....%
oxygen, ideally by Venturi Mask

- Use air compressor supplemented by nasal oxygen at a flow rate of 1–2 litres/min
- Limit oxygen-driven nebulisers to 6 minutes

West Suffolk Hospitals
NHS Trust **NHS**

With thanks to James Paget Healthcare Trust

Oxygen Alert Card

Notes for patient:

Please carry this card with you at all times and show it to Ambulance Staff or A&E Department doctors

When you have an acute deterioration in your COPD (usually due to a chest infection), it is essential that you do not receive too much or too little oxygen. Too much oxygen can cause a rise in the level of Carbon Dioxide in your blood and this can make you drowsy and slow your breathing. Too little oxygen can also be dangerous for you.

The purpose of this card is to make sure that doctors and ambulance staff are aware of your special needs regarding oxygen therapy. Further details can be obtained from your medical records at:

Name: ....

Chest Consultant Dr: ....

Hospital Number: ....

North Essex ACE Services

CFR

ACA

ECA

Q/SAP

TECH

PARA

SP CC

SP PC

COPD Oxygen Alert Card
FAO Ambulance Staff & Emergency Medical Teams

NHS
North East Essex
Services Provider

I have **COPD – use 28% *Venturi* mask** to administer oxygen initially*

I have **COPD and am at risk of type II respiratory failure** with a raised CO_2 level **– use 24% *Venturi* mask** to administer oxygen initially*

Oxygen therapy should aim to achieve:
Oxygen saturation of 88–92% by the use of controlled flow oxygen, ideally by *Venturi* mask as above

Nebulisers should be driven by compressed air and supplemental oxygen should be administered concurrently via nasal connulae to maintain oxygen saturation 88–92% e.g., 1–2 litres/min

North East Essex PCT
COPD Alert Card

Please show this card to the Ambulance staff or Emergency Department doctors.

The purpose of this card is to make sure that the doctor or ambulance team are made aware of your special needs regarding oxygen therapy.

When you have an acute deterioration in your COPD (usually due to a chest infection), it is essential that you do not receive too much or too little oxygen.

Appendix 6

Crew Referral/Feedback Form

Ambulance crew to complete

(*Should patient re-dial 999, subsequent crew to complete and fax back form for audit purposes if patient transported to hospital and RNS does not attend.)

Date: Time of arrival: CAD: PRF:

Crew names and vehicle telephone number:

Patient anonymised details

Ambulance service patient card record number:

Patient initials:

NHS no. (if known):

GP name, address and telephone no:

Any risks to attending RNS (access, pets, etc.):

---

*Patient transported prior to respiratory nurse arrival?:
Yes/No (please delete)
(If yes, please give reason why and hospital transported to):

Attending Respiratory Nurse to complete

Date: Time of arrival:

Patient's condition deteriorated on arrival?:   Yes/No (please delete)

Referral appropriate?:   Yes/No (please delete)

(If no, please give details below):

If matter requires urgent attention please contact the Duty Operations Manager on 07921 028 933

Patient outcome:

Any further comments/suggestions?:

Falls Register and Referrals

Introduction

Falls account for the largest proportion of workload for the East of England Ambulance Service. In 2010 the Trust committed, through one of its quality-account priorities, to contribute to reducing preventable falls. The Falls Register was set up to achieve this aim by storing the details of patients who have fallen.

The register can be accessed 24/7 to record the details of those who have fallen. The information is forwarded onto the patient's GP as part of their health history and to community services, where they exist.

It is recognised that up to a third of falls are preventable with the correct interventions. This scheme supports the agenda by proactively identifying those patients that may benefit from preventative measures.

Who is the scheme for?

The scheme is for patients across the East of England who are over the age of 65 years and who have fallen.

Entries to the register should be made for both patients who have been conveyed to hospital and those who have been treated at home.

Gaining consent

It is vital that patient consent is gained for personal information to be entered onto the register. The patient needs to understand that their information will be stored electronically and may be passed to other healthcare providers where it is felt that this would be beneficial to their care.

Explaining the register and the referral scheme

You need to explain the register to the patient to gain their consent. The following is a suggested template:

- We are all at risk of falling; however, falls in later life are more common and can lead to long-term disability, social isolation and a loss of confidence. We want to contribute to help stop people falling and we need this information to help us to do this. This is why we are keeping a Falls Register.
- All information is held securely and we will only share information with the patient's GP and other healthcare professionals who we believe can contribute to care.
- Not everyone will be contacted by healthcare professionals; this will be based on the provision of care in the area and the assessment undertaken by the ambulance service.
- If the patient has any concerns relating to falls they should contact their GP to discuss.

Process

To enter a patient onto the Falls Register, please telephone the single point of contact on *0845 602 6856* at any time of the day or night (this is the same as the safeguarding number).

Please notify the call handler that you wish to place the patient on the Falls Register. They will ask you the patient's personal details as well as the results of the Cryer and AMT-4 assessments and whether they have atrial fibrillation (AF) (*Table 1* on pages 474–475).

Atrial fibrillation

AF occurs when rapid, disorganised electrical signals in the atria depolarise small islets of atrial myocardium, rather than the atrium as a whole. This causes the atria to contract in a rapid, irregular and unco-ordinated fashion (fibrillation). As a result, blood pools in the atria and is not pumped effectively into the ventricles. This pooled blood can then lead to the formation of blood clots within the atria, which can in turn cause strokes if the clots are carried into the blood stream and lodge in the arteries of the brain. The function of the atria and ventricles is no longer co-ordinated and the atrial contribution to cardiac output is lost, which reduces cardiac output by up to 10–20%.

Why are we doing this?

AF can lead to a wide range of complications, including palpitations, syncope, angina, chronic heart failure, TIA, stroke and systemic arterial emboli. It is associated with a five-fold increase in the risk of stroke; about one-quarter of people who experience a stroke do so in AF.

AF is currently both under-recognised and undertreated. Within our region a significant

ECA

Q/SAP

TECH

PARA

SP CC

SP PC

Table 1 The Falls Register criteria

Cryer assessment	Abbreviated Mental Test 4 (AMT-4)	Does the patient have suspected AF?
A simple assessment tool to identify those likely to fall again.	A simple screening tool that comprises four questions and is used to identify cognitive impairment in older people; it is not a diagnostic tool.	All patients who have fallen should have a baseline set of observations taken. This should include palpation of the pulse. Where a pulse is found to be irregular, a 12-lead ECG should be taken.
Is there a history of a fall in the previous year?	What year are we in?	
Is the patient on four or more medications per day?	What do we call this place you are in?	

ECA

Q/SAP

TECH

PARA

SP CC

SP PC

Does the patient have a diagnosis of stroke or Parkinson's Disease?	How old are you?
	What is your date of birth?
Does the patient report any problems with their balance?	An incorrect answer to any of the four questions indicates cognitive impairment. If they answer all correctly, tell the call handler that AMT-4 is normal, anything else is reduced.
Does the patient need to use their arms to enable them to rise from a chair of knee height?	
Does the patient complain of blackouts or loss of consciousness?	

The characteristic findings of AF are an *irregularly irregular* QRS complex and the absence of recognisable P waves. There may be chaotic electrical activity before the QRS, which will vary in size and shape.

ECA

Q/SAP

TECH

PARA

SP CC

SP PC

number of patients arrive in hospital with an acute stroke who are known AF patients, but are not appropriately medicated.

ECG interpretation

The characteristic findings of AF are an irregularly irregular QRS complex and the absence of recognisable P waves. There may be chaotic electrical activity before the QRS, which will vary in size and shape (*Figure 1*).

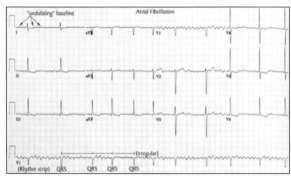

Figure 1 Characteristic ECG with AF

Referral

Patients who present with AF are in two categories:
- non-symptomatic
- symptomatic

Symptoms may include:
- altered mental status
- loss of consciousness
- hypotension
- chest pain

- ECG changes indicative of myocardial ischaemia or infarction
- dyspnoea
- palpitations
- syncope
- dizziness
- fatigue
- weakness
- hypoxia

Where the patient is symptomatic, they should be conveyed to hospital for further assessment. The Falls Register should still be completed.

Where the patient is asymptomatic, it may be appropriate for non-conveyance to hospital, depending on other factors associated with the fall and the clinical condition. This should be a clinical decision made in discussion with the patient.

Where non-conveyance is considered appropriate and with patient consent, the Falls Register should be completed by calling 0845 602 6856. They will ask about the presence of AF as a supplementary question.

The Falls Register system will automatically notify the GP that the patient has fallen and that AF is suspected from the ECG. The patient should be advised that the GP will be notified.

The ePCR/PCR should be completed as normal, with an ECG attached. A copy of the ECG that indicates suspected AF should be left with the patient for them to take to the GP.

ECA

Q/SAP

TECH

PARA

SP CC

SP PC

All GPs in the region are aware of the scheme and will assess the patient's records when deciding the course of action following the fall and potential AF recognition.

What if the patient has already been referred to the Register?

If this is a subsequent fall and the patient has previously been entered onto the Register, then call the Falls Register again so that a history of the falls is recorded.

Follow-up care

If a referral fax number is known for the PCT area that you are calling from, then the referral form (*Figure 1*) will be passed on.

This scheme is for follow-up care only, and may not result in a visit to the patient; if the patient requires immediate intervention, contact the GP or other healthcare providers by telephone to discuss.

Recording on the ePCR/PCR

Record on the ePCR/PCR that the 'patient consented to details being passed to the Falls Register'.

If the patient declines, record on the ePCR that the 'patient declined details being passed to the Falls Register'.

If you have further questions, contact your local Clinical Operations Manager.

Figure 1 The Falls Register and Referral Card

East of England Ambulance Service **NHS**
NHS Trust

Falls Register & Referral

Patient over the age of 65 who has fallen

Full assessment and treatment
Conveyance to hospital if required

Explain to patient purpose of register and gain consent

Call 0845 602 6856

Provide Personal Details and Clinical Details
(Name, Address, Telephone, Gender, Date of Birth)

Modified Cryer Risk Assessment Tool
1. Is there a history of any fall in the previous year?
2. Is the patient on four or more medications per day?
3. Does the patient report any problems with their balance?
4. Does the patient need to use their arms to enable them to rise from a chair of knee height?
5. Does the patient have a diagnosis of stroke or Parkinson's Disease?
6. Does the patient complain of blackouts or loss of consciousness?

Abbreviated Mental Test 4 (AMT=4)
1. What year are we in?
2. What do we call this place you are in?
3. How old are you?
4. What is your date of birth?
An incorrect answer to any of the four questions suggests cognitive impairment may be present.

ECA

Q/SAP

TECH

PARA

SP CC

SP PC

The Major Trauma Pathway (TTT)

Major trauma is a rare event, with about 700 major trauma patients across the East of England each year. As part of the rollout, it is important that everyone feel confident about managing seriously injured patients. The ambulance service always attends these patients and is usually first to the scene, so providing good, basic care on scene makes a fundamental difference to eventual patient survival and quality of life.

The other element is to understand the pathway and what needs to happen to a patient with major trauma. These are critically injured patients with unstable physiology, and so the natural instinct is to get the patient to the nearest hospital as soon as possible. However, evidence presented in the NCEPOD *Trauma – Who Cares?* report quite clearly demonstrates that the outcome for patients with an Injury Severity Score (ISS) of greater than 15 is better if they are taken immediately to a specialist major trauma centre (MTC). Calculating ISS is a retrospective process dependent on in-hospital diagnostics, and is not much use in a pre-hospital setting.

In the East of England, Cambridge University Hospital (Addenbrooke's) is the regional MTC. The Trauma Triage Tool (TTT), explains what to do on identifying a patient who is a major trauma candidate. Some patients in our region will be closer to another MTC, so you may be taking them to London or even to Oxford.

The pathway assumes that major trauma candidate patients will have the TTT applied and that the pathway will be followed. A small degree of over-triage is built in, but it is important not to take patients to the MTC who do not fulfil the major trauma criteria. In our region, the system is built as an 'inclusive' trauma system, which has improved trauma care for patients in local hospitals as well as providing a MTC.

Nearly all of our A&Es are designated as 'trauma units' and will work to a common set of standards that allows them to care for many patients with severe injuries. Over-triage will overwhelm Addenbrooke's and mean that patients are cared for far from home and away from their families when this is not necessary.

The system is set up to help local hospitals manage patients with an ISS <15 promptly and to a high standard. For instance, a patient with two compound fractured tibias would not go to the MTC but will be managed by the local hospital, possibly with advice from the MTC consultants. Some patients will require secondary transfer for specialist treatment after the initial admission to the nearest hospital, and arrangements ensure this is done quickly, so there is no need for 'unofficial' diverts. Patients with burns should be taken to the nearest hospital.

In addition to not over-triaging, it is important to remember that if a patient does fulfil the criteria for going to the MTC, then they are more likely to survive if they are taken there as quickly as possible. This may mean travelling with badly injured patients for up to 45 minutes to the nearest MTC. Again, follow the pathway given and you will receive advice and support to manage these difficult and stressful situations. A number of enhanced care teams and BASICS doctors are available and can be dispatched to provide support.

To find out more information about the pathway and TTT and what you need to do, see the local Trauma Champion or e-mail majortrauma@eastamb.nhs.uk.

Instructions for clinicians using the TTT

To allow EEAST clinicians to recognise consistently and objectively a candidate major trauma patient, and to ensure a consistent approach to patient disposition, the Trauma Network and EEAST created a TTT that is to be applied to all trauma patients.

The TTT identifies a candidate major trauma patient by looking at the patient's physiological and anatomical parameters. If any of these parameters is triggered, the clinician should consider this patient to trigger the TTT positively as a candidate major trauma patient.

The TTT is designed to accompany the patient's primary survey. Upon identifying a candidate major trauma patient, it is imperative that HEOC are informed at the earliest opportunity. This has two main functions: HEOC will be in a better position to ensure the incident is appropriately resourced to include the clinical grade, and HEOC can then also ensure that the East of England Trauma Network is aware of a major trauma candidate within the region, which allows forwards planning of patient flow and care throughout the network. EEAST staff should achieve a situation report (sitrep) within five minutes of identifying a candidate major trauma patient.

The trauma pathway supports hospital diverts where appropriate, with the aim of getting a candidate major trauma patient to a MTC. The TTT supports clinicians through the process of actively diverting to a MTC. If EEAST staff have a candidate major trauma patient and are within 45 minutes' transport time of a MTC with a patient whose airway, breathing and bleeding can be controlled, the patient should be transported to the MTC.

Pre-alert messages must always be provided for all candidate major trauma patients. With this in mind, the TTT standardises the pre-alert message format and uses ATMISTER to achieve this. Pre-alert messages should also be passed through a standard number. This number is for the Network Coordination Service (NCS, the control function of the East of England Trauma Network). By contacting the NCS, staff will be put through to any hospital destination that they are going to pass their pre-alert message to a clinician in the receiving MTC or trauma unit. EEAST staff must pre-alert the receiving MTC or trauma unit via the NCS (number is on the TTT). The pre-alert message should follow the ATMISTER format.

> **Refer to:** *Aide-memoire: ATMISTER, page 4, and Trauma Triage Tool, pages 48–49.*

Q/SAP

TECH

PARA

SP CC

SP PC

Primary Percutaneous Coronary Intervention

Background

Primary percutaneous coronary intervention (PPCI) for ST elevation myocardial infarction (STEMI) was implemented across the East of England (EoE) region with a phased approach in response to the findings of the NIAP final report (NIAP, 2008).

The EoE is served by four 24/7 PPCI Centres at Papworth, Norwich, Basildon (ECTC) and Harefield. Harefield has two linked part-time centres (Monday to Friday 08.30 to 16.30) at Watford and Stevenage (Lister Hospital). All centres have agreed to work to an agreed EoE protocol.

Patients eligible for PPCI are transferred to the nearest PPCI Centre, either from the community or from another hospital in the region using the East of England Ambulance Service NHS Trust (EEAST), which covers the EoE region. The PPCI Centre is activated by the ambulance crew and clinical advice available if required, from either the Clinical Advisor at EEAST or a PPCI Centre.

In addition to the PPCI Centres listed above, this document sets out the PPCI protocol for all acute hospital trusts in the East of England:
- Peterborough and Stamford Hospitals NHS Foundation Trust
- Hinchingbrooke Healthcare NHS Trust
- Papworth Hospital NHS Foundation Trust

Q/SAP

TECH

PARA

SP CC

SP PC

- Cambridge University Hospitals NHS Foundation Trust
- Queen Elizabeth Hospital King's Lynn NHS Trust
- Norfolk and Norwich University Hospital NHS Trust
- James Paget University Hospitals NHS Foundation Trust
- West Suffolk Hospital NHS Trust
- Ipswich Hospital NHS Trust
- Colchester Hospital University NHS Foundation Trust
- Mid Essex Hospital Services NHS Trust
- Southend University Hospital NHS Foundation Trust
- Basildon and Thurrock University Hospitals NHS Foundation Trust
- Princess Alexandra Hospitals NHS Trust
- East and North Hertfordshire NHS Trust
- West Hertfordshire Hospitals NHS Trust
- Luton and Dunstable Hospital NHS Foundation Trust
- Bedford Hospitals NHS Trust

PPCI eligibility criteria

Symptoms compatible with a STEMI <12 hours duration from maximum chest pain, and any of the following ECG criteria:

- ST segment elevation >1 mm in contiguous limb leads or >2 mm in contiguous chest leads.
- LBBB or paced rhythm if the clinical picture is acute myocardial infarction (MI).
- >1 mm ST depression with a dominant R wave in V1–V3 suggesting a posterior MI.

- >1 mm ST elevation in contiguous chest leads if the clinical picture is MI.
- Patients fully resuscitated from cardiac arrest with spontaneous respiration at the scene with ECG criteria for STEMI are eligible.

If a patient has no chest pain, but has symptoms and signs and an ECG that is compatible with a STEMI, then a transfer to a PPCI Centre should still be considered, based on the clinical diagnosis.

PPCI exclusion criteria
The exclusion criteria are:
- acute haemorrhage
- major trauma
- decreased consciousness level of uncertain cause (e.g., suspicion of intracranial event/head injury)
- resuscitated cardiac arrest at the scene, with diagnosis uncertain.

Patients with STEMI who are excluded should be transferred immediately to the nearest Emergency Department.

Management of a community PPCI referral by the ambulance service
If clinical signs and symptoms of STEMI suspected:
- obtain a 12-lead ECG as soon as possible
- examine and assess the patient in accordance with the pre-hospital ambulance assessment and checklist for PPCI (Appendix 1).

If STEMI is confirmed, administer:
- oxygen and analgesia as per ambulance service protocol

- aspirin 300 mg orally
- clopidogrel 600 mg orally.

If there is any doubt about the diagnosis or the suitability of the patient for transfer to the PPCI Centre, contact the Ambulance Trust Clinical Advisor (contact number 07753 950843) in the first instance or the PPCI Centre as advised.

Activation of PPCI Centre team
When they leave the scene, the ambulance crew transferring the patient (or ambulance control) is responsible for contacting the nearest PPCI Centre (Table 1) to activate the PPCI Centre team.

Table 1   PPCI Centres

Hospital	Contact No	Hours of service	Call taken by
Papworth	(01480) 364567	24/7	Nurse in charge of HDU
Basildon	(01268) 394184	24/7	PPCI co-ordinator
Stevenage (Lister)	(01438) 284668	Mon to Fri 08.30 to 16.30	Cardiac cath lab staff
Norwich	(01603) 646599	24/7	PPCI co-ordinator
Harefield	(01895) 824278	24/7	Switchboard staff
Watford	(01923) 436685	Mon to Fri 08.30 to 16.30	Lead Nurse, cath lab

Other PPCI Centres without an EoE protocol are given in Table 2.

Table 2   PPCI Centres without EoE protocol

Hospital	Contact No
Hammersmith	(0208) 3833870
Kettering	(01536) 491458

Ambulance transfer
- The relative/carer information sheets should be given to relatives where appropriate.
- The ambulance crew monitors the patient's condition and observations continuously on the journey to the PPCI Centre, noting any changes on the Patient Record File (PRF).
- On arrival, ambulance crews will provide the top copy of the PRF or the electronic patient record number, together with the checklist and ECG. All will be labelled with the patient's identity and the time. As an audit requirement, details of cardiac arrest or arrhythmia that required intervention in the ambulance must be noted at handover.
- In the event of a cardiac arrest in transit, it is policy for the ambulance to stop before commencing advanced cardiac life support.
- If the patient regains cardiac output and is spontaneously breathing, then they should continue to be transported to the PPCI Centre.
- If return of spontaneous circulation (ROSC) is achieved, but the patient is not able to maintain

their own airway and requires ventilatory support, then they should be transferred to the nearest Emergency Department and the PPCI Centre team should be informed by the ambulance service.

- If resuscitation is not successful, death must be confirmed by a doctor, and the patient must be taken to the nearest mortuary. In the event of death, the receiving hospital should be advised that they are to contact the family of the deceased.
- If the patient's condition deteriorates en route to a PPCI Centre, the crew may need to divert to the nearest Emergency Department. This must be recorded as a deactivation.
- The PPCI Centre team must be informed by the ambulance service.
- The reason for deactivation should be recorded by the PPCI Centre for audit purposes. According to the Ambulance Trust Clinical Instruction 104 (Feb 2011), the ambulance crew should report this using a Datix form.

Arrival at the PPCI Centre
Details for each PPCI Centre are given in Table 3.

The patient should be discussed with the greeting clinician and any additional patient requirements identified immediately (e.g., crash team support). Patients should be transferred with the ambulance crew's defibrillator attached, along with oxygen and emergency drugs from the ambulance.

- Where possible the ambulance crew will establish the next of kin contact numbers.
- The ambulance crew will accompany the patient into the hospital.
- Handover will be to the Cardiology SpR or Sister/Charge Nurse while transferring the patient to the cath lab or the HDU/CCU.

Table 3 Arrival at PPCI Centre

Hospital	Entrance	Met by
Papworth	PPCI entrance (signposted)	Duty cardiology SpR and SHO
Norwich	PPCI entrance through A&E	Cardiology SpR or charge nurse
Basildon (ECTC)	Dry Street ambulance bay	PPCI co-ordinator at ambulance doors
Harefield	Main entrance	Meet at door by team member
Watford	Acute Admissions Unit ambulance bay	Cardiologist at CCL Department
Stevenage (Lister)	PPCI Entrance adjacent to A&E	Consultant Cardiologist or Cardiac Nurse Specialist

Patient in cardiac arrest on arrival at PPCI Centre

- If, on arrival, the patient is in cardiac arrest, the crash team should be paged immediately on 2222 at all centres.
- *Table 4* details the procedures for each PPCI Centre.

Table 4 Procedures for cardiac arrest on arrival at the PPCI Centre

Hospital	Procedure for patient in cardiac arrest
Papworth	Crash call will be initiated by the cardiology SpR
Norwich	Urgent transfer to CCU for assessment/treatment
Basildon (ECTC)	The SpR will assess and establish additional requirements
Harefield	The patient is taken directly to the cath lab by the duty SpR and SHO
Watford	The patient is diverted to the A&E resuscitation room
Stevenage (Lister)	The patient is diverted to the A&E resuscitation room

Patient with non-cardiac medical emergency on arrival at PPCI Centre.

If, on arrival, the patient is having a non-cardiac emergency (e.g., GI bleed), the procedures in *Table 5* apply.

Restocking of clopidogrel
Before leaving, the ambulance crew should replenish their stocks of clopidogrel (except Watford/Stevenage and Harefield) and other replacement items as required according to local protocol.

Table 5 Procedures for a non-cardiac medical emergency on arrival at the PPCI Centre

Hospital	Procedure for patient with non-cardiac medical emergency
Papworth	After discussion with the on-call consultant the patient will be redirected to Hinchingbrooke or Addenbrooke's Hospital, as geographically appropriate
Norwich	The patient will be referred to the appropriate specialty within NNUH and later considered for repatriation to their local hospital, as appropriate
Basildon (ECTC)	The patient will be assessed by the cardiology team and an appropriate management plan made, which may include repatriation to the patient's local DGH as part of the plan
Harefield	The patient is diverted to either Hillingdon or Watford General Hospital
Watford	The patient will be diverted to A&E for further assessment
Stevenage (Lister)	The patient will be diverted to A&E for further assessment

Consent

Witnessed verbal consent for the angiogram and possible PPCI procedure must be taken in all instances. If appropriate (e.g., no sedation has been given to the patient), written consent can be taken.

In emergency/life-threatening situations where the patient is unable to consent, the procedure will be undertaken without consent in the best interests of the patient.

Inter-hospital transfer expected time of arrival notification

When they leave the scene, the ambulance crew transferring the patient (or ambulance control) is responsible for contacting the nearest PPCI Centre to activate the PPCI Centre team.

Appendix 1   Checklist for PPCI

East of England Ambulance Service **NHS**

NHS Trust

Assessment and Check List for PPCI

Patient Name _____

Date of Birth _____

Home Address _____

Date _____ Cad No. _____

IS PPCI INDICATED?

Onset of chest pain/symptoms typical of Acute Myocardial Infarction in the last 12 hours? and is there **one** of the following patterns on the 12-lead ECG:

(a) ST elevation 2mm or greater in 2 or more adjacent chest leads?		Y / N
OR (b) ST elevation 1mm or greater in 2 or more contiguous limb leads (there will usually be reciprocal ST depression in the other limb leads)?		Y / N
OR (c) RBBB with ST elevation in either of the 2 patterns above?		Y / N
OR (d) LBBB with 'classic' clinical picture of AMI (grey, clammy, central crushing chest pain with radiation to jaw/arms)?		Y / N
OR (e) Marked ST depression V1-3 and dominant R wave in V1 suggesting a Posterior MI (they will often have suspicious inferior ECG changes)?		Y / N

If the answer is YES then PPCI is indicated.
Now assess for absolute contraindications to PPCI

2 Is the patient actively bleeding e.g. haematemesis, malaena Y / N

3 Have cardiac arrest resuscitation attempts failed? Y / N

4 Has the patient been resuscitated from a cardiac arrest but the underlying diagnosis is uncertain? Y / N

If the answer to any of the above questions is YES then the patient is not suitable for PPCI and should be transferred to the nearest DGH A/E dept.

If the answers are all NO then go on to assess for relative contraindications

1 Does the history or ECG suggest pericarditis, e.g. ST elevation in all leads except AVR or pain worse on deep inspiration? Y / N

2 Has the patient been involved in an incident causing traumatic bodily injury (not CPR)? Y / N

3 Does the ECG show LBBB or paced rhythm without a clinical picture of AMI? Y / N

If the answer is NO to all contraindication questions then transfer for PPCI is indicated call your nearest PPCI centre: Papworth 01480 364567. Norwich 01603 646599, Harefield 01895 824278, Lister 01438 284668, Watford 01923 436685 or Basildon CTC 01268 394184 to arrange transfer. If the answer is NO to absolute contraindications but YES to any of the relative contra-indications telephone the Trust Clinical advisor on 07753 950843 to discuss management of this case. Also phone if you have any other concerns regarding the patients condition, ECG or any of the contraindications. Please send completed form with PRF and ECG to either Paul Murray (Norwich office) or Sarah Waite (Chelmsford office).

If the patient is to be transferred for PPCI administer Aspirin 300mgs and Clopidogrel 600mgs.

Clinician/Paramedic signature   Print name

SP PC   SP CC   PARA   TECH   Q/SAP

Appendix 2

East of England Ambulance NHS Trust PPCI Pathway

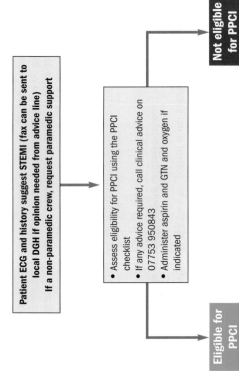

Patient ECG and history suggest STEMI (fax can be sent to local DGH if opinion needed from advice line)
If a non-paramedic crew, request paramedic support

- Assess eligibility for PPCI using the PPCI checklist
- If any advice required, call clinical advice on 07753 950843
- Administer aspirin and GTN and oxygen if indicated

Not eligible for PPCI

Eligible for PPCI

blue lights with pre-alert

- Administer *600 mg clopidogrel orally (paramedic only drug)*
- Blue light transfer with continuous cardiac and haemodynamic monitoring and adequate pain relief en route

Deliver patient to designated entrance at PPCI Centre – a member of the PPCI Centre team will meet you

Additional notes

- Non-paramedic crews can undertake these transfers, but should request paramedic support for the administration of opiates, clopidogrel and heparin. If cardiac arrest occurs during the transfer, stop and treat as per protocol.
- If ROSC and breathing spontaneously, continue transfer to PPCI Centre.
- If ROSC but requiring assisted ventilation (ET or LMA), then divert to nearest DGH.
- If no ROSC, go to nearest DGH or the PPCI Centre if it's closer.
- If have ABCD concerns during the transfer, divert to nearest DGH.
- If diverting from the PPCI Centre en route for any reason, contact them again (or get HEOC to do it), inform them about the deactivation and reason, and allow their team to stand down.
- Complete Datix.

Q/SAP

TECH

PARA

SP CC

SP PC

Appendix 3

Glossary

ACS	Acute Coronary Syndrome
BCIS	British Cardiac Intervention Society
CCL	Cardiac Catheter Laboratory

Single Point of Contact TIA Referral System

Many strokes are preventable; the effective early management of transient ischaemic attacks (TIAs) can reduce mortality and morbidity. The national stroke strategy provides clear direction on the development of stroke care and includes quality markers that relate to the timely referral to a specialist clinic for patients suffering TIA.

This instruction outlines the use of a single point of contact (SPOC) referral system so that ambulance clinicians can refer *low-risk* TIAs direct to specialist clinics without the need either to convey to hospital or to make a secondary assessment and gain referral from the patient's GP.

A low-risk TIA is when a patient has suffered a transient episode of focal neurological symptoms that have *fully resolved* and the $ABCD^2$ score is 3 or less. Any score above 3 indicates a high-risk TIA. *All* high-risk TIAs should be conveyed to hospital for further assessment.

Certain groups of patients are automatically considered high risk irrespective of the $ABCD^2$ score – e.g., patients who are on anticoagulant therapy (warfarin), or have atrial fibrillation, or if this is a second TIA episode within the previous seven days.

Assessment

On attending a suspected TIA, clinicians should undertake a full, comprehensive patient and neurological assessment that includes:

- FAST
- ABCD^2 score
- Full set of baseline observations and BM
- ECG

It is important to record a full set of observations and the time of symptom onset for all patients experiencing a suspected TIA. Blood-glucose measurement is vital, as hypoglycaemia can cause transient focal neurological symptoms (often a right hemiparesis) that mimic a TIA or stroke.

Identifying a TIA

The diagnosis of TIA relies on the recognition of clinical features associated with focal cerebral dysfunction. If the answer to all of the following questions is yes, the symptoms are most likely due to cerebral ischaemia or haemorrhage.

> **Refer to:** *Pathways: Stroke (Appendix 3), pages 519–530.*

Are the neurological symptoms focal?

Neurological symptoms can be divided into focal and non-focal symptoms. Focal neurological symptoms are caused by a disturbance in an identifiable area of the brain (e.g., unilateral weakness, unilateral sensory loss). Non-focal

Q/SAP

TECH

PARA

SP CC

SP PC

neurological symptoms do not suggest a TIA unless they are clearly accompanied by focal neurological symptoms.

Are the focal neurological symptoms negative?

The symptoms of a TIA are usually negative; they represent a loss of function (e.g., arm weakness, difficulty swallowing, loss of vision).

Was the onset of the focal neurological symptoms sudden?

The suddenness with which the neurological symptoms of a TIA develop indicates that they result from a vascular event.

Were the neurological symptoms maximal at onset?

The symptoms of a TIA are usually maximal (greatest) within the first few seconds of onset, rather than developing gradually.

What is the past medical history?

The patient's medical history must be obtained to establish whether focal neurological signs are new or old. For symptoms that are new, i.e., not pre-existing from a previous incident, it is important to establish when they began. If they have occurred before, it is important to establish when they previously occurred.

Referral

When a clinician has concluded that the patient has suffered a suspected and resolved low-risk TIA that is appropriate for referral, they should provide the patient with the TIA patient information leaflet (see Appendix 3) from the ambulance TIA pack (which is located on all emergency resources in the drug locker). The clinician should explain its content in a manner such that the patient fully understands all the advice and guidance. It is important to explain the referral process clearly, as outlined in this instruction, and obtain consent for referral.

If the patient meets all the criteria and consent has been obtained, clinicians should call 0845 602 6856 (available 24/7) to make a referral to the local hospital TIA clinic via the SPOC desk. The call taker will ask a series of questions to attain the information required for the referral form (see Appendix 2).

Once the referral has been accepted, the call centre will forward it to the local clinic who will contact the patient within the next three days to arrange a follow-up appointment. The call centre will also inform the patient's own GP.

Drug administration and supply

* In line with the guidelines (see Appendix 1), when symptoms have resolved fully, and if they are not contraindicated, clinicians should administer a bolus dose of 300 mg of aspirin to

the patient immediately. In addition, clinicians should leave a supply of 300 mg aspirin (which must be in its original box with the information leaflet included).

- The patient must be given instructions that they should take one 300 mg dose of aspirin *per day* starting the day after the first bolus dose is given by the clinician, and they should continue taking this until they attend their appointment at the TIA clinic, as outlined on the patient information leaflet.

- If the patient currently takes 300 mg, they should continue to do so until their clinic appointment; a bolus dose should not be administered and advice should be sought (see below).

- If the patient currently takes 75 mg of aspirin per day, the patient should be advised to continue taking their aspirin as normal until their clinic appointment. A bolus dose should not be administered and advice should be sought (see below).

Aspirin supply guidelines

In the event that a patient has contraindications that prevent them from taking aspirin, or advice is required, the local stroke team should be contacted. The team can be accessed via the relevant hospital switchboard. (If crews do not have the switchboard number then they should contact HEOC.) The team may suggest conveying the patient to A&E or they may advise that the patient is seen in clinic the

Q/SAP

TECH

PARA

SP CC

SP PC

next day. They may also advise the clinician to contact the patient's GP to request an appointment/home visit for review, with a view to prescribing an alternative antiplatelet medication. In the event that a GP appointment is arranged, this should not stop the referral being made. The GP should be informed that a referral has been made so that a duplicate referral is not made.

In the event that the TIA occurs out-of-hours and advice is required, then crews should contact the on-call stroke consultant at the hospital they are referring to. The consultant can be contacted via the relevant hospital switchboard.

Leaving at home

Following the full assessment, administration and supply of aspirin, acceptance of the referral, and with all aspects of care documented appropriately on the ePCR/PCR, low-risk TIA patients can be left at home. Clinicians should insure the patient has full capacity and understands all aspects of the advice given and of what their on-going care will involve. Patients should clearly understand that if any neurological symptoms present again prior to their clinic appointment then 999 *should be called immediately!*

In the event that any clinician has concerns or queries regarding the appropriateness of a patient referral, then the stroke team can be contacted for advice during normal working hours, and during OOH the on-call stroke consultant can be contacted. Where advice has been taken from specialists, clinicians should document this clearly and inform the call taker of the advice given.

On occasion, the call handler may question the clinician on contraindications; this is in no way a reflection of the clinician's ability, but it is a safety-net process to insure no patients are inappropriately left at home during the pilot scheme. Call handlers are required to identify red-flag situations that may mean a referral is inappropriate (see Appendix 4).

This instruction can be summarised in the TIA pathway card (see Appendix 5). Every member of staff should be issued with personal pocket-sized guidelines, and an A4-sized copy should be included in all TIA packs, along with a laminated copy of this instruction. This instruction is viewable on EAST24 and should be displayed on station clinical notice boards. Local COMs are fully aware of all aspects of this instruction and should be approached if clinicians have any questions or require any advice regarding this pathway.

Q/SAP

TECH

PARA

SP CC

SP PC

Appendix 1

TIA Aspirin Supply Guideline

Presentation
- Aspirin 300 mg chewable tablets supplied in a 16-tablet pack.

Indication
- Patients presenting with a possible transient ischemic attack who are being referred to a TIA Clinic.

Contraindications
- Patients who are already prescribed 300 mg aspirin
- Known hypersensitivity to ibuprofen aspirin or other non-steroidal anti-inflammatory drugs
- Children under 16 years
- Current treatment with anticoagulants
- Haemophilia and other clotting disorders
- Hx of active gastric or duodenal ulcer
- Headache

Cautions
- Asthma
- Pregnancy
- Kidney or liver failure

Side Effects
- GI mucosal ulceration and bleeding
- May cause nausea and vomiting
- May cause wheezing in patients with asthma

Dosage and Administration
- One 300 mg dose daily, starting, the day after

the 300 mg aspirin loading dose. Tablets should be dissolved in water or chewed and swallowed immediately with or after food, as indicated on the packet.

Additional Information

- An initial 300 mg loading dose of aspirin must be administered.
- Provide a copy of the TIA patient information leaflet. Advise the patient that there is also an information leaflet inside the aspirin pack.

Appendix 2

East of England Ambulance Service Low-risk TIA Referral

Referred by	
CAD:	Date:
Clinician 1 ID:	Vehicle No:
Clinician 2 ID:	Station:

Patient Details	
Name:	D.O.B. Age Gender
	Tel No (home):
	Tel No (work):
	Tel No (mobile):
Post Code:	NHS No (if known):
Has the patient previously visited this hospital? ☐ Yes ☐ No	Hospital No (if known):

Onset of symptoms:

	Date:	Time:
Duration of symptoms:	Hours:	
First contact with health professional:	Date:	Time:

Symptoms

☐ Hemiparesis/arm weakness ☐ Dysphasia/any speech disturbance ☐ Hemisensory disturbance
☐ Double vision ☐ Loss of vision in one eye ☐ Bilateral limb weakness
☐ Loss of visual field on one side ☐ Other

Relevant past medical history

☐ Hypertension ☐ AF ☐ Angina ☐ Peripheral vascular disease ☐ MI
☐ Hyperlipidaemia ☐ CABG ☐ Diabetes ☐ Heart failure ☐ Smoker

Details of previous stroke or TIA

Any other relevant information

Current medication	Drug	Dose

Q/SAP

TECH

PARA

SP CC

SP PC

Appendix 2

East of England Ambulance Service Low-risk TIA Referral

ABCD2 Score variable			Score given
Age	<60 years	0	
	60 or above	1	
Blood pressure	Systolic BP>140 mmHg or	1	
	Diastolic BP>90 mmHg		
	BP below these levels	0	
Clinical features	Any unilateral weakness (face/hand/leg)	2	
	Speech disturbance (without motor weakness)	1	
Duration of symptoms	Other weakness	0	
	>60 minutes	2	
	10–59 minutes	1	
	10 minutes	0	

Diabetic	Yes		1
	No		0
		Total score	

Checklist

Consent for referral obtained	☐ Yes	☐ No
Patient started on aspirin unless CI or local stroke team/GP contacted for advice if patient is already on aspirin	☐ Yes	☐ No
Patient given TIA advice leaflet	☐ Yes	☐ No
FAST information given	☐ Yes	☐ No
Patient advised not to drive until assessed at clinic	☐ Yes	☐ No
Patient advised to call 999 if they have a further event	☐ Yes	☐ No
Patient advised that anyone who witnessed the event should accompany them to the clinic	☐ Yes	☐ No
ECG performed	☐ Yes	☐ No

Q/SAP

TECH

PARA

SP CC

SP PC

511

Appendix 3

East of England Ambulance Service NHS Trust Patient Advice Sheet – Transient Ischaemic Attack (TIA)

What is a TIA?

A transient ischemic attack (TIA) is often called a 'mini-stroke' or mild stroke. The symptoms are very similar to those of a full-blown stroke, but they do not last as long – anything from a few minutes up to 24 hours. As with a stroke, the symptoms are an indication that a part of the brain is not getting enough blood.

What causes a TIA?

Two large blood vessels, one on either side of the neck, carry oxygenated blood up into the head. These are called the carotid arteries; they branch into smaller and smaller blood vessels; which carry blood to all parts of the brain. Sometimes a blood clot or other debris can clog one of these tiny blood vessels. As a result, the blood supply to nearby brain cells can be disrupted. If this is temporary, a TIA may occur. If the disruption to the blood supply is permanent, it can result in a stroke.

What will happen next?

You will be contacted by your local district general hospital or TIA clinic within the next 3 days. They will give you an appointment for the TIA clinic. Your appointment will be within the next 7 days. At the clinic you may have some or all of the following tests:

• Computed tomography (CT) or magnetic resonance imaging (MRI) head scan

- Blood pressure measurements
- Blood tests
- Electrocardiogram (ECG) to look for unusual heart rhythms
- Ultrasound (Doppler scan) of the carotid arteries to check blood flow
- Echocardiogram to check for various forms of heart disease.

If your local district general hospital do not contact you within the next 3 days you **must phone** your GP to inform them that no call has been received. Your GP will be aware of the situation because the ambulance crew you first saw will have contacted the GP to inform them of your situation.

Medication
You must continue to take all your medication including the aspirin you were prescribed today. **You must take (300 mg/one tablet) of aspirin daily with or after food until you attend your follow-up appointment at your local hospital unless you have any adverse reaction.** (See advice leaflet in the aspirin box.) If you have any adverse reactions to your medication you must contact your GP immediately.

It is essential that you attend your TIA clinic appointment

Driving
You must not drive after a stroke or TIA until you have been medically assessed, and you always need a doctor's approval to resume driving.

If you have recurrence of any of the following symptoms of stroke or TIA you must call 999 immediately.

The FAST (Face Arms Speech Test) will help you to quickly recognise the key symptoms of a TIA or stroke:

- **Facial Weakness:** Can you smile? Has your mouth or eyelid drooped?
- **Arm Weakness:** Can you raise both arms?
- **Speech problems:** Can you speak clearly and can others understand what you say?
- **TIME TO CALL 999.**

If you fail any one of these tests, you must seek urgent medical attention. Other symptoms of a TIA or stroke may include:

- Weakness, numbness. clumsiness or pins and needles on one side of the body – for example, in an arm, leg or the face.

- Loss of or blurred vision in one or both eyes.
- Slurred speech or difficulty finding some words.

Further information can be found on the website www.stroke.org.uk or by phoning 0303 303 3100 (open Monday to Friday, 9am to 5pm).

Useful fact sheets include: Driving After a Stroke and Transient Iscaemic Attack (TIA).

Appendix 4

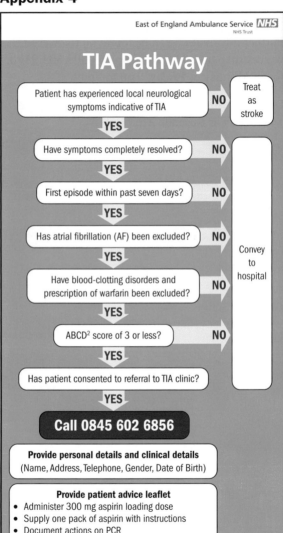

East of England Ambulance Service **NHS**
NHS Trust

TIA Pathway

Patient has experienced local neurological symptoms indicative of TIA — **NO** → Treat as stroke

YES

Have symptoms completely resolved? — **NO**

YES

First episode within past seven days? — **NO**

YES

Has atrial fibrillation (AF) been excluded? — **NO**

YES

Have blood-clotting disorders and prescription of warfarin been excluded? — **NO**

YES

ABCD^2 score of 3 or less? — **NO**

YES

Has patient consented to referral to TIA clinic? — **NO**

Convey to hospital

YES

Call 0845 602 6856

Provide personal details and clinical details
(Name, Address, Telephone, Gender, Date of Birth)

Provide patient advice leaflet
- Administer 300 mg aspirin loading dose
- Supply one pack of aspirin with instructions
- Document actions on PCR

Age 60 years or older	1 point
Blood pressure >140/90 mmHg	1 point
Clinical features:	
• Unilateral weakness	2 points
• Speech disturbance without weakness	1 point
• Other	0 points
Duration	
• >60 mins	2 points
• 10–60 mins	1 point
• <10 mins	0 points
Diabetes	1 points

Note, maximum score of 2 points

ABCD² Score	points (Total score 0–7)

Note: High-risk patients (six to seven points) have an 8.1% two-day recurrent stroke risk.

Q/SAP

TECH

PARA

SP CC

SP PC

Appendix 5

Red flags for call takers regarding low risk TIA referrals

TIA referrals are inappropriate in the following situations:

- ABCD^2 score of 4 or above.
- If a patient is on warfarin or has a blood clotting disorder i.e., haemophilia.
- If this is a second TIA event in less than 7 days.
- If the patient has atrial fibrillation.
- If the patient's symptoms have not **COMPLETELY** resolved prior to referral.
- If symptoms are rapidly resolving this is a good indication that it is a TIA, but it **MUST** be confirmed that symptoms have **FULLY** resolved before accepting referral and the crew leave the scene.

Acute Stroke

> **Refer to:** *Aide-memoire: Patient Assessment: Neurological system, pages 34–35.*

Thrombolysis, including divert criteria

When attending suspected strokes, as clinicians we must assess to see if the patient would benefit from being rapidly assessed for thrombolysis on arrival at A&E. There are many contraindications for stroke thrombolysis, most of which can only be determined in hospital. In the pre-hospital setting we must rule out some of the absolute contraindications in order to determine if a blue light journey and pre-alert (or divert) is appropriate.

It is important to remember that only approximately 10% of stroke patients are eligible for stroke thrombolysis. However, the remaining 90% of patients who do not meet the criteria will still benefit significantly from prompt specialist assessment and access to the hospital acute stroke unit.

This can only be achieved if patients are assessed and managed promptly in the pre-hospital phase of care.

When is a blue light transfer to hospital with pre-alert required? (See Appendix 2)

ECA

Q/SAP

EMT

PARA

CCP

SP

Yes or no?

- Is the patient FAST-positive or do they have persistent focal neurological deficit suggestive of stroke that is of new onset? (See Appendix 3)

- Can a seizure prior to symptom onset be ruled out?
- Can hypoglycaemia be ruled out? (Hypoglycaemia can present with stroke-like symptoms.)
- Can major ABC problems be ruled out?

If NO to any of the above, the patient should be conveyed to the nearest A&E for further assessment.

If YES to all, the patient is likely to be suffering an acute stroke.

Clinicians should then establish the time of symptom onset and, if the nearest hospital provides stroke thrombolysis:

- Is there a clear time of onset of less than 4.5 hours?

If YES:

- Clinicians should establish whether the nearest hospital provides access to stroke thrombolysis at the current time of day/night. (See Appendix 1)

Phillips, D. (2012). Time is brain – all strokes are an emergency. *Acute stroke clinical guidelines*. 1. pg. 1–6.

ECA

Q/SAP

TECH

PARA

SP CC

SP PC

- If the nearest hospital does provide thrombolysis and the patient can be there within 4.5 hours of onset, the patient should be immediately conveyed with blue lights to the hospital with pre-alert to A&E or the stroke team depending on local pathway. (See Appendix 1) RRVs on scene should urgently request immediate backup (NO divert) through priority request to speak, stating that it is a stroke thrombolysis candidate.

If there is NO clear time of onset, or the patient has had symptoms for over 4.5 hours or will arrive at hospital after 4.5 hours, the patient is not appropriate for blue light or thrombolysis divert and should be conveyed to the nearest A&E. This excludes: Queen Elizabeth II Welwyn Garden City Hospital, Barnet and Chase Farm Hospitals, Whipps Cross Hospital, Milton Keynes Hospital and Kettering Hospital; patients in these catchments should be conveyed to the nearest hospital with a stroke unit. (See Appendix 1)

- FAST-positive patients or those with persistent focal neurological deficit suggestive of stroke who have had symptoms for over 4.5 hours from onset should still be managed as urgently as possible with on scene times kept to a minimum. These patients should be conveyed under normal road conditions to the nearest appropriate hospital that has a stroke unit.

ECA

Q/SAP

TECH

PARA

SP CC

SP PC

When the nearest hospital does not provide stroke thrombolysis and the patient is a suitable candidate meeting the following criteria:

- New onset FAST-positive or persistent focal neurological deficit suggestive of stroke
- Clear onset time of symptoms and can be at receiving hospital within 4.5 hours of this time
- NO seizure prior to onset
- Hypoglycaemia ruled out
- NO major ABC problem.

In this situation, clinicians should establish the nearest centre (excluding Broomfield General Hospital) offering thrombolysis. If the patient will arrive at this hospital within 4.5 hours of symptom onset, the patient should be diverted, therefore bypassing the nearest hospital and going to a hospital providing thrombolysis.

- HEOC clinical co-ordinators can be contacted for advice on which hospitals are available and the pre-alert numbers that need to be called (see Appendix 1).

Treatment

- There is limited invasive intervention required for stroke patients in the pre-hospital phase of care. The most important aspects of care being: early recognition, thorough assessment and prompt transfer to a hyper-acute centre.
- However, if clinicians identify any need for intervention then this should be addressed as required.

- Oxygen therapy should only be administered when SpO_2 <95%.
- Due to the time criticality of stroke, any delay on scene should be minimised, and therefore some procedures should be done en route. Performing a 12-lead ECG is only necessary to confirm atrial flutter, fibrillation or when abnormality is detected on a 3-lead trace. If an ECG is necessary before arrival, the patient should be transferred to the vehicle and prepared in transit. A 12-lead ECG can then be performed either by stopping the vehicle briefly to allow capture and printout, or doing the ECG before off-loading on arrival.

Why is diverting occurring?

Not all hospitals within the East of England or its or its borders have 24/7 access to stroke thrombolysis. The following chart shows which hospitals offer what services and the method of alerting appropriate patients.

When a hospital does not provide thrombolysis or does not accept any suspected stroke patients the following chart (see Appendix 1) shows this and highlights which units are appropriate to divert to. The decision to divert and to which hospital is a clinical decision made on scene based on the clinical criteria and the geographical location of the incident in relation to the alternative hospital.

ECA

Q/SAP

TECH

PARA

SP CC

SP PC

Appendix 1

Hospital	Hours of service	Divert when indicated to next appropriate centre	Pre-alert?
Addenbrookes Hospital	24/7	N/A	A&E when in criteria 01223 245306
Peterborough Hospital	24/7	N/A	Stroke team for *all* strokes and high-risk TIAs 01733 67867
Hitchingbrooke Hospital	No thrombolysis service	All strokes indicated for thrombolysis divert 24/7 to nearest unit (usually Addenbrookes)	N/A
Queen Elizabeth Hospital, King's Lynn	24/7	N/A	A&E when in criteria 01553 613896
Norfolk and Norwich Hospital	24/7	N/A	Stroke team for all suspected strokes
James Paget	24/7	N/A	A&E when in criteria

West Suffolk Hospital	24/7	N/A	A&E for *all* strokes 01284 712669
Ipswich Hospital	24/7	N/A	A&E for *all* strokes 01473 716863
Colchester Hospital	24/7	N/A	A&E when in criteria 01206 851619
Broomfield Hospital	24/7	N/A No OOH diverts accepted due to capacity	A&E when in criteria 01245 442577
Princess Alexandra Hospital	7 days/week 09:00–21:00	Thrombolysis indicated to go to Basildon, Addenbrookes, Queens, depending on which is closest. Broomfield is unable to accept *any* diverted patients	A&E when in criteria in hours 01279 416761
Basildon Hospital	24/7	N/A	Stroke team for all suspected strokes 07796 9416613

ECA

Q/SAP

TECH

PARA

SP CC

SP PC

Appendix 1 *continued*

Hospital	Hours of service	Divert when indicated to next appropriate centre	Pre-alert?
Southend Hospital	24/7	N/A	A&E when in criteria 01702 331406
Watford Hospital	24/7	N/A	A&E when in criteria 01923 217654
Lister Hospital	24/7	N/A	A&E when in criteria 01438 357745
Queen Elizabeth Hospital, Welwyn	No service	All stroke PTS to Lister 24/7	N/A
Lantone & Dunstable Hospital	24/7		A&E when in criteria 01582 497497 Stroke team available for advice 01582 497136
Bedford Hospital	Mon-Fri 9-5	Thrombolysis indicated OOH to go to	A&E when in criteria

ECA

Q/SAP

TECH

PARA

SP CC

SP PC

Barnet/Chase Hospital	No service	All suspected strokes to Watford, Lister or PAH. For PAH OOH follow divert for thrombolysis	N/A
Whipps Cross Hospital	No service	All suspected strokes to PAH OOH follow PAH divert for thrombolysis	N/A
Queens Hospital	24/7	N/A	A&E when in criteria 01708 764125
Stoke Mandeville Hospital	No service	Thrombolysis indicated to go to L&D	N/A
Milton Keynes Hospital	No service	All suspected strokes to L&D	N/A
Kettering Hospital	No service	All suspected strokes to L&D	N/A
Northwick Park Hospital	24/7	N/A	A&E when in criteria 02088 643000

Phillips, D. (2012). Time is brain – all strokes are an emergency. *Acute stroke clinical guidelines.* 1. pg. 1–6.

SP PC | SP CC | PARA | TECH | Q/SAP | ECA

Appendix 2

East of England Ambulance Service **NHS**
NHS Trust

Stroke Pathway

Further assessment required
Convey to nearest A&E department

NO TO ANY

- Positive FAST assessment or persistent focal neurological deficit suggestive of stroke?
- Can you exclude hypoglycaemia?
- Can you confirm that there was seizure at onset of stroke symptoms?
- Can you rule out a major ABC problem?

YES TO ALL

Convey to nearest A&E department excluding: Barnet, Chase Farm, Whipps Cross, QE11 Welwyn Garden City, Milton Keynes and Kettering. For these, follow local instructions and convey to nearest hospital with a stroke unit

NO

Is there a clear time of onset of stoke symptoms

YES

Establish nearest hospital offering stoke thrombolysis service

YES

NO

Can the patient be in this hospital within *4.5 hours* from onset of symptoms

YES

Always consider calling clinical advice/EOC clinical co-ordinator line if required for advice on stroke pathway and thrombolysis available

Take to nearest hyper-acute hospital providing stoke thrombolysis

- Pre-alert/discuss with stroke team/A&E in line with local guidance
- Convey rapidly if eligible for fast track specialist assessment, CT and thrombolysis
- ECG monitoring and full observations en route
- Administer oxygen only when SpO_2 below 95%
- Convey patient with a relative/carer

ECA
Q/SAP
TECH
PARA
SP CC
SP PC

Appendix 3
Symptoms of stroke

Focal symptoms include:

Motor Symptoms
- Weakness or clumsiness of one side of the body (hemiparesis)
- Simultaneous bilateral weakness (paraparesis, quadriparesis)
- Difficulty swallowing (dysphagia)
- Imbalance (ataxia)

Speech and Language Disturbance
- Difficulty understanding or expressing spoken language (dysphasia)
- Difficulty reading (dyslexia) or writing (dysgraphia)
- Difficulty calculating (dyscalculia)
- Slurred speech (dysarthria)

Sensory Symptoms
- Altered feeling on one side of the body (hemisensory disturbance)
- Loss of vision in one eye, in whole or in part
- Loss of vision in the left or the right half or quarter of the visual field
- Bilateral blindness
- Double vision (diplopia)

Motion-like Symptoms
- A spinning sensation (vertigo)
- Difficulty dressing, combing hair etc. (visual-spatial-perceptual dysfunction)

- Difficulty performing complex tasks (dyspraxia)

Non-focal Neurological Symptoms:
- Generalised weakness and/or sensory disturbance
- Light-headedness
- Feeling faint
- 'Blackouts' with altered or loss of consciousness
- Incontinence of urine or faeces
- Transient loss of consciousness
- Confusion

Appendix 4

Neurological Assessment

Refer to: *Aide-memoire: Patient Assessment: Neurological system, pages 34–35.*

6

Directory
of Services

South Bedfordshire

Management of seizure in children in an out-of-hospital setting

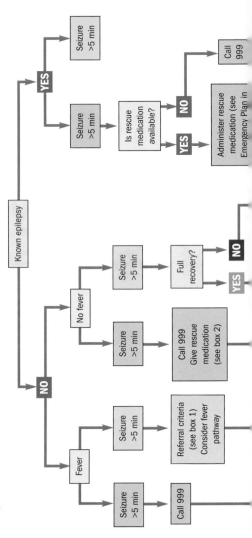

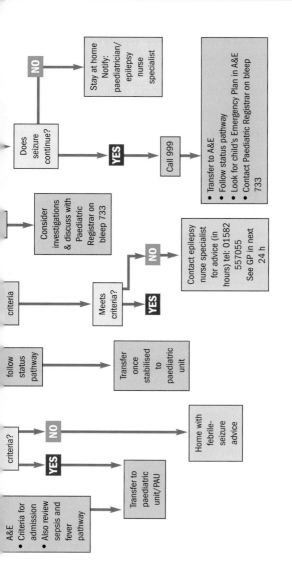

Q/SAP

TECH

PARA

SPCC

SP PC

Children's Seizure Pathway

A seizure is a sudden episode of transient neurological symptoms such as involuntary muscle movements, sensory disturbances and altered consciousness (The American Heritage Science Dictionary).

Obtain blood glucose level at the time of the seizure or as soon after as possible. In the hospital setting, an ECG should be performed for convulsive non-febrile seizures.

Box 1

Criteria for referral/admission:

- Prolonged seizure.
- Recurrent seizures on the same day.
- No focus of infection on examination for febrile seizures.
- Evidence of intracranial pressure (blurred vision, bulging fontanelle in infant, persistent headache associated with vomiting).
- Focal neurological signs (one sided weakness, squint or paraesthesia).
- Drowsy or GCS <15 1 hour post-seizure.
- Age <18 months for febrile seizure.
- Age <2 years or non-febrile seizure.
- Consider parental anxiety/social circumstances.
- Seizure after a head injury (refer to head injury pathway).
- Focal seizures.
- NICE guidelines advise that immediate referral and investigations are not required for a child

---

over 2 years of age who has had a non-febrile generalised tonic/clonic seizure and made a full recovery.

- Second non-febrile seizure with full recovery – refer to paediatric outpatients.

Box 2

Rescue medication (as per Emergency Plan or status pathway)

Buccal midazolam

1–6 months – 300 micrograms/kg (max 2.5 mg)

6 months to 1 year – 2.5 mg

1–5 years – 5 mg

5–10 years – 7.5 mg

10–18 years – 10 mg

Rectal diazepam

1–12 months – 2.5 mg

1–5 years – 5 mg

5–10 years – 10 mg

10–15 years – 15 mg

Over 15 years – 20 mg

Rectal paraldehyde

Dosage as per Emergency Plan

Second dose of midazolam or diazepam can be given if the child continues to seizure 10 minutes after the first dose, but in the presence of paramedics.

This guidance is written in the following context.

This assessment tool was arrived at after careful consideration of the evidence available, including, but not exclusively, NICE Guidelines, EPEN and NHS evidence. Healthcare professionals are expected to fully take it into account when exercising their clinical judgement. The guidance does not, however, override the individual responsibility of healthcare professionals to fully make decisions appropriate to the circumstances of the individual patient, in consultation with the patient and/or guardian or carer.

Welwyn Garden City (WGC) 999 Falls Team

The ambulance service falls teams, otherwise known as the falls partnership vehicles, are pilot schemes that are currently operating within the East of England Ambulance Service in the areas of Hertfordshire, Bedfordshire, Cambridgeshire and Essex.

The Falls Team attends all 999 calls that are coded as a fall. This may be in a private home, residential or nursing home, or a public place. It also attends other 999 calls when they are not dealing with falls – *the Falls Teams only respond to calls via the 999 system.*

The North East Hertfordshire partnership is an association between a Specialist Paramedic (SP) from the ambulance service and a social worker from Hertfordshire County Council. This partnership is based at the WGC Ambulance Station and operates in a specialised vehicle that carries non-emergency equipment for the patient as well as all 999 response equipment. It covers the areas of Stevenage, WGC, Hatfield, Hertford, Ware and sometimes Letchworth, Hitchin and Baldock.

Essential parts of the East Hertfordshire team's ability to leave people at home include the carrying of equipment for immediate dispatch to patients, with items such as commodes, urine bottles, emergency key safes, etc. The ability of the social worker to put immediate care packages in place or organise respite care is also essential, as is the ability of the SP to diagnose any serious illness and minor illness in patients and provide immediate treatment for infections and minor injuries.

The information herein highlights the combined skills partnership of the 999 Falls Team.

Specialist Paramedic

The SP operates as an immediate emergency response in an ambulance or a fast response vehicle.

Complimentary to the emergency equipment, SPs carry antibiotics and analgesics that enable them to treat the patient in the community.

Q/SAP

TECH

PARA

SP CC

SP PC

SP skills

- Full paramedic skills (see below)
- Full in-depth clinical assessment of body systems:
  - cardiovascular
  - respiratory
  - abdominal
  - central nervous system
  - peripheral nervous system
  - muscular-skeletal system
- Differential diagnosis
- Assess and treat uncomplicated infections
- Provide therapeutic interventions (medications)
- Assess and treat minor illness
- Assess and treat minor injuries
- Assess and treat minor wounds, including the use of:
  - suturing
  - glueing
  - multiple and specific dressings
- Use of therapeutic medicines in the treatment of:
  - chest infection
  - urine infection
  - skin infection
  - kidney infection
  - throat infection
  - ear infection
  - infections in the mouth
  - pain relief
  - allergy
  - asthma
  - dyspepsia

- – children's minor illnesses
- – constipation
- Refer patients to the most appropriate clinical pathway
- Referral to physiotherapy via GP
- Liaise directly with other ambulance crews; cardiovascular units; stroke units; GPs; district, diabetic and respiratory nurses; Falls Clinic; Falls Team; carers; family
- Respond to referral from other healthcare professionals

Paramedic competencies
- External defibrillation using manual and AED devices
- Advanced life support (including paediatric)
- Endotracheal intubation
- Airway maintenance
- Intravenous cannulation
- Intramuscular injection
- Subcutaneous injection
- Needle chest decompression
- Needle cricothyroidotomy
- Cardiac monitoring and rhythm recognition (common arrhythmias)
- 12-lead acquisition
- Use of ventilators
- Measurement of peak flow
- Measurement of blood-glucose levels
- Blood pressure monitoring
- Pulse oximetry
- 12-lead ECG interpretation – recognition of acute myocardial infarction (MI)

539

- Burns treatments
- Clinical pathway referral
- Clinical body systems assessments (respiratory/CVS/neurological)
- Treatment in gynaecological/obstetric emergencies
- Major incidents
- CBRN incidents
- Traumatic injuries
- Road traffic incidents
- Use of therapeutic medicines in the treatment of:
  - diabetic emergencies
  - cardiac arrest
  - respiratory difficulties
  - heart failure
  - MI
  - pain relief
  - trauma treatment
  - fluid replacements
  - meningitis
  - allergic reactions
  - drug-misuse treatments
  - seizures
  - sickness (when related to medication)

Drugs carried by the SP (including paramedic drugs)

- Amoxicillin
- Penicillin
- Flucloxacillin
- Co-amoxiclav
- Trimethoprim

- Metronidazole
- Ibuprofen 200/400 mg
- Paracetamol 500 mg
- Co-codamol 30/500 mg
- Diclofenac 50 mg
- Diazepam 5 mg tablets
- Ranitidine
- Gaviscon
- Salbutamol inhaler
- Gentosine ear drops
- Chlorphenamine
- Prochlorperazine
- Lignocaine 1% for wound care

Paramedic drugs
- Adrenaline 1:10,000
- Adrenaline 1:1000
- Atropine
- Aspirin
- Amiodarone
- Benzyl penicillin
- Calpol sachets
- Chlorphenamine
- Dextrose
- Diazepam
- Diazemuls
- Efcortesol
- Entonox
- Furosemide
- Glucagon
- Glucose 5%
- Glucose 10%

- GTN
- Ipratropium
- Metoclopramide
- Morphine
- Narcan
- Oramorph
- Oxygen
- Saline 0.9%
- Salbutamol

SP clinical assessment of the falls patient

The SP takes basic observations:

- pulse
- temperature
- blood pressure (sitting/standing/after walking)
- cardiovascular assessment, including 12-lead ECG
- respiratory assessment
- central nervous system assessment
- abdominal assessment (if indicated)
- peripheral nervous system checks including reflexes
- urine test
- mobility assessment

Overall aims of the SP

- Reduce the number of unnecessary emergency ambulance responses to 999 calls and reduce admissions to A&E departments.
- Improving clinical risk management and patient safety by providing a safety net for those

patients not conveyed to A&E, who may be assessed and, if necessary, referred on to an appropriate service.

- Provide a safe and appropriate level of care for patients whose conditions may be managed in the community in liaison with the community-based multidisciplinary teams (MDTs).
- Refer patients directly to hospital and community-based health and social care agencies to reduce the number of unannounced A&E attendances.
- Provide a reliable and prompt clinical support service to front-line ambulance crews and other NHS staff, allowing them to refer patients directly to an SP.

Falls Team intervention by the social worker and adult care services

Summary of social worker interventions:

- Emergency care package
- Emergency respite/rehabilitation
- Sit-in service
- Financial assessments
- Community-enablement team
- Provision of commodes, toilet frames, perching stools, urine bottles, bed raisers, chair raisers, bed levers, leg levers, pick-up sticks, key safe
- Involvement of ICT
- Referral to other agencies.

This is not a comprehensive list.

The social worker, in partnership with an SP, reduces admissions into an acute hospital. The SP takes control of the medical side of things and makes the decision as to whether the patient needs an acute hospital. Once this decision is made, and if the patient does not need A&E, the social worker can take over and decide what is needed or whether the patient needs to go to a place of safety. The aim of the service is to retain people at home as much as possible and to retain their independence as much as possible. Services range from arranging respite, rehabilitation, equipment, care packages, enablement, referrals and many of the items covered later.

Criteria

The social worker's decisions are based upon the need, risk and adult care services (ACS) criteria that have to be met. Funding is an issue and hardly any services are free. The ACS use other agencies from both the voluntary and private sectors.

The criteria are based upon a critical physical need and not an issue that can be managed through the medical team.

Respite

Respite is not free, so the service user has a means-tested financial assessment to establish support criteria. However, if they are self-funding and willing to pay for their own respite, then this can be arranged privately.

Respite can cost from roughly £700.00–£900.00 a week. Some members of the family, such as daughters, sons, daughters-in-law and other blood relatives, feel that it is up to them to suggest or request respite. Of course, suggestions and requests are considered, but the decision as to whether respite should be provided is made by the social worker, with consideration given to the family members; ultimately, though, the final decision lies with the service user (with capacity). Self-funding service users do not have to use Social Services to engage respite care, but permission is needed from the service user who must have capacity. The social worker arranges the respite care.

The decision for the provision of respite does not sit with GPs, hospital doctors, intermediate care teams, district nurses, any other professionals or family members, unless they wish to fund it. Respite provision can be agreed on the grounds of a carer's breakdown or a carer not managing, but the decision for provision sits with the social worker, with the family views considered, and with the service user. In the community, a GP can request respite via ACS.

Unfortunately, respite under the Falls Team is usually arranged as an emergency and, therefore, any empty bed available will be used. Sometimes this can be difficult if it is not in a preferred place or area.

Rehabilitation

Sometimes rehabilitation is needed after a service user has had a lengthy stay in an acute hospital setting. The decision is usually made by the MDT, which holds weekly meetings at the acute hospital. The MDT consists of a physiotherapist, occupational therapist (OT), consultant, house doctor, social worker, discharge co-ordinators and ward sister or staff nurse, dietician, and speech and language therapist (SALT). The decision for rehabilitation is based upon the physiotherapist's assessment of the service user. However, the social worker can request further rehabilitation if they are able to explain why it would be beneficial to the service user. Many service users who are brought into the hospital were very independent before admission. Owing to the length of stay in a hospital bed, it does not take long for them to lose muscle usage. Service users will lose up to 10% of muscle after one week in bed. The average stay in an acute ward is two weeks or more. The decision for not sending a person to rehabilitation can, and is likely to, be based upon whether the team feel the service user has no rehabilitation potential.

The social worker is able to set up rehabilitation independently of the physiotherapist. On the one hand, rehabilitation is very useful for service users who have stayed in an acute hospital for a long period of time. On the other hand, rehabilitation and respite should not be used as baby-sitting services while families go away on holiday. This is very common. The aim of rehabilitation is to return the service user to their baseline.

Equipment
Equipment while in hospital is provided by the OT. However, measuring a service user's ability in a hospital setting or a ten-minute home visit, which is carried out by the OT (but sometimes the physiotherapist and social worker attend), is not always an accurate guide.

Social workers do not provide hospital beds, scooters, three-wheel trolleys or reclining chairs (except in very special circumstances), stair lifts, or wet rooms and extensions.

The Falls Team usually find that once the service user is at home or their health has deteriorated over time, further equipment is needed. The social worker can provide toilet seats, commodes, bed levers, chair and bed raisers, easy-reach temporary key safe and toilet frames. The social worker can also arrange for rails to be put up for service users. These pieces of equipment and their installation are free.

Hospital beds are for people who are bed bound or terminally ill, not for service users who fall out of their own beds; hospital beds are extremely expensive and there are strict criteria for their use. Service users and families are encouraged to purchase their own bed. Hospital beds are provided by the OT and District Nurses, and, if the patient meets strict criteria, are free.

Q/SAP

TECH

PARA

SP CC

SP PC

Housing

The social worker can help to gain warden-controlled properties, flats, residential, nursing and two-and-a-half housing.

Referrals

The Falls Team can request, via the GP, physiotherapy, incontinence, tissue-viability and district nurses, and a dietician to visit a service user. In all cases this is free, but criteria must be met first.

Advice and information

Advice and information is given out to nearly all service users. Advice can consist of housing issues, equipment, money and benefits, carer's holiday, safety in the home, Age UK leaflets, message-in-a-bottle, and information regarding pendant alarms, key safes, and sitting-in services, which enable people to have someone come to them and chat. Social workers can advise on placements (such as residential, nursing and dementia), rehabilitation, respite, carer's breakdown and day centres.

Enablement team

The enablement team has become the first step in assessing a person's ability for the need of permanent care while in their own home. The enablement team becomes involved after discharge from an acute hospital, community hospital, or as a direct referral from either a Falls Team social worker or a community social worker. Service users are able to self-refer. The enablement team works with the service user from two weeks up to six weeks on many aspects. This service is free at the point of delivery, once the criteria are met. However, if a permanent care service is needed, the service user will have to pay.

Continuing Healthcare Checklist

A Continuing Healthcare Checklist is used when a service user is terminally ill and needs care. The checklist is completed by the district nurse and social worker. It establishes whether further assessment is needed and, if so, a full assessment and report is completed. If a service user meets the criteria and once the report is completed, it is presented to the Continuing Healthcare Panel by the district nurse and social worker.

If successful, care becomes free, whether in the service user's own home, or in a nursing or dementia placement. Everyone has a right to apply for continued healthcare funding. Funding is not easy to secure, but as long as health is the overruling factor and not social issues, then it should be granted. Professionals are not always willing to complete the Continuing Healthcare Checklist as it is a lengthy report that is time consuming and needs input from all the other professionals involved.

Service users who are almost at the end of life can be fast-tracked to the Panel. This entails reports from the doctor or consultant and district nurse, who do not have to be present at the Panel. The

Panel only meets twice a month and a decision is made within 24 hours. People have the right to appeal if they do not agree with the Panel's decision.

Packages of care
Care, and the different packages, can be set up by the social worker. Care can be as little as one hour a week or there can be two carers four times daily. Various packages are available that are designed to meet the different needs of individuals. The social worker team can also arrange for day-centre visits, a sitting-in service, telephone service, meals on wheels, frozen meals and transport.

Intermediate care team
The intermediate care team is a service that consists of nurses and carers working in a team. This team is accessed by the hospital team. The aim is for a quick, sharp and short-term intervention designed to get the service user back to their baseline and, hopefully, no longer in need of care. This service is used when the service-user problems are based more on medical issues. The Falls Team can access the intermediate care team via the Lister hospital.

Capacity (as determined by the social worker)
Capacity is and has always been a difficult area. The Mental Health Act 2005 (MHA) states that everyone is deemed to have capacity unless proved otherwise. A person cannot be assessed for capacity while there is any sort of infection or trauma. The professional (e.g., social worker) has to make every

effort to help the person who is being assessed. Before completing a capacity assessment, such things as hearing, speech and environment must be considered. Capacity is question-specific and not based on perceptions as to why the house is not tidy. If a Capacity Form has to be completed by the social worker, this is done over a three-day period.

If and when a service user is proved not to have capacity, then decisions are made by the family, and a tool called Best Interests is used. However, if a person has no family or friends, the vulnerable person can be made a Ward of Court under the Court of Protection.

Summary of Falls Team skills
- Full clinical assessment
- Diagnosis and treatment of minor illness and injury
- Provision of immediate therapeutic intervention
- Treatment in the community
- Referral to hospital
- Referral to community teams and GP
- Referral to GP for physiotherapy and OT assessment
- Organisation of transportation to hospital/respite
- Provision of emergency-care packages
- Enablement teams
- Full social care needs review
- Referral to respite/rehabilitation care
- Immediate provision of equipment

Q/SAP

TECH

PARA

SP CC

SP PC

Summary of Falls Team operations

- 999 caller response only
- All falls coded calls
- Any 999 as required (if not on a falls call)
- Overnight referrals from 999 crews
- Mobilisation on a blue light vehicle
- Full paramedic response
- Full SP response
- Full social worker skills package
- Equipment provision

Contact details, WGC Falls Team

Hours of operation: 8.30–16.30, Monday–Friday
Sarah or Tracey: 07795 626 869

Cambridgeshire

Falls Partnership Vehicle

Who is it for?

This is a new service consisting of an SP and social care practitioner/ therapist from Cambridgeshire Community Services. It will operate in Cambridge City and its villages for patients who are over 65 years of age and have fallen at home. The service will be available to respond to AMPDS Code 17 (falls) calls (excluding potential major injury) within a 30-minute drive of Brookfields Hospital, Cambridge.

Its aim is to provide medical and social support and intervention, in order to help prevent hospital admissions and to promote falls prevention. The team will provide expertise from a social care environment, along with the medical assessment provided by the SP.

Treatment of minor injury and illness, acute wound care, treatment of infection, and pain management are provided alongside a holistic assessment of the patient's social and physical needs.

The Falls Partnership Vehicle (FPV) will be able to implement social care packages, such as enablement, input regarding carers, home alterations, meals on wheels, life lines, key safes, referral to admission prevention, beds, etc. The vehicle will also carry some commonly used mobility equipment, which can be provided at the point of access.

ECA

Q/SAP

TECH

PARA

SP CC

SP PC

The service is happy to accept referrals from crews for patients they have been dealing with. These patients will have been appropriately assessed by the attending crew as not requiring acute admission to hospital. The referring crew will retain responsibility to inform HEOC of the referral and will remain with the patient until the referral is confirmed, accepted by the FPV, and a time frame is agreed. The FPV will then confirm with HEOC that the referral has been accepted.

During the hours of operation, if a clinician is not on duty the social care therapist will be able to offer telephone advice to crews relating to mobility and social care issues.

Contact details
Hours of operation: 8.30–16.30,
Monday–Friday
Last referral accepted 15.00
Mobile: 07595 551143
Digital Radio: 2264
e-mail: cambs.fpv@eastamb.nhs.uk

Essex

The falls/admission avoidance car

At present the admission avoidance car, which has been commissioned for 12 months by South East Essex PCT, is tasked by the Health Emergency Operations Centre at the East of England Ambulance Locality Office in Chelmsford, Essex. Most of the patients attending come via the 999 system, wherein a call taker decides that the patient fits the criteria for an admission avoidance car response. Other sources of referral are from ambulance crews who find patients that need extended interventions, such as wound closure or UTI. The Specialist Paramedic (SP) then decides if onwards referral to intermediate care services is needed and what service is required.

The SPs have a well-developed directory of services they can refer to, but choosing the right pathway can often be confusing and so inappropriate referrals can result. At the very least, busy intermediate care staff have a lengthy discussion about each patient and may then be involved in the onwards referral to the appropriate team. This lengthens the patient pathway and reduces capacity throughout the team.

The admission avoidance car is also a net user of community services, which is not the best use of the resource or the skills of the staff manning it. To date, progress on making SPs available to intermediate care teams without the need to call 999 has been slow.

To streamline the patient pathways, a single point of referral (SPOR) staffed by a team that is experienced in community health and social care allows all intermediate-care teams to obtain access to the right service quickly and easily, enabling community staff to spend more time caring and less time navigating.

In the case of the admission avoidance car, a SPOR would give SPs the confidence to refer appropriate patients. However, it is vital that the car interacts with the intermediate care team so that the SPOR can use the resources provided by the car to support and instigate admission avoidance. In particular, the ability of SPs to provide basic wound closure, treat with antibiotics and analgesics under PGDs, and lend their risk-management expertise to patient assessment means that the admission avoidance car resides within intermediate care.

As all SPs who work in the admission avoidance car also work a 24-hour shift roster, there is also the possibility that an out-of-hours SPOR could be provided. The planned provision of Toughbook laptops and the integrated use of Adastra, with its ability to pass information electronically to GPs, and the use of assessment and treatment skills, should allow a seamless and efficient patient pathway at all times, without large set-up costs.

In conclusion, there are opportunities for the admission avoidance car, to be integrated further into intermediate care, and for that integration to help improve the capacity, efficiency and cost effectiveness of the community team.

East of England Ambulance Service NHS Trust community and intermediate care directory

Introduction

For over five years, the SPs working for the ambulance service in Southend-on-Sea have developed and maintained strong working relationships with the local community, intermediate care services and the South East PCT.

Following the inception of the drive to navigate patients away from hospital admission and manage their health requirements more effectively within the community, and the successful implementation of the falls car in the Southend and Castle Point locality, it is clear that these links must be further developed and strengthened as the ambulance service takes its place at the core of these changes.

To help ambulance staff choose the appropriate pathway for their patients into intermediate care, this directory was compiled following meetings with our partner organisations. In addition, a number of voluntary organisations were contacted and information gathered that may not result in a referral pathway, but may inform the patient or their relatives that these organisations do exist, which may reduce the number of desperation calls received.

Age Concern Toenail Cutting Service

Hours:	09.00–16.00, Mondays–Thursdays; 09.00–13.00, Fridays
Tel:	(01245) 423333
e-mail:	info@ageconcernessex.co.uk
Address:	Age Concern Essex 112 Springfield Road Chelmsford CM2 6LF
Website:	www.ageconcernessex.co.uk
Services:	An appointment-only toenail cutting service Staff trained in correct technique Cannot help diabetics, ingrowing toenails, some circulatory disorders
Leaflet:	Yes

Age UK Befriending Service

Area covered:	Castle Point and Rochford only
Hours:	Normal office hours, Monday–Friday, Basildon
Tel:	(01268) 525353
e-mail:	befriendingthurrock@ ageukessex.org.uk
Address:	Age UK Essex 112 Springfield Road Chelmsford Essex CM2 6LF
Services:	Provide a befriender to phone or visit regularly Be a listening ear Link to other services
Criteria:	Over 60 years of age who are socially isolated/lonely

Details:	Volunteers are not medically trained and do not perform care tasks (e.g., shopping, housework, personal care)
Leaflet:	Yes

Basildon Careline

Hours:	Service operates 24 hours a day
Tel:	0800 121 4545
Address:	The Basildon Centre St Martin's Square Basildon SS14 1DL
Services:	24-hour telephone care service and also supply fall detectors Can contact relatives/friends/ emergency services in event of incident
Leaflet:	Yes

Carers Emergency Planning Service

Hours:	24 hours a day, seven days a week
Tel:	(01245) 434375
e-mail:	carersinfo@essexcc.gov.uk
Address:	Carer's Strategy Team Essex County Council Freepost CL3636 County Hall Chelmsford CM1 1XZ
Services:	To assist carers in completing an emergency contingency plan Issue a Carer's Emergency Card to be carried by the carer at all times Single point of contact number and PIN

ECA

Q/SAP

TECH

PARA

SP CC

SP PC

Anyone phoning the number on the card will alert the EDT

Leaflet: Yes

Collaborative Care Community Response Team

Area covered: Castle Point and Rochford only

Manager: Rhonda Holbrook

Hours: 08.00–20.00, seven days a week

Tel: 07717 867003

Address: Rayleigh Clinic
Eastwood Road
Rayleigh
Essex SS6 7JP

Services: Provides short-term rehabilitation service for patients who would have needed an acute hospital admission because of an immediate nursing or rehabilitation need

Criteria: Ensure full patient assessment and CRF is completed
Short-term interventions for patients who:
- suddenly cannot manage at home because of an underlying medical need, but who do not really need to be in hospital
- are medically stable, but require additional support to promote their independence
- have been seen in the previous 24 hours by a GP or an SP

Patients who have gone 'off their feet' because of a medical condition such as a chest infection or urinary infection

Patients who have had an accident, such as a fall, and have lost their confidence.

Team: Qualified community nurses
Occupational therapists
Physiotherapists
Associate practitioners
Healthcare assistants

Community Stroke Team
Hours: 08.00–17.00, Monday to Friday
Tel: Office:
(01702) 606954
Case Manager: 07949 505944
OT: 07949 507213
Stroke Nurse: 07538 478441
Support Worker: 07908 966351
e-mail: communitystroketeam@nhs.net
Address: Community Stroke Team
Cumberledge Intermediate Care Centre
Pantile Avenue
Southend on Sea
Essex SS2 4BD
Services: Advice and support post-stroke, including equipment referrals to community rehabilitation services, returning to work and leisure activities

ECA

Q/SAP

TECH

PARA

SP CC

SP PC

Medication
Mobility
Washing and dressing
Meal preparation and shopping
Continence
Memory and attention
Communication and swallowing
Driving
Sexual health
Smoking cessation
Health education and promotion
Episodes of illness
Social security benefits

Leaflet: Yes

Diabetes Primary Care Service

Area covered: Southend, Castle Point and
                 Rochford
Manager: Any team leader
Hours: 09.00–1700, Monday–Friday
Tel: (01268) 464542 (advice/referrals)
Fax: (01268) 464584
e-mail: diabetes.hadleigh@nhs.net
Address: 12 Castle Road
                 Rayleigh
                 Essex SS6 7QF
Services: Support for individuals with
                 diabetes, promoting self-
                 management to help each person
                 lead a full, healthy and active life
                 Provide individual planned care
                 Provide education and training
                 programmes

Work closely with consultants, GPs, practice nurses, district nurses, pharmacists, dieticians and chiropodists

Run drop-in clinics and regular community clinics

Criteria: All diabetic patients – use referral form for hypoglycaemic patients not conveyed

Leaflet: Yes

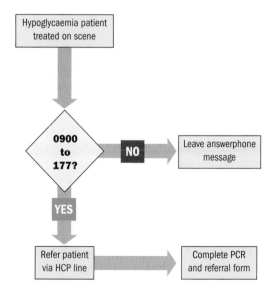

Figure 1 Hypoglycaemic referrals to diabetes primary care service.

The pathway in *Figure 1* should not negate the need to treat and transport patients with life-threatening conditions.

- Health Care Professionals: (01268) 464590
- Advice Line: (01268) 464542
- Fax Line: (01268) 464584
- Paediatric: (01268) 464549

Fax the referral form at the earliest opportunity and attach the fax receipt. Submit with PCR at the end of the shift.

Diabetes nurse will contact the patient within 48 hours. Please consider leaving a leaflet for the patient's information.

As part of our clinical performance indicators for hypoglycaemia, we have to demonstrate that a direct referral was made following treatment of these patients.

To facilitate this, the Diabetes Primary Care team have agreed to accept referrals from crews, either directly during office hours, or by answer phone at all other times. In addition, a referral form will be completed by the crew and faxed at the earliest opportunity to the Diabetes Team. They aim to contact the patient within 48 hours. If you consider that the patient is not safe to leave for this length of time, alternative pathways, such as the patient's GP, should be explored. SPs and the SHARC car have access to a variety of community services and will be able to assist in finding suitable pathways to allow the patient to stay at home safely.

Please remember that this is not an acute service, and does not negate the responsibility of the clinician on scene to treat all presenting problems appropriately.

The telephone and fax numbers are printed on the back of the referral forms. When you fax, please retain the fax receipt and staple it to the form, then hand it in with your PCRs at the end of the shift. If you experience any problems with this pathway, please see DOM or COM in the first instance.

District Nursing

Hours:	Liaison staff man phones during the day, phones divert to night sister at other times
Tel:	(01702) 608250
Fax:	(01702) 390761
Address:	District Nurse Liaison Suffolk House
	Baxter Avenue
	Southend on Sea
	Essex
Services:	Domiciliary nursing, including wound care and review
	Catheter care
	IV administration
	Ulcer care
Leaflet:	No
Referral Form:	Yes

ECA

Q/SAP

TECH

PARA

SP CC

SP PC

End-of-Life Care Team

Area covered:	Southend, Castle Point and Rochford
Contact:	Kim Hooper 07976 725773 Case Manager for Great Wakering, Hockley, Rochford, Shoebury, Southend
	Sharon Dines 07966 792630 Case Manager for Canvey, Kent Elms, Leigh, Rayleigh, Thundersley
End of Life Care Team:	Telephone (01268) 366831; Fax: (01268) 569021
Hours:	Normal office hours – fax 24 hours
Services:	Recruitment of patients in the last year of life to the End-of-Life Care Register
	Assistance with completion of Preferred Place of Care documents and liaise with other healthcare professionals for placement of DNAR decisions
	Management of recruited services
Leaflet:	Decision flowchart and referral form with information sharing letter for patients

Essex Dementia Care

Manager:	Dr Tessa Perrin PhD, MSc, DipCOT
Hours:	No stated hours
Tel:	(01376) 585225
e-mail:	info@essexdementiacare.org.uk

Website:	www.essexdementiacare.org.uk
Services:	Offers support in own home
	Mutual support of other people who have similar difficulties
	Provides activities and days out
	A key worker/companion who understands the patient's needs and builds a relationship
	Back-up team ensures support is consistent and uninterrupted
Method:	Leaflet in blue folders
Other linked services:	Oasis Drop-In Centre

Falls and Osteoporosis Management Service

Tel:	(01702) 606907
Fax:	(01702) 606960
Address:	Cumberledge Intermediate Care Centre
	Pantile Avenue
	Southend on Sea
	Essex SS3 9DA
Services:	Assessment of patients who repeatedly fall
	Team includes physiotherapist and OT
	Onwards referral if appropriate
Leaflet:	No
Referral form:	Yes
Note:	Patients who have fallen should be referred via the SPOC.

ECA

Q/SAP

TECH

PARA

SP CC

SP PC

Headway Essex

Tel:	(01206) 768797
Fax:	(01206) 547486
e-mail:	communitysupport@headway essex.org.uk
Website:	www.headwayessex.org.uk
Address:	Headway Essex
	Community Support Services
	58b Head Street
	Colchester
	Essex CO1 1PB
Services:	Telephone support and information on brain injury
	Home visits
	Hospital visits
	Monthly support-group meetings
	Day-centre referrals
	Support for individuals and families to cope with the effects of brain injury
	Help access to education, leisure, voluntary and employment opportunities
	Support individuals and families to pursue their own interests and achieve independence
	Advocacy
	Provide training for informal and formal carers
	Signpost to other organisations
	Benefits advice

Oasis Drop-In Centre

Hours:	11.00–15.30, every Wednesday
Tel:	(01376) 585225
e-mail:	info@essexdementiacare.org.uk
Website:	www.essexdementiacare.org.uk
Address:	Rayleigh Baptist Church
	High Road
	Essex SS6 7QA
Services:	Drop-in centre for anyone living with dementia
	Can provide short-term care for dementia sufferers
	Provides morning coffee, hot lunch and activities
	All incur small charge
Leaflet:	Yes
Other linked services:	Essex Dementia Care

Papworth Trust

Tel:	(01702) 465182
Fax:	(01702) 465049
e-mail:	homesolutionssouthend@papworth.org.uk
Address:	Papworth Trust Solutions Unit 1
	225–235 West Road
	Westcliff on Sea
	Essex SS0 9DE
Services:	For anyone who is older, has a disability or is on a low income
	Provides practical information and guidance on funding and benefits

Adaptations to homes to aid
independent living
Repairs, maintenance and
improvements
Advice on alternative accommodation
Home safety assessments
Handyperson service

Leaflet: Yes

Rapid Response Nursing Team

Area covered:	Southend, Castle Point and Rochford
Deputy Manager:	Lisa Hilbery
Manager:	Diane Higgs
Hours:	08.00 to 22.00, seven days a week (last referral, 20.00)
Tel:	Direct 07710 929672, 08.00–17.00, Monday–Friday Via SPOR, (01702) 314321/ 314322, 08.00–17.00, Monday–Friday All other times 07710 929478
Address:	Cumberledge Intermediate Care Centre Pantile Avenue Southend on Sea Essex SS2 4BD
Services:	Provides nursing care to patients experiencing an acute episode of illness in their own home Provides health education and promotion

Administers medications, including intravenous

Arranges short-term loan of necessary equipment

Onwards referral to other healthcare professionals (e.g., physiotherapists, occupational therapists)

Criteria: Patients must have a care plan in place

Do not refer young asthmatics

Staff are willing to discuss patients and provide pathway advice

Blood tests

Cardiac failure

Cannulation

Cellulitis

Chest infection

COPD and exacerbations

Crisis intervention

Degenerative/disabling conditions

Dehydration

Dermatology

Diarrhoea and/or vomiting

Diabetes

Elderly care

Family support

Infectious diseases

Medication compliance

Nutrition

ECA

Q/SAP

TECH

PARA

SP CC

SP PC

Oncology
Pulmonary fibrosis
Rheumatoid arthritis
Smoking cessation
Urinary tract infection
Wound closure

South East Advocacy for Older People

Hours: 09.00–16.00, Monday–Friday,
24-hour answering machine
Tel: (01702) 340566
Fax: (01702) 340388
e-mail: southeastessexadvocacy@btopenworld. com
Address: 181 London Road
Southend on Sea
Essex SS1 1PW
Services: Support for over 60s within the Southend
Borough
Help with a wide range of issues
(e.g., a finance and debt, housing)
Leaflet: Yes

Southend Careline

Hours: Service available 24 hours a day
Tel: (01702) 236195
Website: www.southessexhomes.co.uk
Address: South Essex Homes Cheviot House
70 Baxter Avenue
Southend on Sea
Essex SS2 6HZ
Service: Provides 24-hour telephone-care service
within the Borough of Southend on Sea.
Can contact family/friends in the event of

an emergency
Chargeable monthly
Mobile response if appropriate

Leaflet: Yes

Southend Treatment and Recovery Team

Area covered: Southend, Castle Point & Rochford
Manager: Shirley Lough
Hours: 07.00–23.00 Monday–Sunday
(last referral 21.30)
Tel: 07967 614370 – this number will
divert to SPOR in hours
Address: Cumberledge Intermediate Care Centre
Pantile Avenue
Southend on Sea
Essex SS2 4BD
Services: Provides assessment and care of
patients over the age of 17 years with
acute social care needs
Ability to supply mobility equipment
if required.
Criteria: Ensure full patient assessment and
PCR is completed
Use single contact number to talk to
senior staff
If capacity exists, staff will try to
attend while the ambulance is on the
scene
Will also provide care for dependents
if the carer is admitted to hospital or
unable to cope due to illness
Will arrange onwards referral to
other services as necessary

ECA

Q/SAP

TECH

PARA

SP CC

SP PC

ECA

Q/SAP

TECH

PARA

SP CC

SP PC

Suffolk
East Suffolk admission avoidance

Service	Scope	How to access	Hours of operation
EAU at Ipswich Hospital Trust	Calls taken between 09.00 and 17.00, Monday to Friday, will be answered by the EAU consultant. The consultant is available for advice about a potential admission, triage and will agree a patient-care plan with you. Calls taken outside these times will be taken by a senior EAU nurse. Nurse-led service for patients needing intensive nursing, therapy and care to avoid a hospital admission. Examples of services provided are: • IV antibiotic therapy • thromboembolic treatment for DVT and PE re loading on warfarin	Ipswich Hospital Trust switchboard Tel: (01473) 712233 and ask for bleep 620.	24/7 24/7 Will attend to the patient within two hours.

nursing service (now known as Admission-prevention service)	by the District Nurse but between the hours of 16.00 hrs and 08.00 hrs e.g., wound care, catheter care, bowel care, provision of equipment out of hours.	ring. Tel: 07970 847449 (including out-of-hours period). Tel: (01473) 704259, 08.00–20.00, Mondays–Fridays.	
COPD Admission Avoidance	**Refer to:** *Pathways: Chronic Obstructive Pulmonary Disease Admission Avoidance, pages 445–453.*		
End-of-life/ palliative care, St Elizabeth Hospice	Clinical advice and information about the hospice and palliative-care issues. Referrals to hospice at home, a nurse-led 24-hour reactive service.	First, telephone 0800 567 0111.	24/7

ECA

Q/SAP

TECH

PARA

SP CC

SP PC

575

East Suffolk admission avoidance   *continued*

Service	Scope	How to access	Hours of operation
Local health care teams	The teams consist of community and district nurses, community matrons, physiotherapists and occupational therapists, with the support of generic workers, therapy assistants, healthcare assistants and administrative staff. The service: • provides a holistic assessment of needs, including falls assessments • promotes/maintains independent living through the process of rehabilitation • prevents inappropriate admissions and facilitates timely discharge from a hospital or other bedded unit	Ipswich Tel: (01473) 322 131 Fax: (01473) 322130 Aldeburgh Tel: (07966) 809181 Fax: (01728) 451603 Felixstowe and Woodbridge Tel: (01394) 458882 Fax: 01394 458863 Stowmarket, Hadleigh, Eye & Sudbury Tel: (01449) 614769	09.00–16.00, Mondays–Fridays Any other time Tel: Healthcare professional line on 01189 902167

ECA

Q/SAP

TECH

PARA

SP CC

SP PC

		09.00–16.30, Mondays– Fridays
	Ipswich team Tel: (01473) 301025 Fax referrals through COM	
• prevention of ill health • palliative/end-of-life care • signposting/referral on to other services as required • nursing skills – wound care, catheter management, continence, etc.		
Total care team (TCT, community matrons and social workers)	The TCT provides integrated social and nursing case management for patients with complex long-term conditions and social needs who are at high risk of future hospital admission and who would benefit from having their care co-ordinated and reviewed regularly.	

ECA

Q/SAP

TECH

PARA

SP CC

SP PC

East Suffolk admission avoidance *continued*

Service	Scope	How to access	Hours of operation
Home First – social services	Home First is a short-term service that supports and assesses people after a hospital stay or in a crisis – the team support people to regain their independence and then help them decide on future options.	Telephone the professional line 08456 066167, 08.00–18.45, Mondays–Fridays All other times, Tel: 0808 800 4005	24/7
Mental health – older people crisis resolution and home-treatment team	Provide treatment to meet mental health needs in their own home. Can help prevent the need for hospital admission.	First, telephone (01473) 329822, 09.00–17.00, Mondays–Fridays	

| Following a crisis assessment, if home treatment is indicated, a care plan will be agreed with the individual, aimed at meeting their current mental health needs.

This may include daily visits from the team, adjustment of medication, referral/signposting on to other agencies and reassessment of the need for hospital admission. | All other times, Tel: (01473) 329000 and ask for adult crises team | 24/7

Fax urgent referrals to: (01473) 329371

Fax non-urgent referrals to: (01473) 329821 |

ECA

Q/SAP

TECH

PARA

SP CC

SP PC

Suffolk

Rapid Response Team

The Rapid Response Team (RRT) is a 24/7 nursing and therapy service available to adults aged 18 and over who are registered with a GP in Suffolk. The team aims to respond within two hours to assess patients who are appropriate for supporting care closer to home.

Below are guidelines to assist decision making regarding the most appropriate pathway for the patient.

For all referrals made you should ring and discuss with the RRT nurse.

Condition	Inclusion	Exclusion	Comments
Low back pain/minor injuries (e.g., sprains/ strains)	• Able to weight bear, sit to stand, stand to sit	• Paraesthesia • Shooting pains in limbs • Bowel/bladder dysfunction • Osteoporosis/history of RA • Trauma associated with central, cervical, thoracic and lumbar spine pain	
Elbow/ shoulder pain or injury	• Localised swellings with or without bony tenderness • Minor injury	• Gross deformity in children and adults • Underlying bone health condition	
Knee pain or injury	• Minor injury • Weight bearing (see exclusion)	• Inability to weight bear (knee injury) in the elderly	

ECA

Q/SAP

TECH

PARA

SP CC

SP PC

Condition	Inclusion	Exclusion	Comments
Wrist/hand injury with/without superficial lacerations	• Good grip • Able to supinate • Wrist injury • Wrist pain	• Obvious gross deformity • Neurovascular compromise • 'Hot' wrist with acute pain/temperature	
Lower leg/ankle/foot injury	• Ankle injury associated lacerations/superficial wounds	• Obvious gross deformity • Deformity with significant overlying wound See at IHT	
Falls	• Mobile patients with single-limb trauma and no bony injury • No injury but history of falls	• Multiple-site injury, non-mobile	

Unwell adult with pyrexia	• Generally unsuitable but could be assessed by nurse: observation, bloods, urinalysis	• Illness presentations to GP or out-of-hours service
Palliative care	• Symptom control, syringe-driver management, family support	
Stoma care	• Leaking bag • Constipation	• Necrotic stoma • Bleeding • Suspected obstruction • Sepsis • Urostomy – no output for more than four hours • Ileostomy – no output for more than than 10 hours

ECA
Q/SAP
TECH
PARA
SP CC
SP PC

Condition	Inclusion	Exclusion	Comments
Abdominal pain caused by constipation	• Suitable if assessed by doctor	• History of underlying bowel condition	Crew to contact GP first
Abrasions	• Minimal foreign body contamination	• Deep facial/cosmetically sensitive areas, especially in children • Chemical involvement	Widespread abrasions often require GA to scrub-out to prevent 'tattooing' of the skin
Infected wounds Skin problems	• Cellulitis, insect bites/stings • Redness around wounds • Wound ooze • Blocked catheter, bypassing, fallen out	• Immuno-compromised • Pilonidal/anal abscess • Spreading cellulitis – involving enlarged nodes ± pyrexia • History of severe reaction/anaphylaxis	RRT can assess and liaise with GP for prescription if necessary

ECA

Q/SAP

TECH

PARA

SP CC

SP PC

Catheter problems including suprapubic	• Blocked catheter, bypassing, fallen out	• Frank haematuria, underlying complex bladder conditions	RRT hold a special patient list for those who cannot be catheterised in the community; therefore discuss with RRT in the first instance
Lacerations	• Adults • Minor head wounds • Pretibial lacerations • Limb, digit wounds	• Deep wounds with associated head injury (see HI criteria*) • Deep facial wounds where plastic surgery opinion is likely to involve wounds to the lips, crossing the vermillion border, eye-lids • Suspected involvement of facial bones and significant dental damage	

ECA

Q/SAP

TECH

PARA

SP CC

SP PC

585

ECA

Q/SAP

TECH

PARA

SP CC

SP PC

Condition	Inclusion	Exclusion	Comments
		• Uncontrollable major haemorrhage • Where suicidal intent is still suspected or responsible adult is not in place to observe	
Vomiting/dehydration	• Adults unwell through D/V	• D/V exceeding two days • Diabetic	
Eye contamination requiring irrigation	• Adults	• Associated trauma • Possibility of FB, which will require examination with slit lamp and local anaesthetic • Contaminant acidic in type	

To make a referral or to discuss other patients outside of the list call:

East 07970 847449

West 07985 365544

*Guidance for the referral of a patient directly to an emergency department:

- Any previous loss of consciousness ('knocked out') as a result of an injury from which the injured person has now recovered.
- Amnesia for events before or after the injury ('problems with memory'). The assessment of amnesia will not be possible in pre-verbal children and is unlikely to be possible in any child aged under 5 years.
- Persistent headache since the injury.
- Any vomiting episodes since the injury.
- Any previous cranial neurosurgical interventions ('brain surgery').
- History of bleeding or clotting disorder.
- Current anticoagulant therapy, such as warfarin.
- Current drug or alcohol intoxication.
- Age 65 years or older.
- Suspicion of non-accidental injury.
- Irritability or altered behaviour ('easily distracted', 'not themselves', 'no concentration', 'no interest in things around them'), particularly in infants and young children (that is, aged under 5 years).

Admission avoidance West Suffolk County Council

The Admission Prevention Service provides rapid, high-quality assessment and treatment by health and social care staff to people in their own home to prevent inappropriate admissions to hospital and to facilitate a quick return to an optimum level of independence.

Scope of the team
- Seven days per week
- 24 hours a day

Criteria
- Aged 18 years and over
- Registered with GP within West Suffolk
- Patients who are medically suitable for a care-in-a-community setting

Who can refer?
- GPs, Community Healthcare Teams, Ambulance Service, A&E, EAU, Outpatients, Suffolk Adult Services

Examples of reasons for referral
Nursing, social care and functional assessment for health crisis, including urgent bloods to aid diagnosis.

Reasons for referral can be:

- administration of intravenous antibiotics for conditions such as cellulitis or infections not responding to oral antibiotics (e.g., UTI, chest infection, wound infection)
- management of dehydration using subcutaneous infusion therapy
- anti-coagulation management, including administration of oral vitamin K and monitoring for unstable INR
- first catheterisations following medical assessment
- co-ordination of integrated packages of care incorporating relevant health and social care professionals – nurse, social worker/CCP, occupational therapist, physiotherapist and domiciliary carers
- co-ordination of referral to specialist services, such as community matron, falls prevention co-ordinator, specialist nurses.

Contact
Office
Tel: (01284) 718250
Fax: (01284) 718275
Mobile: 07985 36554

ECA

Q/SAP

TECH

PARA

SP CC

SP PC

NHS 111 Service

The NHS 111 telephone number was introduced to make it easier for members of the public to access urgent healthcare services.

The free-to-call 111 number is available 24 hours a day, seven days a week, 365 days a year to respond to people's healthcare needs when:
- medical help is needed fast, but it's not a 999 emergency
- the public don't know who to call for medical help or don't have a GP to call
- the public need another NHS urgent care service
- the public need health information or reassurance about what to do next.

Impact on HEOC

111 calls that have resulted in a 999 response are automatically presented to the correct dispatch desk for allocation of the appropriate resource. The normal assignment process applies to 111 calls.

111 calls are presented as a call type 111Red or 111Green on the pending stack with the priority displayed as appropriate. All HEOC staff have been given a short training session to explain the new process. Where a call cannot be passed automatically by the 111 service, a verbal handover takes place to the HEOC call handler – an appropriate script has been agreed.

Impact on crews

The MDT system

Data are being passed to crews in exactly the same way as for normal 999 calls. The actual content of the data being passed to MDT is slightly different. This is because the 111 service uses NHS Pathways software for triage, not AMPDS.

All call types from the 111 automated dispatch service are presented in Table 1. Figure 1 is a sample 111 call for information.

Table 1 Call types

111Red/R1	111Green/G2
111Red/R2	111Green/G3
111Green/G1	111Green/G4

Diagnosis code

The diagnosis code is (*Figure 1*) the actual description of the patient problem as taken by the call taker. This is a free-format field as defined by NHS Pathways.

Summary AMPDS information

The summary AMPDS information (*Figure 1*) is not available at this point as it is not provided by NHS Pathways.

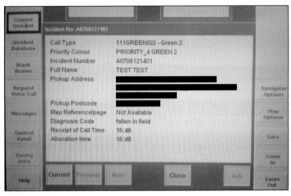

Figure 1   Sample 111 call for information

Mobile phone paging
The only change is that the type of call shows either as 111Red or 111Green.

Digital radio
No changes.

ePCR Toughbook
Obtain call details via the CAD Pull facility as normal by appending the last four digits onto the preformatted Incident Number displayed. The following information is downloaded via the CAD interface to the Toughbook as appropriate to the type of call:

Incident screen information
- Incident date/time
- Incident number
- Call type (emergency)
- Dispatch complaint (NHS111 Red or NHS111 Green)

- Dispatch complaint code (111R1, 111R2, 111G1, 111G2, 111G3 or 111G4)
- Incident location address
- Caller address and telephone number if details are present.

Identification screen
This shows the patient's first and last names including gender if the details are available.

Use the Reconcile Patient Data facility if a number or question mark appears in the small box next to the two communications lights, located at the top right-hand corner of the screen. This indicates that patient information from the CAD system has not yet been fully applied to the ePCR record.

Times/details
Details of the dispatch, mobile, arrival at scene, departure from scene, arrival at destination and available times are automatically pushed out to the Toughbook via the CAD interface, as normal.

Portal
Incidents are presented in the portal and split into R1 or R2 and G1–G4 as appropriate, with some slight differences:
- the pickup and clock start time are exactly the same
- no phone ring time is available
- because the 111 service uses Pathways, no ProQA information is available and clinical

ECA

Q/SAP

TECH

PARA

SP CC

SP PC

information from 111 Pathways comes through to the CAD as notes. Clinical details regarding the patient are therefore now included in the comment section in Portal.

> **If a problem is identified, please contact the IT service desk on 0845 6012509 or e-mail itservicedesk@eastamb.nhs.uk**

ECA

Q/SAP

TECH

PARA

SP CC

SP PC

7

Policy
Summaries

Introduction

The Trust has a number of policies which relate to clinical practice – these can be found on the intranet. The clinical policies are as follows: best practice policy, capacity to consent policy, clinical audit policy, clinical supervision policy, community responder policy and procedures, conveyance and discharge policy, infection control, IPC audit, medical diagnostic and therapeutic equipment, medicines management, obstetric management, paediatric care training, patient care record, patient feedback policy, research policy, resuscitation policy, safeguarding children and young people, safeguarding vulnerable adults, and stroke.

This section summarises key points from some of the policies. It is a requirement to understand and follow the up-to-date policies in use by the Trust, and while this section can be used for reference, the full policies should be accessed as required.

Non-conveyance check sheet – discharge check list

Questions to consider before making the decision to leave a patient at home.

DATE .... PCR/ePCR Number ....

	Yes	No
1. Capacity to consent		
Does the patient have capacity to consent?	☐	☐
(If no, complete the proforma and best interests)		
2. Have you completed a		
Patient history	☐	☐
Primary examination	☐	☐
Relevant secondary examination including observations	☐	☐
2. Have you identified the reason/cause why the patient called the ambulance service?	☐	☐
3. Have you identified any illness or physical deficit which the patient did not have before?	☐	☐
4. Do you feel there is a need for you to seek further advice?	☐	☐
Please tick the source of advice:		
The patient's GP	☐	
Clinical Advice Line	☐	
Other appropriate agency	☐	
(please state ....)		
5. Are you able to provide advice or if appropriate treatment to the patient which will allow them to return to their normal level of daily living activity?	☐	☐
6. Do you feel the patient can be left at home safely?	☐	☐
7. Have you completed a Patient Care Record/ePCR?	☐	☐
8. Has the patient or their relatives/carers agreed with the proposed pathway?	☐	☐
9. Have you provided the patient or their relatives/carers with worsening/condition advice?	☐	☐
State which Trust patient information sheet was used:		
10. Have you informed the patients GP or the out of hours service or if required arranged for follow-up assessment or care?	☐	☐
11. Is there a safeguarding concern with the patient?	☐	☐
If yes, has a referral been undertaken?	☐	☐

The purpose of the above questions are to ensure an adequate clinical assessment has taken place. If you have ticked any of the grey boxes then you should carefully consider your decision to leave the patient at home. Advice and guidance must be given to the patient and/or carers about how to seek further help if that were to be needed

Side tabs: CFR, ACA, ECA, Q/SAP, TECH, PARA, SP CC, SP PC

Capacity to Consent Assessment Form

CFR
ACA
ECA
O/SAP
TECH
PARA
SP CC
SP PC

Capacity to Consent Assessment Form

■

	Incident Date		Incident Number

Patient Surname		Patient First Name	

Date of Birth   /   /

Male ☐   Female ☐

Any psychiatric history?   If Yes, complete details:
☐ Yes   ☐ No

Brief outline of events preceding incident

Name of Service	Name of Contact

Who called for assistance?
☐ Patient   ☐ Police   ☐ Public
☐ Relative   ☐ GP   ☐ Other

Police ID Number

Mental Capacity Assessment

1   Is the patient able to understand the information relevant to the decision - can they tell you about it?   ☐ Yes ☐ No

2   Can the patient retain that information - can they accurately describe it to you?   ☐ Yes ☐ No

3   Can the patient understand, or weigh up the information, as part of the decision making process?*see below   ☐ Yes ☐ No

4   Is the patient able to understand the options available?

598

Contact Name

Organisation

Contact Phone Number

Time of Referral [ ] : [ ]

JRCALC Suicide and Self Harm Risk Assessment

Yes No

Is the patient male?

Is the patient 19 years or younger?

Is the patient 45 years or older?

Is the patient showing signs of depression/hopelessness?

Has the patient experienced previous attempts at suicide/self-harm?

Is the patient's rational thinking absent?

Has the patient experienced an organised or serious attempt at suicide?

Does the patient have no close/reliable family, job or active religious affiliation?

Is the patient determined to repeat actions or ambivalent about their future?

0-3=Low Risk   4-6=Medium Risk   6>=High Risk   Total 'Yes'

Important Note

*If the patient has attempted suicide, complete the JRCALC Suicide and Self Harm Risk Assessment Tool. If the score is 3, or more, this alone is enough for there to be reasonable belief that the patient lacks capacity (it is recognised in law that both physical and emotional trauma have a negative impact on an individual's cognitive functioning).
There is a legal understanding that patients who have experienced such trauma, are not truly able to weigh up the information needed to make a decision- Q3 above (Ref: NICE CG16, 2004).

Has the patient consumed drugs or alcohol within the past 24 hours?   If YES, please detail what was consumed and when

[ ] Yes   [ ] No   [ ] Unknown

■

CFR

ACA

ECA

Q/SAP

TECH

PARA

SP CC

SP PC

Best Interests Record

Best Interests Record

East of England Ambulance Service **NHS**

PCR Unique Number

Time Assessment Commenced

Q1 Is an advanced directive in place?

- [ ] Yes
- [ ] No
- [ ] Unknown

Q2 What actions were taken to encourage participation/involvement of the patient in this decision?

Q3 Is the patient likely to regain capacity?

- [ ] Yes
- [ ] No
- [ ] Unknown

If yes, when

Q4 What relevant factors/circumstances have you considered?

600

Q 6 Views of others involved i.e carers, friends appointed deputy including any disagreements between parties

Q 7 Actions taken in Best Interests of the Patient

Q 8 Was the Patient restrained?

Yes ☐ No ☐

If yes, reasons for use

I have taken reasonable steps to establish the patients capacity to make decisions. To the best of my belief and knowledge the patient lacks this capacity and the decision is in the Best Interests of the patients care and well-being

Signed

Date ☐ ☐ / ☐ ☐ / 2 0 ☐ ☐

Name

Employee Number

CFR

ACA

ECA

Q/SAP

TECH

PARA

SP CC

SP PC

When should you complete a form?

A form must be completed for the following patient groups:

- Patients who have a known mental health / psychiatric history
- Patients who have **refused** treatment/conveyance
- Patients who have self-harmed or attempted suicide
- Patients who have had to be restrained by ambulance staff for their own safety (in their best interests)
- Other patients who lack capacity at the time of assessment/treatment

How to complete the form?

The form is fairly self-explanatory however it is very important that all relevant boxes are completed in full and with as much information as possible.

As the form is in a scan-able format, it is important that the following points are followed:

- Information is contained within boxes.
- Tick boxes must be marked with a cross.
- Any boxes or areas of the form where documentation is not required must be left empty – please do not strike through.

Where the patient has been restrained in their best interests to keep them safe, full details should be documented including; type of restraint used, why the patient was restrained, etc. Restraint must only be used in line with the Mental Capacity Act as defined within Trust policy.

Use of restraint (EEAST Capacity to Consent Policy, 2.10)

2.10.1 EEAST has a policy of no restraint being used when attending to patients except under exceptional circumstances under common law. However, under the Mental Capacity Act restraint may be used by staff when it is considered to be in the Best Interests of a patient who lacks capacity but then ONLY restraint that is proportionate and reasonable may be used.

2.10.2 Under the Mental Capacity Act, a person is defined as using restraint if they:
- Use force – or threaten to use force – to make someone do something that they are resisting, or
- Restrict a person's freedom of movement, whether they are resisting or not.

2.10.3 Any action intended to restrain a person who lacks capacity will not attract protection from liability unless the following two recommendations are met:

- The person taking action must reasonably believe that restraint is necessary to prevent harm to the person who lacks capacity, and
- The amount or type of restraint used and the amount of time it takes must be a proportionate response to the likelihood and seriousness of harm

2.10.4 In addition, the common law imposes a duty of care on healthcare and social care staff in respect of all people to whom they provide services. Therefore if a person who lacks capacity to consent has challenging behaviours, or is in the acute stages of an illness causing them to act in a way that may cause harm to others, staff may under common law, take appropriate and necessary action to restrain or remove the person in order to prevent harm both to the person concerned and anyone else. Acts under common law would not provide sufficient grounds to deprive someone of their liberty.

What to do with the form?

Top copy → Clinical Quality Department, Bedford.
Bottom copy → Remains with the patient unless it is inappropriate to do so. In those circumstances, forward the bottom copy to the patient's GP.

CFR

ACA

ECA

Q/SAP

TECH

PARA

SP CC

SP PC

Guide to assessing capacity with flow chart

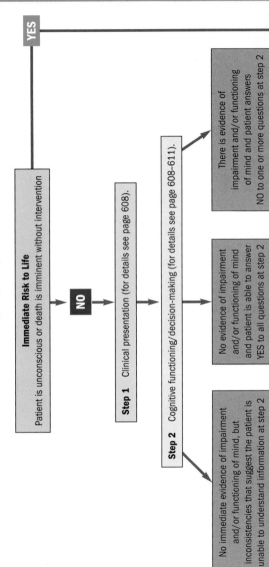

Immediate Risk to Life
Patient is unconscious or death is imminent without intervention

YES

NO

Step 1 Clinical presentation (for details see page 608).

Step 2 Cognitive functioning/decision-making (for details see page 608-611).

No immediate evidence of impairment and/or functioning of mind, but inconsistencies that suggest the patient is unable to understand information at step 2

No evidence of impairment and/or functioning of mind and patient is able to answer YES to all questions at step 2

There is evidence of impairment and/or functioning of mind and patient answers NO to one or more questions at step 2

CFR

ACA

ECA

Q/SAP

TECH

PARA

SP CC

SP PC

606

Patient to be considered to lack capacity to make decision

Act in patient's best interests
Check for any advance decisions

Make every effort to provide the necessary treatment or care. Where appropriate, consider involving or referring to other health or social care professionals.

The use of appropriate restraint or reasonable force may be required to ensure the patient's best interests are met.

Send copy of capacity assessment and PCR to locality office.

Patient to be considered to have capacity to make decision

Patient has capacity to make decision

Respect wishes of patient. Provide advice should they change their mind or their condition worsens. Further risk to patients or others should be considered when in a public place.

Send copy of capacity assessment and PCR to locality office.

Patient to be considered to lack capacity to make decision

CFR

ACA

ECA

Q/SAP

TECH

PARA

SP CC

SP PC

Step 1: Clinical Presentation

Is the patient suffering from an impairment or disturbance in the functioning of the mind or brain? This may include:

- Conditions associated with some forms of mental illness
- Dementia
- Significant learning disabilities
- The long-term effects of brain damage
- Physical or medical conditions that cause confusion, drowsiness or loss of consciousness
- Delirium
- Confusion following a head injury
- Symptoms of alcohol or drug abuse

Then check:

Q1. Is the person orientated for time place and person?

Q2. Is the patient able to identify or locate familiar objects? Example – location of medicines in the home, identification of a personal item such as wallet, purse, keys

Q3. Is the patient able to follow simple commands? Example – lifting arm to allow BP to be taken, standing or sitting when asked (if appropriate)

Step 2: Cognitive functioning

Q4. Does the patient have a general understanding of what decision they need to make and why they need to make it?

Example – does the patient recognise their current health situation and what actions are required to provide further assessment or treatment?

Q5. Does the patient understand the consequences of making, or not making, the decision, or of deciding one way or another?

Example – can the patient state what will happen if they elect not to follow recommended course of action?

Q6. Is the patient able to understand and weigh up the importance of the information relevant to the decision?

Example – can the patient state what factors they are taking into account when making the decision?

Q7. Is the patient able to retain the information as part of the decision making process?

Example – can the patient demonstrate recall of what has been discussed?

Q8. Can the patient communicate their decision using any means available to them?

The Mental Capacity Act will cover individuals and organisations, provided that they can evidence that they acted in the best interests of the patient who lacks capacity.

There are 6 courses of action that ambulance crews will have to follow to evidence that they have been compliant with the Act and taken appropriate action in the best interest of the patient. These are:

1. (The crew) must consider whether it is likely that the patient will at some time have capacity in relation to the matter in question, and if it

appears likely that the patient will, when that is likely to be;

2. (The crew) must, so far as reasonably practicable, permit and encourage the patient to participate, or to improve the patient's ability to participate as fully as possible in any act done for the patient and any decision affecting the patient;

3. Where the determination relates to life-sustaining treatment (the crew) must not be motivated by a desire to bring about the death of the patient when considering what is in the patient's best interests;

4. (The crew) must consider, as far as is reasonably ascertainable, the patient's past and present wishes and feelings (in particular any relevant written statement made when the patient had capacity), and any beliefs and values (e.g. religious, cultural or moral) that would be likely to influence the decision in question and any other relevant factors.

5. As far as possible (The crew) must consult with other people if it is appropriate to do so and take into account their views as to what would be in the best interests of the patient lacking capacity. This would especially be anyone named by the person lacking capacity as someone to be consulted, carers, close relatives or close friends or anyone else interested in the person's welfare, and any attorney appointed under a Lasting Power of Attorney, or deputy appointed by the Court of Protection to make decisions for the person.

6. The person making the determination about best interests must not make it merely on the basis of the patient's age, appearance, their condition, or an aspect of their behaviour which might lead others to make unjustified assumptions about their best interests.

Capacity to Consent Forms

As part of its priorities within the Quality Account 2012/13 the Trust is committed to improving accurate records for known mental health patients and/or those who or may lack capacity to consent at the time of assessment and/or treatment.

The Trust has reviewed its Capacity to Consent Forms to ensure that they meet the needs of patients and also provide an easier mechanism for staff to complete. The forms are in a scan-able format which means that the Trust will be able to measure actions taken and also, where necessary, liaise with Mental Health teams.

Who should complete them?

All clinicians are required to complete these forms, this includes: Paramedics, Specialist Paramedics, Nurses, Emergency Medical Technicians, QSAPs, SAPs, ECAs and Doctors.

When should you complete a form?

A form must be completed for the following patient groups:

- Patients who have a known mental health / psychiatric history
- Patients who have **refused** treatment/conveyance
- Patients who have self-harmed or attempted suicide
- Patients who have had to be restrained by ambulance staff for their own safety (in their best interests)
- Other patients who lack capacity at the time of assessment/treatment

How to complete the form?

The writing shield contains useful information such as the 'Best Interests Guidance' which should be taken into account when completing the form.

It is also very important that full documentation is provided when a patient has been **restrained** in their best interests to keep them safe.

Use of restraint (EEAST Capacity to Consent Policy, 2.10)

2.10.1 EEAST has a policy of no restraint being used when attending to patients except under exceptional circumstances under common law. However, under the Mental Capacity Act restraint may be used by staff when it is considered to be in the Best Interests of a patient who lacks capacity but then **ONLY** restraint that is proportionate and reasonable may be used.

2.10.2   Under the Mental Capacity Act, a person is
         defined as using restraint if they:
         - Use force – or threaten to use force – to
           make someone do something that they
           are resisting, or
         - Restrict a person's freedom of
           movement, whether they are resisting or
           not.

2.10.3   Any action intended to restrain a person
         who lacks capacity will not attract
         protection from liability unless the
         following two recommendations are met:
         - The person taking action must
           reasonably believe that restraint is
           necessary to prevent harm to the person
           who lacks capacity, and
         - The amount or type of restraint used
           and the amount of time it takes must be
           a proportionate response to the
           likelihood and seriousness of harm

2.10.4   In addition, the common law imposes a
         duty of care on healthcare and social care
         staff in respect of all people to whom they
         provide services. Therefore if a person
         who lacks capacity to consent has
         challenging behaviours, or is in the acute
         stages of an illness causing them to act in a
         way that may cause harm to others, staff
         may under common law, take appropriate
         and necessary action to restrain or remove
         the person in order to prevent harm both

to the person concerned and anyone else. Acts under common law would not provide sufficient grounds to deprive someone of their liberty.

As the form is in a scan-able format, it is important that the following points are followed:

- Information is contained within boxes.
- Tick boxes must be marked with a cross as shown here $\boxed{\text{X}}$

- Any boxes or areas of the form where documentation is not required must be left empty – please do not strike through.

What to do with the form?

- **Top copy** → Clinical Quality Department, Bedford.
- **Bottom copy** → Remains with the patient unless it is inappropriate to do so. In circumstances, forward the bottom copy to the patient's GP.

NEW – Capacity to Consent Forms

As part of the Trust's Quality Account for 2012/13 the Trust has implemented priorities around mental health and learning disabilities. As well as the introduction of aide memoire prompt cards to help staff communicate with patients who have learning disabilities, it is also introducing Capacity to Consent forms. These forms will shortly be arriving on stations and are presented as A3 duplicate pads – 1 pad per vehicle.

The form will enable clinicians to record decisions and actions taken for particular patients.

A form must be completed for:
- Patients who have a known mental health / psychiatric history
- Patients who have **refused** treatment/conveyance
- Patients who have self-harmed or attempted suicide
- Patients who have had to be restrained by ambulance staff for their own safety (in their best interests)
- Other patients who lack capacity at the time of assessment/treatment

The form is fairly self-explanatory however it is very important that all relevant boxes are completed in full and with as much information as possible.

As the form is in a scan-able format, it is essential that; Information is contained within boxes, tick boxes must be marked with a cross and any boxes or areas of the form where documentation is not required must be left empty – please do not strike through.

Where the patient has been restrained in their best interests to keep them safe, full details should be documented including; type of restraint used, why the patient was restrained, etc. Restraint must only be used in line with the Mental Capacity Act as defined within Trust policy.

The form also contains the JRCALC self-harm and suicide risk assessment toolkit and comes with a printed writing shield which provides information around best interest guidance as well as the best interest flow chart.

If you require any further information, please contact Natalie Mudge at Natalie.Mudge@eastamb.nhs.uk or 01234 243147.

Medicine Management Policy

Aim for a safe regime

The overriding consideration of the attending doctor, nurse, paramedic or technician is the clinical safety and well-being of the patient.

The key principles that govern the management of medicines within the Trust are compliance with the items in *Figure 1* on the next page.

Principles of the management of controlled drugs

Authority to possess and supply

- Paramedics have a group authority to possess and supply morphine injections at a strength not exceeding 20 mg/ml (Schedule 2) and diazepam – all forms (Schedule 4). As such, these are the only controlled drugs in Schedules 2–4 that may be held as stock within ambulance stations and on ambulances and other Trust clinical vehicles. Paramedics are also authorised to possess and supply morphine oral solution 10 mg in 5 ml (Schedule 5, see Appendix 1).
- Paramedics may only supply morphine injections or oral solution 10 mg/5 ml, or diazepam (all forms) to a healthcare professional authorised to possess these drugs – in the Ambulance Trust this will only be another paramedic or a doctor, and the paramedic can only do so for immediate use in the treatment of a patient.
- Nurses working with Ambulance Trusts do not have authority to possess any controlled drugs in

617

Current prescribing legislation

Management of the risks to patients and staff arising from the physical handling processes involved in the initiation of treatment

Prescribing

Procurement

Acquisition

Storage

Distribution

Dispensing

Preparation

Administration and safe handling/disposal of any residual product

Observance/consideration to guidance from DoH

Figure 1 Key principles that govern the management of medicines within the Trust.

Schedules 2–4, including diazepam.

- Doctors and pharmacists have general authority to possess, supply and procure all controlled drugs except those in Schedule 1.
- Additional controlled drugs, midazolam and ketamine, are carried on the air ambulance on the authority of the Trust Medical Director, who, as a doctor, is authorised to possess and supply all controlled drugs. Midazolam and ketamine may only be carried by doctors on the authorisation of the Medical Director.
- Primary-care services, such as out-of-hours services, operated by the Trust may carry a range of controlled drugs, including midazolam, morphine and diamorphine, again on the authority of a doctor who remains totally responsible for the secure and safe management of the out-of-hours service.
- Only registered paramedics, the Medical Director and Associate Medical Directors are permitted to have morphine and diazepam in their custody or possession. Other ambulance staff are not permitted to have morphine in their possession at any time.
- Trust vehicles (excluding air ambulances) may carry the controlled drugs morphine, diazepam and Schedule 5 drugs approved for Trust use, which include oral morphine 10 mg in 5 ml.
- Air ambulances carry a wider range of controlled drugs, including midazolam and ketamine. Stocks of controlled drugs for air ambulances are ordered by medical practitioners only and remain their responsibility.

Storage of controlled drugs

- Each locality ambulance station must have a small, lockable metal cabinet bolted to the floor or wall. Within this cabinet there must be sufficient personal fixed trays and space for use by paramedics to store stocks of morphine and/or drug keys when they are off duty. The key for the outer cabinet and the master key for the drug safe trays must be kept within a key press.

- Paramedics will store their individually issued stock of morphine in a personal Trust drug safe, to which they alone hold the key, at an ambulance station or, when they are on duty, in a drugs safe to which they alone hold the key, in a Trust vehicle.

- Vehicle storage:
  - ambulance – in a locked compartment
  - car – in a locked compartment, in the locked boot of the car
  - air ambulance – in a locked tray within a locked unit.

- Primary Care Centres' (PCCs) controlled drugs may be stored in the doctor's bag during each shift, but must be removed and placed into the main controlled drugs cupboard when their shift ends. Whenever a controlled drug is placed into a doctor's bag, a physical balance of that medicine must be taken.

- On the air ambulance, morphine sulphate must be stored in the crew room in the lockable cupboard (safe). The keys must be kept in a

number-pad lockable key safe.
- Morphine must be stored in the aircraft in a number-pad lockable box in a lockable cupboard. Other controlled drugs for use by doctors must be stored in the aircraft in a numbered lockable box in a lockable cupboard to which only the doctors have access.

Carriage
- The security of controlled drugs is paramount. The individual paramedic is responsible for the security of their personal stock of morphine sulphate. In agreed situations, a paramedic may transport their personal supply in a locked container from their normal duty station to their allocated place of work where it must be secured as per the local arrangements.
- The locked container (e.g., small cashbox) must be in a locked boot out of sight of the public. The vehicle must be roadworthy and secure.
- Transfer to a Trust locked store should be undertaken at the earliest opportunity, whether it be at a drugs safe at a station or a drugs safe in a Trust vehicle.
- The locked container must not be left in an unattended vehicle overnight.
- The paramedic should ensure that the paramedic's controlled drug stock is checked against the paramedic's drug register and that this is witnessed as being correct by a Trust colleague. This will ensure that any discrepancy is noticed at the earliest opportunity. This should

be done as soon as possible when working away from the duty station and again on return.

Morphine stores on vehicles

- For vehicles with key-lock controlled drug compartments, there are two keys: one (which may be a master key to all the drug trays in the store) is to be kept in the station key press and the other (which is individual to the drug tray) is to be held by the paramedic during the shift. The paramedic's key is to be passed to the next paramedic coming on duty on the vehicle or, in the case of there being no paramedic to pass the key to, the key is to be placed in the station drug store and a note made in the station log.

- Where the drugs are stored in a compartment with a digital lock, only paramedics will have access to the code and/or to the key that is required to set the code.

- Each paramedic will ensure that they hold a minimum of two ampoules and a maximum of 15 ampoules of morphine at the beginning of each shift. Where there are two paramedics on a vehicle, only one paramedic can take their morphine stocks on the vehicle and they will have sole responsibility for the secure and safe handling of these stocks.

Controlled drugs in PPCs

- Controlled drugs received must be checked and signed for by a doctor and entered into the PCC Controlled Drugs Record Book.
- The balance must be checked and recorded as correct at the beginning and end of each 'out-of-hours' shift. This check must be carried out by two people, one of whom will be the doctor assigned to that shift. This check must be recorded with both people identified. This record may be kept at the back of the register or in a separate book, but must not be recorded on the pages that record drugs obtained or supplied.
- If a controlled drug is prepared by a nurse or doctor and not used, it must be destroyed by the paramedic who administers the drug, and recorded against the replenishment record to identify each ampoule individually by batch number.
- When a clinician administers morphine to a patient, they must record the following:
  - date and time
  - patient's name
  - dosage administered
  - PCR/ePCR number
  - name and signature of the person who administered the drug
  - name and signature of witness
  - stock balance
  - expiry date
  - batch number.

- If a mistake is made when completing the book, then a line must be drawn through the middle of the written text and the corresponding row. The correct information should then be recorded in the next row down. Do not tear the page out of the book.
- All administration of controlled drugs should be witnessed. However, it is recognised that with solo responders it may be difficult to have the administration of controlled drugs witnessed, but they should make every attempt to obtain a witness. Where there is no witness available, the clinician should record 'No witness available' in the witness column.
- At the earliest opportunity following an unwitnessed administration, the paramedic should have their register and stocks checked by a second paramedic.

Destruction of controlled drugs
- Expired medicines containing controlled drugs in Schedules 22–4 must be denatured prior to disposal.
- The denaturing of Schedule 2 stock controlled drugs must only take place in the presence of an appropriately authorised person. There are no special requirements for the witness of the destruction of all other controlled drugs over and above standard procedures for the safe disposal of medicines.
- When a controlled drug is destroyed, details of the drug must be entered into the controlled

drug register. This should include the name of the drug, its form, strength and quantity, and the date it was destroyed, as well as the signature of the authorised person who witnessed the destruction and the person who destroyed it (i.e., two signatures).

Loss of controlled drugs

- Any apparent loss of controlled drugs must be reported to the GM and the Controlled Drugs Accountable Officer as soon as possible. A Datix form should also be completed.
- In the event that the drug cannot be accounted for within 24 hours, then the Police must be notified and a Serious Incident form must be completed that will be notified to the SHA/PCT.

Refer to: *Medicines Management Policy: Available on EAST 24.*

Appendix 1

Overview of drug schedules

Schedule	Example of drug types
Schedule 2	Includes opioids, (e.g., diamorphine, morphine, methadone), major stimulants (e.g., amphetamines), remifentanil, secobarbital
Schedule 3	Includes minor stimulants, temazepam, diethylpropion, buprenorphine, midazolam, flunitrazepam, barbiturates (except secobarbital)
Schedule 4 (Part 1)	Part 1 includes benzodiazepines
Schedule 4 (Part 2)	Part 2 includes anabolic steroids, clenbuterol, growth hormones
Schedule 5	Includes low-strength opioids

Variations in Clinical Practice and Clinical Competence

Purpose of the policy

- This policy aims to establish a clear pathway for dealing with issues of adequacy of performance and competency of clinical staff, and any variations that relate to clinical practice. It establishes a clear separation between these issues and those that pertain to matters of personal misconduct and capability.

- The purpose of the policy is to encourage employees to discuss patient-care issues openly in a supportive environment, without the threat of blame, and to improve clinical practice for the future, which will provide real benefits for patients.

- In addition, the policy deals with 'near misses' and 'adverse clinical incidents' so that measures can be taken to avoid reoccurrence, and any lessons learned can be shared with the organisation so that standards of care can be maintained and, where possible, improved.

Stage 1 – Local resolution via a clinical debrief

- Having decided to seek a local resolution via a clinical debrief, the manager conducting it should consider incorporating additional expert assistance within the debrief if it is deemed necessary.

ECA

Q/SAP

TECH

PARA

SP CC

SP PC

- The clinical debrief should be conducted in an informal and relaxed atmosphere, with the emphasis placed on learning lessons and improving clinical practice. Confidentiality of the issues discussed must be ensured.
- Individuals must be advised that they can be accompanied by a Trade Union representative or fellow worker (i.e., another of the Trust's workers).
- If as a result of the clinical debrief it is decided that no further action is required, this must be documented on the Clinical Debrief Form (Appendix 1), which should be dated, signed by and copied to all relevant parties involved in the debrief.
- If needed, an action plan should be agreed with the individual at the end of the debrief, and recorded in writing on the Clinical Debrief Form, which should be dated, signed by and copied to all relevant parties involved in the debrief. An action plan may include:
  - a period of mentoring (length of time to be mutually agreed)
  - additional training and education
  - formal assessment (simulation or 'live')
  - reviewing or recommending changes to equipment, guidelines or practice
  - case-study submission, which is relevant to incidents or areas of poor practice/competence
  - changes to working practices.

- If necessary, a review date is agreed to assess progress and this should involve those present at the debrief. It may not be necessary to convene another meeting to review progress, as this can often be done using other communication links.
- A summary of the debrief should be forwarded to the Clinical General Manager and Senior Operational Manager for that area. This summary should be recorded on a Clinical Debrief Form. Anonymised summaries of clinical debriefs will be discussed at local clinical review groups.
- If at any point during Stage 1 it is considered more appropriate to deal with the matter under either Stage 2 (Clinical Performance Panel) or the Trust's Disciplinary Policy (Managing Performance and Conduct), the Stage 1 process will stop. The employee will be informed in writing of the reason why and of the more appropriate pathway to be followed.
- If the manager conducting the Stage 1 clinical debrief feels it is more appropriate to move the matter to either Stage 2 or the Trust's Disciplinary Policy, then the relevant section of the Clinical Debrief Form (Appendix 1) should be completed, outlining the reasons for their decision, and forwarded to the Clinical General Manager and Senior Operational Manager for that area.
- Should there be an inconclusive outcome following the debrief, then the matter should move forwards to Stage 2.

ECA

Q/SAP

TECH

PARA

SP CC

SP PC

Stage 2 – Clinical Performance Panel

- For more serious clinical issues for which the matter has been progressed from Stage 1, or for multiple complaints or for those that cannot be resolved at Stage 1, then Stage 2 is invoked and a Clinical Performance Panel convened. This should occur within 28 calendar days of the investigating manager's clinical review of the facts or the date of the Stage 1 outcome. All paperwork should be shared immediately after the decision is taken to progress to Stage 2. If the timescale cannot be adhered to for legitimate reasons, then the nominated chairperson should document the reasons and reassign another date that is agreeable to all parties.
- The panel will be organised by the Human Resources (HR) Department in conjunction with the Chair, and will comprise the following:
  - a Chairperson (normally the relevant clinical lead)
  - a staff peer whose skill level is representative of the employee attending the clinical review panel
  - a staff representative nominated by UNISON who should have extensive clinical experience and credibility
  - an appropriate manager from the domain the individual is employed in.
- In special circumstances, the panel may invite an independent or an expert view if this will help to improve the quality of the conclusion or decision of the panel.

- While the initial investigating manager should not be invited to sit on the panel, they may be required to attend the panel hearing for clarity.
- The member of staff will be invited to attend and be advised that they can be accompanied by a Trade Union representative or fellow worker (i.e., another of the Trust's workers).
- The panel members will have a meeting prior to the commencement of the panel hearing to discuss the case and formulate questions and outline an agenda of proceedings.
- If as a result of the panel's findings it is deemed that the issue is better dealt with under the Trust's Disciplinary Policy (Managing Conduct and Performance), the Chairperson will complete the relevant section of the Clinical Debrief Form (Appendix 1), outlining the reasons for their decision and copy it to the HR Department, who will then make arrangements for a disciplinary hearing to be convened. In these circumstances, the individual must be informed of this decision prior to, during or at the end of the meeting.
- The panel should consider what the current clinical standards of the individual are, along with any current or previous issues. If a deficit in clinical performance is identified, the panel must formulate a plan of action. This may include:
  - additional training, mentorship or personal learning plan
  - reviewing or recommending changes to equipment, guidelines or practice

- – a programme of reviewing performance to ensure that high standards of clinical practice are maintained
- – changes to working practices
- – taking no further action.
- If the panel is reviewing a GP, then a report from the panel should be sent to the PCT on whose provider list the doctor is registered.
- Upon reaching their decision, the panel chair must communicate this to the individual. This should be done at the end of the panel hearing with written confirmation within eight calendar days.
- If required, the panel will set a review date in line with their recommendations, which should normally be within six months of the hearing date.
- The panel Chairperson will confidentially report its conclusions to the Trust's Medical Director, with a copy forwarded to the HR Department for the employee's personnel file.
- The HR Department will keep a complete copy of all the documentation used by the panel.
- The Medical Director is responsible for the preparation of biannual anonymised reports for the Trust's Governance Committee that summarise the incidents considered, and undertakes an annual review of the functionality of the panel composition in partnership with staff.

Referral to the professional body

- The Trust will meet its requirements with regards to reporting matters to Professional/Registration bodies, as advised by, and in compliance with, the relevant professional body. Further advice or information is available from:

The HR Department
Health and Care Professions Council
General Medical Council Nursing and
Midwifery Council
Tel: 020 7582 0866
www.hcpc-uk.org – 0845 357 8001
www.gmc-uk.org – 020 7333 9333
www.nmc-uk.org

Appendix 1

QA3 Clinical Debrief

Those Present at Debrief

Description of Events/Issues

Debrief Findings

Recommendations/Conclusions (Provide Detailed Reasoning for Decision)

Lessons Learnt/Action Plan

Signatures

Manager (Print Name)

Signature

Crew's Name (Print Name)

Signature

Crew's Name (Print Name)

Signature

Index